GW00536805

GRASSHOPPERS AND ALLIED INSECTS OF GREAT BRITAIN AND IRELAND

GRASSHOPPERS
AND ALLIED INSECTS
of Great Britain and Ireland

Judith A. Marshall BSc & E. C. M. Haes BSc

with colour plates and text figures
by Denys Ovenden

Harley Books (B. H. & A. Harley Ltd.),
Martins, Great Horkesley,
Colchester, Essex, CO6 4AH, England

Text set in Linotron 202 Plantin by
Saxon Printing Ltd., Derby and
Rowland Phototypesetting Ltd., Bury St Edmunds, Suffolk
Page make-up by Rowland Phototypesetting Ltd.
Text printed by St Edmundsbury Press Ltd., Bury St Edmunds, Suffolk
Colour originated by Adroit Photo Litho Ltd., Birmingham
and printed by Jolly & Barber Ltd., Rugby, Warwickshire
Bound by Hunter and Foulis Ltd., Edinburgh, Scotland

British Library Cataloguing-in-Publication Data

Marshall, Judith A.
Grasshoppers and allied insects of Great Britain and Ireland
1. Great Britain. Orthoptera. Identification Manuals
I. Title II. Haes, E. C. M. (E. Christopher M.)
595.7'26'0941

ISBN 0 946589 13 5

Contents

Foreword

The British Isles have arguably the best-known fauna in the world. Our relatively dense human population has an unusually strong interest in our natural history, and numerous books are available on such popular groups as birds and butterflies. Even our grasshoppers and crickets, traditionally regarded as a neglected group, have formed the subject of no fewer than five books since the turn of the century. In a nature-loving country like ours this is not really surprising, since these attractive and often large insects, their songs so closely associated with warm, sunny days, are among the most rewarding to study, both in the field and in captivity. The fact that they make poor museum specimens no longer affects their appeal, since the growing interest in conservation has shifted the emphasis from dead specimens to live insects – to the study of their life histories and habits in nature. The large size and attractive appearance of many of our grasshoppers and their allies make them ideal subjects for the nature photographer, and their characteristic songs present a challenge to the wildlife sound recordist. For some years now there has been no comprehensive handbook available on these insects, my own book being long since out of print, and so this new work, quite different from any of its predecessors, will fill a long-standing need.

Judith Marshall and Chris Haes have produced a text that should appeal to layman and expert alike. They have usefully included the Channel Islands in their geographical coverage, and the insects treated include the earwigs – a truly neglected group – in addition to the crickets, grasshoppers, cockroaches and stick-insects. Embellished by Denys Ovenden's beautiful and accurate paintings, and with short contributions from John Burton, Ron and Christine Foord and myself, the book is sure to fulfil Basil Harley's intention: to produce an authoritative and comprehensive text that will be the standard reference work for many years to come.

David R. Ragge

April, 1988 — Purley, Surrey

To those whose enthusiasm for the study of Orthoptera knows no bounds

Acknowledgements

In this work the authors have been individually responsible for certain chapters, and have collaborated on others. Further chapters have been contributed by specialists in the appropriate field – David Ragge, John Burton, and Ron and Christine Foord, to whom the authors are much indebted – so that the book incorporates a wide range of expertise on orthopteroid insects. That it does so is due to the enthusiasm and support of the publishers; both authors are extremely grateful to Basil and Annette Harley for their high standard of editing and meticulous attention to detail, as well as for their important contributions to the text and their preparation of the charts and the index.

The outstanding abilities of Denys Ovenden will be appreciated by all who see his work; both authors and publishers are grateful for his superb paintings and line drawings, reflecting not only his capability as an artist but also his interest in Orthoptera; he has the feel or 'jizz' of the insects in his paintings, which one could almost see walking off the page.

Judith Marshall is grateful to colleagues at the British Museum (Natural History), particularly David Ragge, and also Theresa Howard and Jim Reynolds, for their advice and helpful comments during the preparation of this work. Chris Haes is indebted to David Ragge for all his help and encouragement during the last 25 years, and also to his co-author, Judith, and to Jim Reynolds and Bruce Townsend for their efforts in identifying the various British and Continental specimens which he has sent to the Museum over the years. The Orthoptera Section is equally grateful to Chris for all his material which has benefitted the collection considerably. Both are also grateful to all orthopterist colleagues world-wide as the result of whose work the study of orthopteroid insects has progressed in recent years. Specialists and centres of study in the U.K. and elsewhere are fully acknowledged in the text.

Individual contributors to the Orthoptera Recording Scheme are too numerous to mention here by name. However, for their special help and advice with details of distribution and habitat requirement, Chris Haes must particularly thank K. N. A. Alexander (National Trust); D. W. Baldock; P. D. Brock; Mrs. P. Copson; D. C. F. Cotton; R. S. Cropper; R. Cumming; M. Davies (Royal Society for the Protection of Birds); B. C. Eversham; A. P. Fowles (Nature Conservancy Council); D. J. R. Haigh; R. D. Hawkins; Mrs. A. Kelham; R. Long; R. McGibbon (NCC); I. K. Morgan; Mrs. M. J. Morgan; Dr. J. Paul; D. G. Rands; M. J. Skelton; Mrs. S. M. Turk; A. J. Wake; A. R. and Mrs. N. Welstead; J. R. White (NCC); and R. Williams.

Both authors and publishers would like to record their gratitude to Paul Harding and other staff at the Biological Records Centre of the Institute of Terrestrial Ecology, Monks Wood, for their considerable help with the preparation of the distribution maps and the gazetteer. Chris Haes supplied the information derived from the Orthoptera Recording Scheme and S. M. Hewitt and C. Ronayne prepared these maps specially for this book, using base maps supplied by the Biological Records Centre.

Authors and publishers would also like to thank John Burton for producing the companion *Sound Guide to the Grasshoppers and allied Insects of Great Britain and Ireland* and David Ragge for writing and recording the commentary; individual recorders are acknowledged on the cassette. Thanks are also due to Ron and Christine Foord for their superb colour photographs used on the book jacket and cassette sleeve.

On a personal note, Judith acknowledges the encouragement given by her husband John, and is grateful for the very practical assistance given by the use of his computer. Chris acknowledges the immeasurable degree of help and encouragement given to him, both in the field and in the preparation of the manuscript, by his late wife, Jane. All involved in this work feel the tragedy that she did not live to see the completed book.

Judith A. Marshall
Farnborough,
Hampshire

E. C. M. Haes
Angarrack, Hayle,
Cornwall

September 1988

Preface

The Appeal of Orthoptera

The hot sun of late July beats down on a dry grassy bank by a path. From this turf comes a chorus of brief, crisp, rasping chirps of field grasshoppers. Many of the small, slim 'stick-like' males are taking jerky little walks around the much stouter, sun-basking females, stridulating urgently, doubtless with amorous intentions, until an incautious movement by the observer sends them in all directions on their dry papery wings. Such a small but memorable incident demonstrates that Orthoptera are essentially to be enjoyed alive, for few insects fade and shrivel as unattractively after death. A cabinet of crickets or grasshoppers might have great scientific interest but it is only in life that they really exert an undoubtedly powerful aesthetic appeal. Their relatively large size and the way they are able to move their highly articulated bodies make them seem more mammalian in behaviour than most insects. This is particularly the case during feeding and courtship. The courtship of several British species is well worth watching – none more so than the fascinating courtship 'dance' of the male rufous grasshopper, which is locally common in warm, tree-sheltered places in the Cotswolds and chalk downland of southern England. Most naturalists who have witnessed the performance become imbued with an enthusiasm for the Orthoptera and a determination to learn more about the group.

Orthoptera certainly appeal to the ear. Many species make distinctive and often attractive sounds within the range of human hearing. Most stridulate only in fine warm weather and the sound readily becomes associated with memories of good summers. This is perhaps especially the case with the impressively large great green bush-cricket, which is common around many holiday resorts on the South Coast. W. H. Hudson, in his evocative book, *Hampshire Days,* published in 1903, considered that 'crystal beads dropped in a stream down a crystal stair would produce a sound somewhat like the insect's song'. Another species very familiar to the ear in much of southern England is the dark bush-cricket. Its chipping stridulation may usually be heard well into November, and becomes associated with subdued leaf-colours and the haunting, plaintive autumn song of a robin.

Our comparatively few species of native Orthoptera produce a surprisingly diverse range of sounds, most of which are highly specific and a valuable guide to identification in the field. Two hundred years ago, Gilbert White wrote enthusiastically about the calls of the field- and mole-crickets, but, although there is no mistaking the lovely eventide purring of mole-crickets or the ringing chirp of field-crickets in early summer, sadly both species are today very rarely heard in Britain, unless one is fortunate enough to locate their few surviving colonies. But visit the New Forest any time from the end of June until late autumn and it will be difficult to miss the gentle trilling of the tiny wood-cricket as choruses of many males stridulate beneath the fallen leaves, the ventriloquial sound seeming to come from a considerable distance, but in reality probably no more than a metre or two from one's feet.

Also in the Forest, from dangerously quaking bogs, may be heard at this time the odd 'bubble-popping' stridulation of the large marsh grasshopper. Whereas most of our other Orthoptera have more conventional rasping chirps, the local stripe-winged grasshopper produces a weird metallic scouring sound quite unlike that of any other species; while for those with the ability to hear high pitched sound, the continuous stridulation of Roesel's bush-cricket can become almost unbearable at close range!

At first glance, our grasshoppers and their relatives are not as immediately appealing as butterflies or dragonflies: most of our native species look to be somewhat leggy green or brown insects often with rather vague colour patterns. What is revealed through the close-up lens of a camera, however, invariably arrests attention: the prominent veining of the wings; the herring-bone muscles on the hind legs; the sharply chiselled faces with complex biting mouthparts – like those of some futuristic robot – and glassy compound eyes; the intricate colour schemes full of minute but clean detail. All invite close scrutiny and arouse interest even in those who have little natural enthusiasm for insects. Orthopterans are undoubtedly photogenic and make excellent sport for wildlife photographers (see page 56). They are often exceedingly alert and it is usually difficult to obtain a really satisfactory photograph without a great deal of patience and the expenditure of much costly colour film, but the shots that are satisfactory seem to justify all the trouble.

The mature male of the woodland grasshopper is probably the most surprising when closely examined. Seen from above it looks to be a rather nondescript species of uniform charcoal colour but, close-up from the side, the chalk white palps by the mouth and the scarlet tip to its black abdomen adorned with thin white rings make it as showy as a spotted woodpecker. The same is more or less true of most of our other grasshoppers and bush-crickets; some variants of the mottled grasshopper exhibit the most complex patterns of all, reminiscent of those of the dazzle-paint camouflage patterns used on shipping during the First World War, with sometimes hardly any two individuals identical in a sample.

Nearly all thirty-five species of our native orthopteroids are thought to be close to the edge of their natural range in Britain where our mild but comparatively sunless, oceanic climate is far from ideal for them. However it is this very limitation which provides a further and perhaps most potent aspect of the appeal of our Orthoptera – that of discovery. From the historical survey which follows (p. 21), it will be apparent that, despite this small number of species, very few entomologists had made detailed studies of them until well into this century and they are a surprisingly under-researched group for such large and often conspicuous insects. A very great deal remains to be discovered, as is obvious from the remarkable facts which have come to light only in the last twenty or so years. At professional level, research by Dr J. C. Hartley and colleagues at Nottingham University during the 1960s and 1970s revealed, amongst other details, the protracted life-cycles of most of our bush-crickets; while work by Dr V. K. Brown at Imperial College in the early 1970s demonstrated a similar situation with our native cockroaches. Subsequent post-graduate work from both centres has added much more information that was unsuspected or only guessed at, particularly about our grasshoppers and bush-crickets.

In *British Grasshoppers and their Allies* (1936), Dr M. Burr stressed the neglect of the British Orthoptera and noted that there had been 'no unquestioned addition to our list for a century'. Since then five additional species have been confirmed. Professor K. G. Blair recognized the long-winged cone-head as a British species in the very year Burr's book was published. Subsequently, the scaly cricket, Cepero's ground-hopper, and the heath and lesser mottled grasshoppers have been added to our fauna (see historical account, p. 23). Almost as intriguing as the discovery of new species has been the discovery of long-recognized species in entirely new localities and even in quite unexpected habitats. The majority of such discoveries have been made by contributors to the national Orthoptera Recording Scheme during the last twenty years and include the recent finds of Roesel's and the dark bush-crickets in the Republic of Ireland, and the long-winged cone-head and lesser marsh grasshopper as substantial populations in places from which they were hitherto quite unknown and in habitats quite distinct from those in which they had previously been recorded.

Detailed ecological studies, especially of grasshoppers, have revealed that most of our more local native species are important as indicators of good habitats for other local animals as well as plants. Here both professionals and amateurs have contributed valuable observations but a vast amount remains to be discovered. It seems very probable that many further exciting discoveries await fortunate orthopterists carrying out distribution surveys in these islands, even of such familiar insects as the common earwig. It will be particularly interesting to see the effects (if any) on distribution of some species of the opening up of previously densely wooded areas resulting from the wholesale destruction of woodland in south-east England by the 'hurricane' of October 1987.

E. C. M. H.

PART I: INTRODUCTION

1. The Scope of the Book

This book lists and describes all the orthopteroid insects which are either native species or established aliens in the British Isles, including the Channel Islands. These comprise the bush-crickets, crickets, grasshoppers, cockroaches, earwigs and stick-insects. All the species included are known to be capable of breeding here, though sometimes in protected conditions such as greenhouses, *without* the assistance or encouragement of human agency. Many of the casual introductions may be capable of breeding here under similar circumstances but have not yet done so, or have succeeded only for a very brief time before being eradicated, or only when given the encouragement of a suitable, protected environment. For example, some of the cockroach species which are casual introductions with bananas from the West Indies have been bred in culture, but would not survive naturally.

The study of orthopteroid insects in Britain was revolutionized by the publication of *Grasshoppers, Crickets and Cockroaches of the British Isles* (Ragge, 1965). For anyone interested in Orthoptera, possession of a copy of 'Ragge' has been of prime importance, and such a copy will be very well worn. Unfortunately it has been out of print for many years, and good copies have become collectors' items.

The present work sets out to update and supplement Ragge – long established as the 'orthopterist's Bible'. In addition to new material on the orders covered by Ragge, the seven species of Dermaptera (earwig) found in Britain are also described and illustrated. The current status and distribution of a total of fifty-two orthopteroid species is given in detail, supported, in most cases, by dot-distribution maps compiled by the BRC in association with the Orthoptera Recording Scheme, set up in 1977. Following the destruction of habitats and their wildlife as a result of the use of herbicides and pesticides and of land 'development' over the past twenty years, the importance for our native Orthoptera of the conservation of suitable remaining habitats is given due emphasis in the three final chapters of this book. In chapters contributed by outside authors who are specialists in their fields, successful methods of taking photographs and making sound-recordings of these insects are also described.

As mentioned in the preface, which draws attention to the appeal of Orthoptera, much progress has been made in the study of this group since 1965. In addition to Hartley & Warne, and Brown and her associates, valuable developmental studies are being undertaken by Hewitt and colleagues at the University of East Anglia. Moreover, there are now many Continental workers on orthopteroid insects and some of their work has relevance to the British fauna. The results of these studies, particularly on distribution and biology, are referred to whenever possible; and there is an extensive Reference section in addition to a Select Bibliography of works that are essential reading for the serious student of orthopteroid insects.

2. Nomenclature and Classification

All animals as well as plants, both living and fossil forms, are given scientific names. This name usually describes some aspect of the creature or its habitat, or perhaps the name of the person who discovered it, and is formed of two parts – the generic and the specific name. The generic name, although it comes first, can be thought of as the surname of an individual, and the specific name, which follows it, as the 'forename'. Within each genus there may be many species, all having different specific names; each generic name is different from all the others but species' names may be repeated within different genera. Thus any pair of scientific names can refer to only one species of animal or plant.

When the different forms of animal and plant life were first described in the seventeenth and early eighteenth centuries, the practice was established for each one to be given a short description so that it could be distinguished from the others. The language used among scientists at that time was Latin, and so the whole descriptive sentence would be in Latin. The great Swedish naturalist, Carl Linnaeus (1707–78), developed the system of binominal nomenclature by which a precise pair of names is given to each creature. His method of naming all members of the animal kingdom, and indeed many of the names in use today, date from the publication of his *Systema Naturae* in the tenth edition, the date of publication being arbitrarily fixed as 1st January, 1758. Linnaeus had already published a similar system for names in the plant kingdom but the two kingdoms are treated separately. Thus the generic name *Bacillus* meaning 'a little rod' is used for a group of stick-insects as well as for the group of bacteria commonly referred to in the plural as bacilli.

As the early names were all in Latin, scientific names have continued to be in Latin or latinized Greek, or in a latinized form of some other language. The generic name always begins with an upper case (*i.e.* capital) letter and the specific name with a lower case letter, even if the species is named after a person or country. The specific name, when adjectival, should always agree in gender with that of the generic name. This is sometimes easy to follow, as when both have the masculine *-us* ending, e.g. *Omocestus viridulus*, though less clear when a masculine generic name ends in *a*, as in *Acheta domesticus*.

The name of the person or 'author' who originally described a species should be cited after the scientific name, at least on the first occasion to which it is referred within a publication. When a species has been transferred from the genus in which it was originally placed to another, this is indicated by the author's name being put in parentheses.

For the scientific name of an animal or plant to be considered valid it must be published in a recognized scientific journal or book, with an adequate description fulfilling universally accepted criteria. The complexities of scientific nomenclature were to become such that an International Commission on Zoological Nomenclature was established to set down and, from time to time, amend the rules and recommendations covering the formation and usage of scientific names, and these are collectively published as the *International Code of Zoological Nomenclature* (ICZN). The third and most recent edition of this (ed. Ride *et al.*) was published in 1985. Though these rules and recommendations may seem complicated and difficult, to quote from the preface to the first edition of 1961, 'biological nomenclature has to be an exact tool that will convey a precise meaning to all persons in all generations'. A similar commission and rules exist to govern the names of plants.

Unfortunately not everyone has the interest or opportunity to study the Code – and some of those who do so are none the wiser – in consequence of which many biologists remain unfamiliar with the 'rules of the game', and misapply names. This can lead to years of confusion in the naming of otherwise easily-recognizable species, as in the case of the laboratory stick-insect, *Carausius morosus* (*q.v.*, p. 143).

Another problem is that the rules are occasionally changed, or at least interpreted in different ways, as with the woodland grasshopper, which was described by Zetterstedt (1821) in the genus *Gryllus* using two specific names – *ventralis* for the females and *rufipes* for the males. He had not appreciated that they were the same species. Later entomologists recognized that the two were synonymous though, as the males are easier to identify, some used *rufipes* whereas others preferred *ventralis* because that name appeared on the page before *rufipes*. They were observing the rule of 'page priority': if two names are published for the same species, the one published first takes priority, even if the priority is by only one page. However another rule has also been agreed, which is that if a later scientific worker publishes a revisionary work and selects the later of two names, perhaps for the reason that it describes the more easily identified male, then this name shall take priority on the 'first reviser' principle. Such is the case with *Omocestus rufipes*.

When a species is named after a person, the specific name is correctly formed with a genitive ending, as in *Ectobius panzeri* (named after Georg Wolfgang Franz Panzer (1755–1829)). However, if the original author had incorrectly derived the name, the original spelling is still retained, as in *Metrioptera roeselii* (named after August Johann Roesel von Rosenhof (1705–59)) which is sometimes written linguistically correctly but scientifically wrongly as *M. roeseli*.

All genera are grouped together within wider categories of related organisms known as the 'family-groups', which are also subject to the provisions and recommendations of the ICZN. These family-group taxa are recognizable by their endings: the families, such as Tettigoniidae and Gryllidae (ending -idae), are placed within the higher groupings of superfamilies Tettigonioidea and Grylloidea (ending -oidea), but at a lower level they are subdivided into subfamilies (ending -inae) and further into tribes (ending -ini). Thus the family Tettigoniidae in Britain includes the Meconematinae, Conocephalinae and others, as well as the nominate, or name-bearing, subfamily Tettigoniinae. According to the rules of the code, each family-group name must be based on a genus – the 'type genus' – and derived from the plural form of the name, hence the subfamily name Meconematinae is derived from 'Meconemata', the plural of *Meconema*.

Again, the misuse of family-group names may also occur. In Volume 2 of his comprehensive *Orthoptera of Europe* (1975), Harz resurrected the subfamily name 'Locustinae'. This family-group name had not been in use for many years and was originally applied to the group of Orthoptera now known as the Tettigoniidae. Since the name is apparently derived from *Locusta* which is now the generic name of the migratory locust, Harz used the subfamily name to include all the European grasshoppers in the previously recognized 'Oedipodinae'. Harz disregarded the ICZN rules governing the usage of family-group names, as within the subfamily Locustinae he placed the tribes 'Vichetini' and 'Oedipodini' – but no Locustini! Furthermore, he included *Locusta* within the Oedipodini (not the 'Locustini'), and invented 'Vichetini', instead of deriving it from a generic name. Understandably though unfortunately, several European entomologists have followed his usage of Locustinae: in such a comprehensive and invaluable work as the Harz trilogy (1969, 1975 & [with Kaltenbach] 1976) errors of this nature are not anticipated. It may be necessary for the Commission to make a ruling in this case; in the meantime the previous usage of Oedipodinae is followed here, to include *Locusta* and, of course, *Oedipoda*.

There are no accepted rules for names above the family-group level, nor any rules for their formation, which is why a group of insects may have several different names, used either in different countries or simply by people who have different ideas. The principle grouping of insects within the Class Insecta is that of Order. Between Class and Order there may be major groupings such as Division and Cohort, and between Order and Family there may be Suborders and Infra-orders. The names of many Orders end in -ptera and are descriptive of the wings of that Order; Orthoptera means straight-wings, referring to the usually fairly-straight wing venation. The name Phasmida was the first name of ordinal status given to this group of insects, and is derived from their supposedly spectral appearance. Since this was published in 1815, the names Phasmatodea, Phasmoptera, Phasmatoptera and Cheleutoptera have all been created and may still be used by some authors.

It is important to recognize the relationships between groups of insects, both the similarities and the degree of difference. The Gryllidae (true crickets), and the Gryllotalpidae (mole-crickets) have for many years been recognized as belonging to different families, though Vickery & Kevan have since 1967 considered them sufficiently different to warrant their placement in different superfamilies. Upgradings of this nature may result in the eventual upgrading of almost every other family or tribal name within the Orthoptera, without actually changing the basic pattern of relationships. Indeed, studies by Dirsh (1973, 1975) resulted in his division of the Orthoptera Saltatoria into ten distinct Orders!

In 1976, a symposium was held at the XVth International Congress of Entomology on the subject 'The Higher Classification of Orthopteroid Insects', the proceedings of which were published the following year. As Kevan (1977) pointed out, 'almost no two works are alike in their treatment; there is no stability in the nomenclature of such higher categories as are recognized;...the situation...is probably less stable than for any other group of insects'. It was his hope that orthopteroid classification could be organized into 'some sort of logical plan' but this has not yet materialized, although he has since (1982, 1986) made further suggestions for orthopteroid classification. At the same meeting, whilst discussing the Tettigonioidea, Ragge (1977) also made a plea for stability, pointing out that raising subfamily ranks to family and above in order to emphasize the differences between groups does not actually help in understanding the relationships between them, and often leaves the lower categories of subfamily and tribe unemployed. It is important to keep an eye on balance; it seems that a specialist tends to raise the level or rank of the group on which he is working, to emphasize its importance. A conservative view is followed here whilst acknowledging that there are often excellent reasons for changing status by raising ranks or even by downgrading them, as did Rentz (1980) with the Decticinae (see p. 68).

3. Pronunciation of Scientific Names

It may be thought that it is difficult enough to worry about the correct spelling of a scientific name without considering the pronunciation. However, having learnt the scientific names of insects, communication with entomologists of different nationalities will be assisted if everyone uses a more or less standard form of pronunciation. Keen gardeners will appreciate the problems of communication which are involved here; if one knows the scientific name of a plant but not the 'accepted' pronunciation, it can be difficult to make oneself understood at nurseries or garden centres.

Unfortunately there are two distinct ways of pronouncing Latin for English-speakers: the traditional English form, used by gardeners and many biologists, and the academic or classical pronunciation, which approximates to the sound of the language as it was spoken by educated Romans. A detailed comparison of the two forms is given by Stearn (1973). Unfortunately for English-speaking biologists, the classical pronunciation is closer to that used on the Continent. Vowel sounds should be pronounced as follows:

'a' as in 'cat' 'i' as in 'it' 'u' as in 'put'
'e' as in 'egg' 'o' as in 'on'

Thus in *Meconema* the second 'e' should not be heard as 'ee'. For many years the name *brunneus* has here been pronounced as 'brunneus', when it should more accurately be pronounced 'brunneus'.

In addition, 'Ch' is always pronounced as 'k'
'c' before a, o and u is hard (as 'k')
'c' before e and i is soft (as 's')

Thus *Conocephalus* could phonetically be rendered as 'konosefalus' and *verrucivorus* should be pronounced as 'verrucivorus. (N.B. The 'c' here is soft, being before 'i', although in 'verruca' it is hard, being before 'a'.)

In view of this situation, when considering the announcements to be made for the accompanying cassette of Orthoptera songs, it was agreed that an attempt should be made to pronounce the scientific names in a manner approaching the classical form. They should thus be easily recognizable to Continental ears, without being totally unrecognizable to traditional 'English-Latin' users.

4. Common Names

Following Ragge's (1965) example, English common names have been quoted for all species. At his suggestion, one name has been changed. The species previously called the common field grasshopper, *Chorthippus brunneus*, is now known as the field grasshopper, since this is a better description of its Continental distribution. Only in the British Isles can *C. brunneus* be regarded as a 'common' field insect. Though previously thought to have been common and widespread in southern Europe, specimens from areas such as Spain have now been correctly identified as closely related species (Ragge, 1987b).

The name 'bush-cricket' is used in preference to the earlier term 'long-horned grasshopper' for all members of the family Tettigoniidae. 'Bush-cricket', first used by Burr in 1936, emphasizes the closer relationship of this family with the true, ground-dwelling crickets, Gryllidae, rather than with the grasshoppers, Acrididae. However in North America, Australia and other parts of the world where there is 'americanization', the common name of 'katydids' is often applied to bush-crickets. Since the name 'katydid' was originally imitative of the song produced by a particular North American bush-cricket whose distant European relatives do not make the same sounds, the term is not in general use here nor is it encouraged.

The vernacular name of a creature in one country may be very different even in a neighbouring country. Thus the ubiquitous *Blattella germanica*, known here as the German cockroach, was known in Germany as the 'Russian' cockroach, and in Russia as the 'Prussian'. In Britain it has also been called the 'shiner' and 'steamfly' from its shiny appearance and liking for humid environments; and in the U.S.A. it was named the 'Croton bug' when it appeared in large numbers after the building of the Croton Aqueduct to supply water to New York. Thus only by reference to the scientific name can one be sure of the identity of the species in question, particularly internationally.

Among the stick-insects, only *Acanthoxyla inermis* did not already have an English name and, since it is a smooth-bodied species in a usually fairly prickly-bodied genus, the 'unarmed' stick-insect is both a useful description and a literal translation of the scientific name.

The common name of most species is closely related to the specific scientific name, or even a direct translation of it. Thus 'the wart-biter' was named '*verrucivorus*' by Linnaeus, as he (being Swedish) knew that Swedish peasants had used them to bite off their warts!

In Scotland, and also in North America and Australia, the ground-hoppers are referred to as 'grouse locusts'; in Wales, grasshoppers are variously referred to as 'ceiliog y rhedhyn' (cock of the bracken), jac-y-jwmper' (Jack the Jumper), 'sioncyn/

sboncyn gwair' (sprightly one of the hay/grass) and, on Anglesey, as 'Robin sbonc' (sprightly Robin) (Elias, 1985). A standardized list of Welsh Names for Orthoptera is in preparation (Davies *et al.*, unpub.). Other local or dialect names no doubt exist in other regions. See Appendix V.

Although the common English names are given with the species descriptions, the scientific names have been quoted almost exclusively elsewhere throughout this work. However, it is appreciated that many will prefer to use the common name because this is either more familiar or easier to use. Moreover, quoting a common name orally avoids the problems of pronunciation of scientific names! (see also p. 19). Ideally, both common and scientific names should be known – not difficult for such a small group as the British orthopteroid insects. In order to assist the reader in recognizing a species under either its common or its scientific name, a book-mark is provided which lists both names and may be used for rapid reference at any point in the text.

5. Historical Account of the Study of Orthoptera

Of the 52 species of orthopteroid insects (including the 14 aliens) currently recognized as breeding here, only 11 were recorded in 1770, including three already-established alien species. There is no real evidence that the number of native species has increased since that time, though our knowledge of them certainly has, with five of them having been identified here with certainty only during the present century. The number of established aliens has, by contrast, actively increased over the years, with the potential for more to follow.

One of the earliest published works to include references to orthopteroid insects was *Theatrum Insectorum* by Thomas Moffet [Muffet, Moufet or Mouffet], whose daughter is still remembered, perhaps apocryphally, in the nursery rhyme as 'Little Miss Muffet' because of her fear of spiders. *The Theatre of Insects* was published in Latin in 1634 (though Moffet had prepared it before his death in 1604) incorporating information from the works of Gesner, Penny and Wotton, who had all predeceased him during the sixteenth century. An English translation of Moffet's book was published in 1658, as the third volume of *The History of Four-Footed Beasts and Serpents and Insects*.

Moffet discussed *Gryllus campestris* in some detail; he knew that they sing by 'rubbing their wings one against the other', and that they live in holes they dig in the ground, describing an ancient method by which children supposedly enticed them from their burrows with an ant 'tied about the middle with a hair'. However he preferred the method of inserting a 'small twig or straw' (or a 'pliant stalk of grass' (Gilbert White, 1789)) into the hole and then gently withdrawing it, the inhabitant following to chase it out.

The earliest published lists of named Orthoptera are those of Forster in 1770 and Berkenhout between 1769 and 1795, naming eleven different species of which eight were natives and three were established aliens. The native Saltatoria, which were all named at that time as species of *Gryllus*, included *viridissima* (as *verrucivorus*), *campestris*, *gryllotalpa*, *brunneus* (as *grossus*), *undulata* (as *bipunctata*) and *subulata*. That *viridissima* is the species to which they referred is likely from Berkenhout's description although the name used was '*verrucivorus*' (Kevan, 1952); and the name *grossus* can be interpreted as referring to *Chorthippus brunneus* and probably other grasshoppers too; Berkenhout called it the 'common grasshopper', and described it as having 'a ridge in the form of an X on the Corselet' [= pronotum]. It is often difficult, particularly with a poorly preserved specimen, to be sure of an identification, and where no specimens are in existence even a written description may be woefully inadequate. It may thus be impossible to decide exactly to which species the earlier authors were referring. Names were also misused, or may since have been applied to other species or synonymized; and several European species have been listed in the past and since discarded as erroneous entries in the 'British List'.

Two native Dermaptera were recorded by Forster: *Forficula auricularia* and (*Labia*) *minor*, though the only Blattodea listed were both established aliens. *Blatta orientalis* and (*Blattella*) *germanica*. The third alien listed at that time was *Acheta* (as *Gryllus*) *domesticus*.

Forster had addressed himself to those collecting insects, requesting them 'to favour him, if possible, with specimens of such insects, as they can spare, and which he is not possessed of' marking in his list those which he required. This must have aroused some interest, and when Curtis produced his *Guide to an Arrangement of British Insects* (1829–31), the number of known species of Orthoptera had increased to 27 natives and five established aliens, although he actually listed over 50 species because he included many names now known to be synonyms, varieties and misidentifications. In his Guide, Curtis incorporated information from Donovan's *Natural History of British Insects* (1792–1813) and from his own *British Entomology* (1825).

The species listed by Curtis included the Tettigoniidae *Meconema thalassinum* (as *varium*), *Decticus verrucivorus* (and also the named 'brown' variant *bingleii*), *Pholidoptera griseoaptera* (appearing in these early records as *cinerea* and *aptera*), *Platycleis albopunctata* (also as *grisea* and *denticulata*), *Metrioptera brachyptera*, *Conocephalus dorsalis* (misnamed as *fuscus*), and *Leptophyes punctatissima* (as *standishii* and *virescens*). Some of the Acrididae were similarly misnamed; *Stethophyma grossum* (as *flavipes*) was listed under *Locusta* with *Omocestus viridulus* and *Stenobothrus lineatus*, whilst *Gomphocerus* included *Chorthippus brunneus* (as *biguttulus*) and *C. albomarginatus* (as *elegans*) as well as *Gomphocerippus rufus* and *Myrmeleotettix maculatus* (as *caledoniensis* and *ericetarius*). *Nemobius sylvestris* was also listed, and all three native *Ectobius* species, although five different names were used. The established aliens by this time included *Periplaneta americana* and *Labidura riparia*.

The first work to provide any information on the distribution of orthopteroids was that of Stephens (1835) in his *Illustrations of British Entomology*. He quoted localities known to him for each species, added (*Metrioptera*) *roeselii* to the British list, and also included (*Omocestus*) *rufipes* and (*Chorthippus*) *parallelus*. However he listed many more names than there are recognized species, *e.g.* for *Tetrix undulata* (as *bipunctata*) he said 'no two examples are found precisely alike' and gave eleven named varieties, based on colour pattern, adding that numerous intermediate varieties are known!

The list published by White (1855) included *Oedipoda caerulescens*, although he indicated that this species had been introduced by shipping. He also included a number of other species, several of which had previously been listed by other authors, and which have since been discounted as 'British' inhabitants: these include such southern European species as *Podisma pedestris* and *Oecanthus pellucens*. One more dermapteran species was added: *Apterygida media* (as *albipennis*).

In his *Synopsis of the British Orthoptera*, Shaw (1889–90) was able to record the arrival of *Periplaneta australasiae* in Belfast, and gave useful descriptions, and analytical tables to the genera and species – at the request of 'several entomological friends'. He also quoted information on localities collected from by several colleagues, after modestly introducing the work by stating that his 'knowledge of the British Orthoptera is but imperfect and scanty'. The first published book solely on the British Orthoptera was that of Burr (1897), in which he included the alien species, (*Pycnoscelus*) *surinamensis*, (*Euborellia*) *annulipes* and (*Marava*) *arachidis*, and the native *Forficula lesnei*. The known natives remained unchanged with the publication of *A Monograph of the British Orthoptera* by Lucas (1920). In this he gave a comprehensive account of each species, including the original description and information on habits and habitats, much of it drawn from his previously published notes in *The Entomologist* to which he continued to contribute after 1920. The established aliens recognized by Lucas included *Tachycines asynamorus*. He also included *Phaneroptera falcata* as a possible British species, based on two reports, including a specimen, from Cornwall; and there is also a dubious sight record from Dorset. Ragge (1965) considered that these records were 'inadequate for the acceptance of this insect as British', although Payne (1969) hopefully – but disappointedly – searched for it in Cornwall.

Lucas listed seventeen species recorded on the Channel Islands, which included *Oedipoda caerulescens* 'not uncommon in Guernsey, also from Jersey'; *Chorthippus vagans* from 'Jersey, apparently rather common'; a specimen from Jersey referred to as *Omocestus haemoroidalis* (but of questionable status (Kevan, 1952)); and a reference to *Euchorthippus pulvinatus* as 'doubtfully recorded for Jersey'.

When describing the 'brown' form of *Decticus verrucivorus*, which Curtis had named as *D. bingleii*, Lucas mentioned a greenish tinge which is not normally seen in the Continental brown specimens. It is probable that all the 'brown' forms in British collections are actually faded green specimens: Dalton (1953) recorded a var. *bingleii* from Corfe Castle, collected in 1923. There were two specimens, both of which are in the BM(NH) collection, and both are brown with a greenish hue. However, the specimens were recorded at the time by Campion (1923), who stated 'both specimens were of the green form, the brown not having been met with'.

Two rather dubious records quoted by Lucas, *Myrmecophilus acervorum* and *Gomphocerus sibiricus*, both reputedly collected from Netley in Shropshire, can certainly be discounted.

Since 1920, five more species have been recognized as British natives. The first, just in time to be put into an addendum to Burr's *British Grasshoppers and their Allies* in 1936, was *Conocephalus discolor*, first collected by Blair in 1931, although he assumed he had 'the rare fully-winged form' of the brachypterous species *C. dorsalis*. Only on seeing a genuine macropterous *C. dorsalis* a few years later did he appreciate *C. fuscus* as it was then known (Blair, 1936). The next species to be recognized as a British native and confirmed by Uvarov (1940) was *Tetrix ceperoi*. Uvarov (1922) had also suspected the presence of the third new species, *Chorthippus vagans*, which was confirmed by Frazer (1944) from specimens he had collected in Dorset in 1934. Fourthly, *Pseudomogoplistes squamiger* (as *Mogoplistes*) has been regularly found on Chesil Beach, Dorset since its discovery in 1949 (Bowen & Williamson, 1950), though whether it is truly native is open to question (see p. 98). The fifth native species, *Stenobothrus stigmaticus*, was discovered on the Isle of Man in 1962 (Ragge, 1963).

During this century three species of Phasmida from New Zealand have established breeding colonies here: (*Acanthoxyla*) *geisovii* (Kirby, 1910), *Clitarchus hookeri* (Uvarov, 1950), and most recently, *Acanthoxyla inermis* (Brock, 1986). One Asian species, *Carausius morosus*, cultured in Europe since the turn of the century (Ragge, 1973) has also established temporary breeding colonies in greenhouses.

The first 'distributional' maps, on a county basis, were provided by Burr (1936) with the purpose of 'stimulating interest and collecting in the districts left blank'. For the same purpose, Ragge (1965) produced more detailed maps using the Watson–Praeger vice-county system, and it is with similar intentions that Skelton (1973) and Haes (1979) have since published their provisional distribution atlases based on the 10km square Ordnance Survey grid.

A number of important local surveys have been published since the work of Lucas: a study of the Littlesea, Dorset area (Diver & Diver, 1933); county surveys of Norfolk (Ellis, 1943) and Somerset (Cowley, 1949), and of the London area (Payne, R. M., 1958b); and the classic population study in Silwood Park in 1947–51 (Richards & Waloff, 1954). A major contribution to the study of British Orthoptera has been the summaries of known distribution of the species by Kevan (1952, 1953, 1954 and 1961).

Much information drawn from these papers, and from other biological studies by various authors, was incorporated by Ragge (1965) in his monograph, *Grasshoppers, Crickets and Cockroaches of the British Isles*, covering all the British orthopteroids except earwigs. Among the discoveries up to that time he also included *Supella longipalpa* (as *supellectilium*), the most recent of the established aliens. In that invaluable work, Ragge provided accounts of the habitat, life history, habits and song of both native and alien species, drawn mainly from his own observations, with identification keys to all species as well as to the colour varieties of the grasshoppers. An updating supplement by the same author was published eight years later (Ragge, 1973), and a detailed historical account of the British Orthoptera since 1800 was given by Marshall (1974).

In her *Grasshoppers*, which covers bush-crickets as well as grasshoppers, Brown (1983) writes particularly for those such as sixth-formers and others without university training but with the opportunity and inclination to study local natural history. The work usefully draws attention to areas of scientific research already covered, and to others within the capability of the amateur naturalist that still await study.

6. The Distribution and History of the British Orthoptera*

by D.R. Ragge

The patchy distribution of many of our Orthoptera may seem puzzling at first sight. It may seem strange that the stripe-winged and rufous grasshoppers (*Stenobothrus lineatus* and *Gomphocerippus rufus*), common in many places in southern England, should not occur in the usually favoured New Forest area; that the bog bush-cricket (*Metrioptera brachyptera*) should be found only on heathy bogs and not on grassy ones; or, perhaps, that there are about twice as many different kinds of Orthoptera to the south of a line drawn from the Bristol Channel to the Wash as there are to the north. These, and most other features of the distribution of the British Orthoptera, largely result from the operation of three factors – climate, geology and vegetation: a brief account of the influence of each of these is given below.

Climate

Orthoptera, like most other insects, are lovers of warmth and sunshine, and this is of course the main reason for their greater abundance in southern England than in any other part of the British Isles. The southern and south-eastern coasts of England have an average of nearly five hours of bright sunshine per day; most of the remaining parts of our isles have fewer than four.

On a smaller scale, climatic effects can be enhanced by the lie of the land. A south-facing slope is warmer and sunnier than one with a northerly aspect; it is also sheltered from cold north winds. Some of the best localities in the country for Orthoptera are in the form of south-facing hollows or 'amphitheatres' in a hillside; such places are sun-traps where the air is often still and where the conditions approach those of more southerly latitudes.

Climate also partly accounts for the poverty of our orthopterous fauna as compared with that of northern Germany and Poland, which lie in the same latitudes as the British Isles: these countries have a continental climate with a rather warmer summer than our oceanic one. However, some of these north German species could doubtless thrive in southern England, and the reason for their absence here lies in our comparatively recent geological and climatic history. Although our knowledge of this history is very poor and the evidence extremely scanty, a very brief account of the events that are now generally agreed to have taken place is given below.

Our reconstruction begins with the onset of the Great Ice Age (*Pleistocene* period) over a million years ago. The very warm conditions of the preceding (*Pliocene*) period, when animals such as elephants, rhinoceroses and the sabre-toothed tiger occurred in England, were interrupted by a number (possibly five) of very cold periods, or *glaciations*; each of these glaciations consisted in turn of glacial phases with brief temperate phases between them. In each glacial phase an enormous ice-

*Reproduced, with minor amendments, from Ragge, 1965.

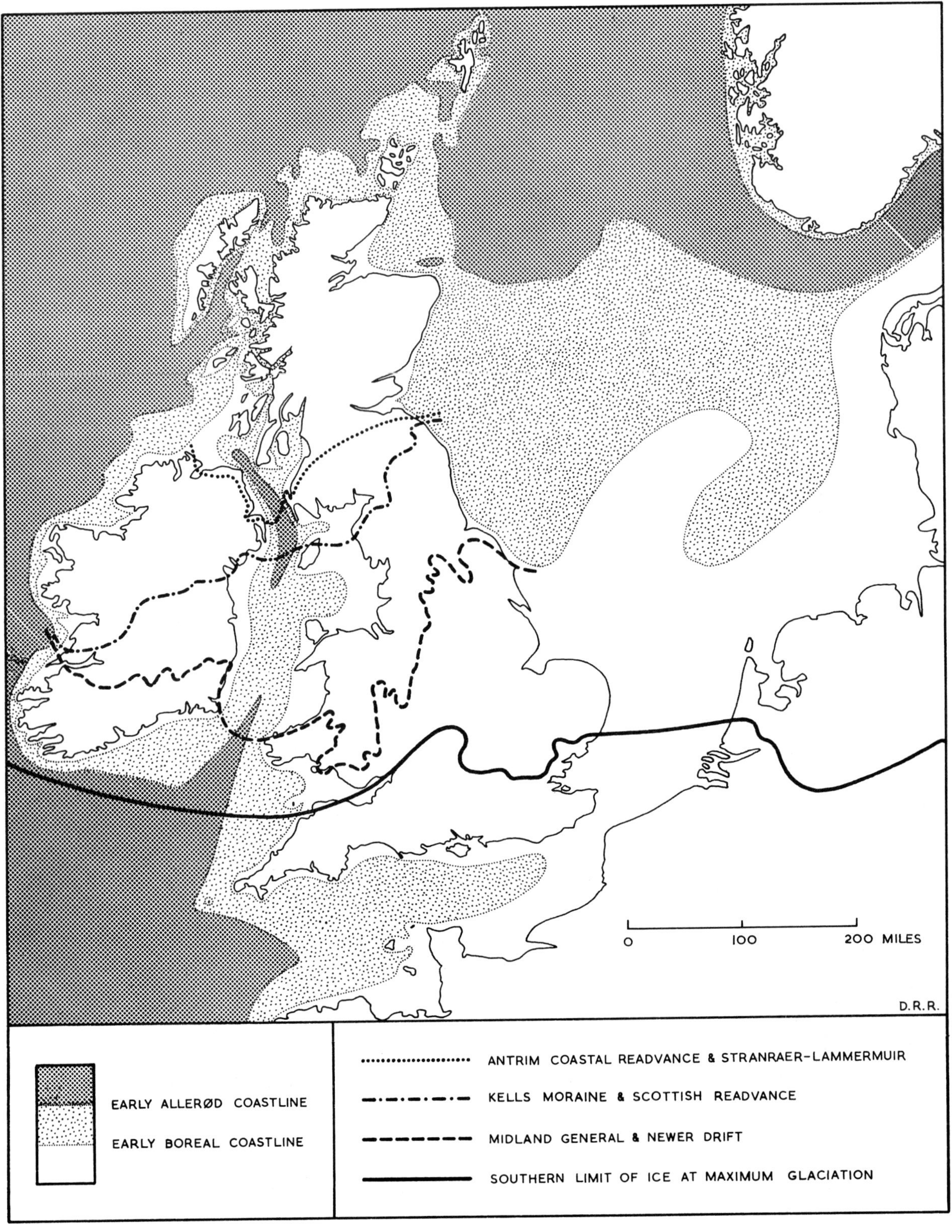
0
100
200 MILES
D.R.R.
EARLY ALLERØD COASTLINE
EARLY BOREAL COASTLINE
ANTRIM COASTAL READVANCE & STRANRAER-LAMMERMUIR
KELLS MORAINE & SCOTTISH READVANCE
MIDLAND GENERAL & NEWER DRIFT
SOUTHERN LIMIT OF ICE AT MAXIMUM GLACIATION

sheet, first forming on the mountains of Scandinavia, spread southwards across northern Europe, and so much water became ice that the sea-level sometimes fell by over a hundred metres. Large areas of land at present covered by sea became exposed, so that Great Britain was joined to the Continent by a broad land bridge and Ireland was in turn connected to Great Britain.

When the most extensive ice-sheets were formed over the British Isles, perhaps during the third and fourth (but not the last) glaciations, the whole of Ireland, except possibly for one or two small areas in the south, and almost all of Great Britain north of the Thames were covered with ice (see text fig. 1). Conditions in the small area of southern England that escaped glaciation were perhaps rather like those of Spitzbergen today, and it seems certain that none of our Orthoptera could have survived in this tundra-like environment, either within the present confines of the British Isles or in the areas that are now covered by the English Channel and North Sea. It is possible, however, that species that occur today in northern Scandinavia and the Alps, such as *Melanoplus frigidus* (Boheman), managed to survive the glaciations in the southernmost parts of the British Isles, and many other species would have entered this country during the warmer periods between glaciations.

Towards the end of the last glaciation, perhaps 12,000 years ago, the comparatively warm conditions that still prevail today set in, and it seems likely that it was during this late-glacial period (from the early part of the Allerød period onwards – see text fig. 2) that our present Orthoptera began to arrive in this country. The earliest arrivals were probably such cold-tolerant species as the field and common green grasshoppers (*Chorthippus brunneus* and *Omocestus viridulus*), the common ground-hopper (*Tetrix undulata*) and the speckled and oak bush-crickets (*Leptophyes punctatissima* and *Meconema thalassinum*). It seems that these species, together with the mottled, large marsh and lesser marsh grasshoppers (*Myrmeleotettix maculatus*, *Stethophyma grossum* and *Chorthippus albomarginatus*) and the mole-cricket (*Gryllotalpa gryllotalpa*), must have reached Ireland while it was still connected to Great Britain by a land bridge. At this time the only land connection was probably between Northern Ireland and Scotland, and the present-day islands of Islay and Jura would have formed part of it. When the sea-level was at its lowest during colder periods, however, further connections would have existed between Eire and Wales (see text fig. 1). The most interesting fact that the meadow grasshopper (*Chorthippus parallelus*), so common over most of the Highlands, does not apparently occur in Ireland or the Isle of Man suggests that these islands must have been cut off from Great Britain before this species had penetrated very far north; its inability to fly may have accounted for its slow northward spread.

It can be seen from text figures 1 and 2 that at the time when the first of our Orthoptera were arriving in this country, Shetland and the Outer Hebrides were already nearly surrounded by sea and that, by the onset of the Boreal period (about

---

Text Figure 1 Map of the British Isles and adjacent parts of the Continent, showing possible past coastlines and the retreat stages of the last ice-sheet. The lines showing edges of ancient ice-sheets refer to periods well before the times of the two past coastlines (from Ragge, 1963, 1965)

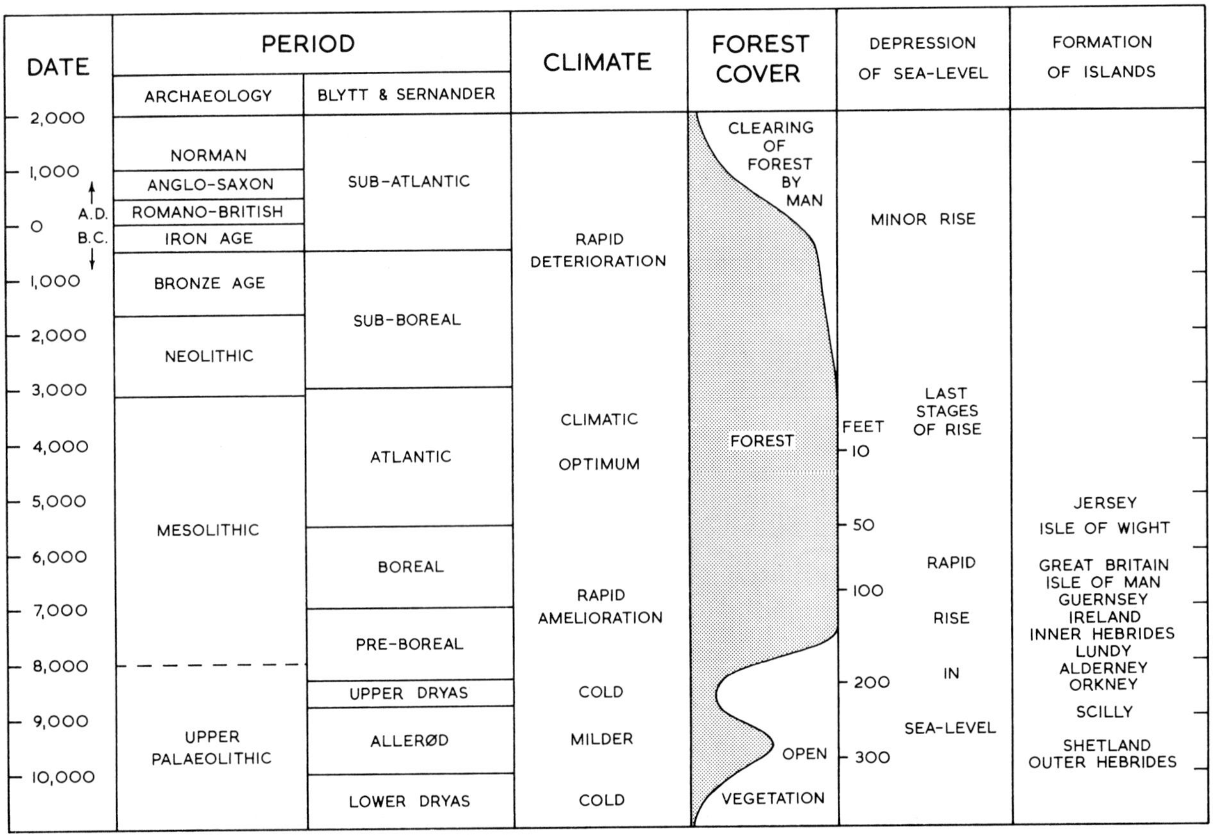

DATE	PERIOD: ARCHAEOLOGY	PERIOD: BLYTT & SERNANDER	CLIMATE	FOREST COVER	DEPRESSION OF SEA-LEVEL	FORMATION OF ISLANDS
2,000	NORMAN	SUB-ATLANTIC		CLEARING OF FOREST BY MAN		
1,000 A.D.	ANGLO-SAXON					
0	ROMANO-BRITISH				MINOR RISE	
B.C.	IRON AGE		RAPID DETERIORATION			
1,000	BRONZE AGE	SUB-BOREAL				
2,000	NEOLITHIC					
3,000	MESOLITHIC	ATLANTIC	CLIMATIC OPTIMUM	FOREST	LAST STAGES OF RISE	
4,000					FEET 10	
5,000		BOREAL			50	JERSEY ISLE OF WIGHT
6,000					RAPID	GREAT BRITAIN ISLE OF MAN GUERNSEY
7,000		PRE-BOREAL	RAPID AMELIORATION		100 RISE	IRELAND INNER HEBRIDES LUNDY
8,000	UPPER PALAEOLITHIC	UPPER DRYAS	COLD		200 IN	ALDERNEY ORKNEY
9,000		ALLERØD	MILDER		SEA-LEVEL	SCILLY
10,000		LOWER DRYAS	COLD	OPEN VEGETATION	300	SHETLAND OUTER HEBRIDES

Text Figure 2 Table summarizing various aspects of the past 12,000 years of the history of the British Isles. The first four columns are based on Godwin (1956); the remaining two columns represent no more than tentative suggestions (from Ragge, 1965)

7,000 B.C.), Scilly, Orkney and Lundy had become islands. Ireland and the Inner Hebrides were also cut off from the mainland at about this time, and the Isle of Man and Great Britain probably became islands a little later, during the Boreal period. The final separation of Great Britain from the Continent, which took place perhaps 8,000–9,000 years ago, prevented the invasion of the British Isles by further species of Orthoptera. The Orthoptera that occur in northern Germany and the Low Countries but not in this country, and which could undoubtedly find conditions favourable to their existence in southern England, had probably not yet reached northern France at the time when England became separated from the Continent. This seems to be the most likely reason for the absence from the British Isles of such species as *Chorthippus biguttulus* (L.), which is very common in the vicinity of Calais and Boulogne. These small grasshoppers and bush-crickets seldom fly more than a few yards, and a stretch of water of a few miles (perhaps much less than this) seems to form an effective barrier to the spread of species such as these, even allowing for the effect of a strong wind.

The comparatively recent discovery of the lesser mottled grasshopper (*Stenobothrus stigmaticus*) on the Isle of Man, and its apparent absence from any other part of the British Isles, has posed something of a problem. Our Orthoptera show a strong preference for the more southerly parts of the British Isles, and only half of the native species extend their ranges as far north as the Isle of Man; only five species had in fact been previously recorded from the island itself. Even the species that occur as far north as Orkney are common along the south coast of England, and the lesser mottled grasshopper is the only species that has not been found south of the Thames.

The possibility of this species having been recently introduced into the Isle of Man from a Continental source seems very unlikely, especially as the Manx specimens are noticeably smaller than Continental ones. There is no known case of a native Continental species of Orthoptera being accidentally introduced into the British Isles, and the Isle of Man is one of the least likely places for this to happen (although introduction at the time of the Viking invasions and settlement is a remote possibility). A natural origin of this grasshopper on the island is nevertheless very difficult to explain, as it implies that the species was at one time distributed over much of southern England. However, its subsequent (apparent) extinction on the mainland could perhaps have been brought about by competition with the meadow grasshopper, which is so abundant throughout England on a wide variety of habitats, but which does not occur on the Isle of Man. For a fuller discussion of this problem, see Ragge (1963).

Geology

Many of the best British localities for Orthoptera owe their attraction for these insects to the underlying soil and rock. This is often because the local geology makes the land undesirable for agriculture; for example an underlying bed of clay may make the land waterlogged, or an extensive outcrop of hard rock may have produced a hill too steep to be used for arable farming. Areas of sand or gravel are often too infertile to be used for agricultural purposes, and the soil on chalk downland may be too shallow to be ploughed. Infertile soils are particularly favourable to grasshoppers; they do not support a lush vegetation, which would prevent much of the sunlight from reaching the ground, and they are often exposed in bare patches where these insects can lay their egg-pods and bask in the sun. As arable land and closely-grazed pasture, which form a large proportion of the land in the British Isles, are usually unsuitable for Orthoptera, areas where the land cannot be used for these purposes are likely to be of particular interest to the orthopterist.

One of the most striking examples of the influences of geology on the distribution of our Orthoptera is the Hampshire Basin (text fig. 3). Here, a large area of Tertiary beds, largely made up of sands and clays, is entirely surrounded by chalk downland and has produced in the New Forest, Isle of Purbeck and Isle of Wight the best localities for Orthoptera in the British Isles. The characteristic bogs of the New Forest and northern Purbeck, providing suitable habitats for the large marsh grasshopper and bog bush-cricket, are a direct result of the local geology.

In the New Forest, they are formed where there are valleys in the Barton Beds; the Barton Clay, which forms the lower part of these beds, causes the ground above to become waterlogged. Such bogs as Matley Bog, Denny Bog, Crabtree Bog,

Hinchelsea Bog and the large bog in Harvest Slade Bottom are all formed in this way. It is because of the waterlogged nature of the soil that the stripe-winged grasshopper does not occur in the New Forest area and the field grasshopper is rather scarce there. These two species are confined to well-drained habitats.

In the northern part of the Isle of Purbeck very similar bogs occur wherever there are dips in the heathland. This heathland is on the Bagshot Beds, which are similar to the Barton Beds of the New Forest and were laid down shortly before them; they consist of white and yellow sands with seams of pipe-clay, and it is these seams that prevent the free drainage of water and cause the formation of bogs. The bog known as Hartland Moor, now a Nature Reserve, was formed in this way, and provides a very suitable habitat for the large marsh grasshopper and bog bush-cricket.

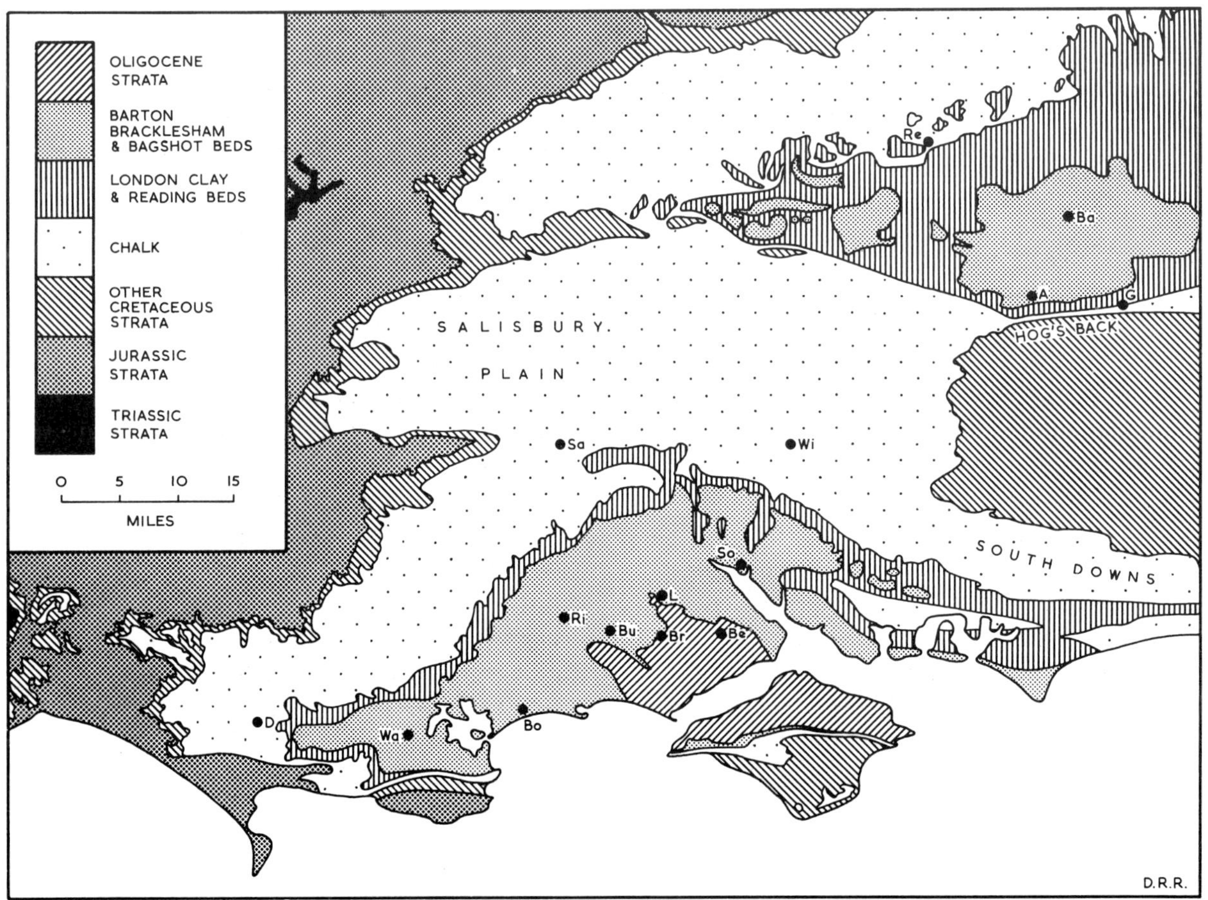

Text Figure 3 Map showing the geology of the Hampshire Basin and surrounding areas. A = Aldershot, Ba = Bagshot, Be = Beaulieu, Bo = Bournemouth, Br = Brockenhurst, Bu = Burley, D = Dorchester, G = Guildford, L = Lyndhurst, Re = Reading, Ri = Ringwood, Sa = Salisbury, So = Southampton, Wa = Wareham, Wi = Winchester (from Ragge, 1965)

Conditions ideal for the stripe-winged grasshopper are to be found on the southern slopes of the Purbeck Hills. These are composed of steeply inclined beds of the Cretaceous rock chalk, forming an east to west ridge from Lulworth to Ballard Point. The Isle of Wight has a similar chalk ridge, once connected to the Purbeck ridge, and here again the stripe-winged grasshopper occurs on the southern slopes.

One can say, then, that in the Hampshire Basin area such species as the heath grasshopper (*Chorthippus vagans*), large marsh grasshopper and bog bush-cricket are associated with the Tertiary beds, and the stripe-winged grasshopper is characteristic of the chalk. The conditions provided by the Tertiary beds can support a much richer orthopterous fauna than those provided by the chalk, and this is why the New Forest and Isle of Purbeck, in comparison with the large surrounding area of downland, are such good hunting grounds for the orthopterist.

A knowledge of local geology sometimes enables one to predict the occurrence of certain species of Orthoptera in areas that one has not yet explored. A glance at a geological map of southern England will show at once that the geological features of the Hampshire Basin are repeated in the London Basin (part of which can be seen in text fig. 3): Tertiary beds lie between the chalk of the Chiltern Hills to the north and the North Downs to the south. We have seen how the infertile sands and clays of the New Forest area and the northern part of the Isle of Purbeck have produced the barren heaths and bogs that are characteristic of these regions. This kind of terrain is produced by the Bagshot, Bracklesham and Barton Beds, and if we look for the recurrence of these beds in the London Basin we should expect to find a similar terrain there. This is indeed so: these beds occur over a large area centred round Sandhurst, Bagshot and Chobham, and associated with them are heaths of the New Forest type. To the east of the Chobham ridges is an area of low-lying heathland on the Barton and Bracklesham Beds that is very reminiscent of the New Forest heaths, which are on the same beds. The lower parts are waterlogged and form quaking bogs of exactly the same type as those of the New Forest and the northern Purbeck. The bog bush-cricket is common and the large marsh grasshopper maintains a small colony in this area. The view northwards from the Hog's Back, which is a ridge composed of steeply inclined beds of chalk (see text fig. 3), vividly recalls the northward view from the similarly composed Purbeck Hills; the effect of the local geology on the terrain and vegetation is striking.

Another species whose distribution is much influenced by geology is the rufous grasshopper. This insect seems to have a definite preference for alkaline soils in this country and is almost always associated with limestone: it does not occur, for example, on the acid soils of the Hampshire Basin. The best localities are provided by the chalk of the North Downs and the oolite of the Cotswolds, and the main distributional centres of this species follow these two formations closely.

Vegetation

Let us first look briefly at the recent history of the vegetation of the British Isles. Towards the end of the last glaciation of the Great Ice Age, about 12,000 years ago, the open, tundra-like vegetation that occurred near the ice-sheets retreated northwards and woodland, composed mainly of birch, began to take its place. As the climate became warmer the woodland spread over the whole of the country; the woods of the Allerød period (see text fig. 2) were gradually replaced by pine and hazel in the pre-Boreal and Boreal periods, and these trees were in turn replaced during the Atlantic and sub-Boreal periods by alder, oak, elm and lime. The development of these forests must have greatly impeded the northward and westward spread of most of our Orthoptera, and, indeed, during the 8,000 years that elapsed from then until the clearing away of the forest by man, many of our species must have been confined to small areas where, for some reason (including perhaps the activities of Middle Stone Age (*Mesolithic*) man, the vegetation was more open.

About 3,000 years after the forest cover of the British Isles had been established, the climate reached its optimum and was quite distinctly warmer than it is now. Conditions were fairly dry in the first part of this climatic optimum, but later they became much moister and more oceanic, perhaps partly as a result of the British Isles being cut off from the Continent by the rising sea. With the increase in rainfall, the mountainous regions of the country, previously forest-clad, developed a cover of boggy moorland, and a similar change in vegetation took place in some low-lying areas near the coast.

It was in the New Stone (*Neolithic*) Age, about 3,000 B.C., that the activities of man first began to have an important effect on our vegetation. With their newly-developed polished stone axes, primitive men of this period were able to fell trees over large areas, and it was almost certainly at this time that the forest was cleared from the Breckland area of East Anglia. New Stone Age man was probably also responsible for the clearing of trees from the other limestone uplands of southern England – the Cotswolds, Mendips, North and South Downs and Salisbury Plain. This deforestation continued through the succeeding Bronze Age, and there is some suggestion that a drier climate during this period may have helped to make conditions on the thin chalkland soils unfavourable for trees.

By the onset of the Iron Age (about 2,500 years ago, or 500 B.C.), the climatic optimum was over and the conditions of our present oceanic climate, with cooler summers and less severe winters, set in. Many boggy areas that had become rather dry and, in some cases, covered with birch woodland now became waterlogged again. In the forest, birch once more became an important constituent and beech became much more widespread, colonizing parts of the chalk and oolite hills that had probably been deforested during the New Stone Age.

From the Iron Age onwards the clearing of the forest by man proceeded very rapidly; charcoal was needed for smelting iron, and timber was soon in demand for a great many purposes. By the end of the Roman occupation, only about half of our original forest cover remained, and our Orthoptera must have been able to distribute themselves much more freely. In Norman times came the reservation of the royal forests, which were not all woodland, and the orthopterous fauna of these areas has probably remained much the same during the last thousand years. At the present time, less than eight per cent of the British Isles is wooded; only a small fraction of these woodlands is composed of remnants of our original forest cover and about a third is new woodland planted by the Forestry Commission.

The effect of the recent history of the vegetation of the British Isles on the distribution of our Orthoptera must clearly have been profound. The almost complete forest cover that persisted for some 5,000 years much have restricted these insects to very small areas, including perhaps coastal districts, riversides and bogs. The northward and westward spread of Orthoptera during the early post-glacial period must have been greatly hampered by the scarcity of open vegetation, and even as recently as 2,000 years ago the limestone downlands of southern England must have provided the only large areas that could be extensively colonized by our more common grasshoppers. The scrubby vegetation favoured by the dark, great green and speckled bush-crickets must also have been very sparse until recent historic times. It seems likely that those of our species that are found only in the vicinity of the coast, such as the lesser cockroach (*Ectobius panzeri*), grey bush-cricket (*Platycleis albopunctata*), long-winged cone-head (*Conocephalus discolor*) and Cepero's ground-hopper (*Tetrix ceperoi*), still have the restricted distribution that was forced on them by the forest cover when they arrived some 8,000 years ago, and have for some reason been unable to spread inland since the clearing of the forest by man. These species show no preference for coastal localities on the Continent.

Some idea of the effect of the present vegetation of the British Isles on the distribution of our Orthoptera may be gained from the remarks on habitat given in the account of each species and in Part III of the book (p. 149). One or two general remarks, however, may be made here. Few of the British Orthoptera are able to exist on arable land, in dense woodland or in built-up areas, and as these categories together constitute about half the area of the British Isles they very much reduce the amount of land available to our Orthoptera. A further third of our land-area is composed of permanent pasture, and other minor categories that have undergone agricultural or economic development. These areas are also unsuitable for most of our Orthoptera, though pasture-land often supports a sparse population of our most common grasshoppers. This means that less than twenty per cent of the British Isles can be regarded as providing really favourable habitats for Orthoptera.

Of this twenty per cent, the greater part consists of heathland and moorland, often lightly grazed by sheep and cattle; about a third of this rough pasture (four per cent of the land area in England and Wales) is common land. Most of this moorland is in Wales, northern England, the Highlands of Scotland and the Irish uplands, so that in southern England, to which a third of our Orthoptera are confined, these favourable areas are much scarcer; they include, however, such well-known areas as Bodmin Moor, Dartmoor, Exmoor, the New Forest and Ashdown Forest, all of which are excellent hunting grounds for the orthopterist. There are innumerable smaller areas of heathland in southern England, but many of these are being divested of their Orthoptera, both by being trampled on by large numbers of people during fine summer weekends and through becoming overgrown with bracken. The increasing amount of urban development is also destroying many areas suitable for Orthoptera and some that provide habitats for our rarities. It is clear that the British Isles have long since passed their peak of favourability to Orthoptera (this was perhaps some 500 years ago) and some of our rarer species, particularly the field-cricket (*Gryllus campestris*) and mole-cricket, are certainly approaching extinction.

7. Orthopteroid Morphology

Insects, being invertebrates (*i.e.* without backbones), have segmented bodies with an external, chitinous skeleton, with bilateral symmetry (text fig. 4a). The segments are formed of sclerites, linked by membranes to permit movement. The body has three main divisions: head, thorax (carrying the legs and wings) and abdomen.

Head

The head capsule (text figs 4b,c), which is formed by the embryonic fusion of six segments, bears the paired antennae and compound eyes, with (usually) three ocelli between the eyes, and the mouthparts. The top of the head (or *vertex*) may have a broadened apex (or *fastigium*), or project beyond the antennae as a conical elongation. The Acrididae have a pair of depressions (or *foveolae*) on the vertex.

The compound eyes are large and efficient in the perception of movement, particularly in the carnivorous Mantodea and Tettigoniidae. The simple eyes (or *ocelli*) merely detect the presence of light. When three ocelli are present, one is placed centrally on the front of the head (or *frons*). The Blattodea have only the lateral pair of ocelli, also known as *fenestrae*.

The mouthparts comprise the uppermost lip (or *labrum*), covering the paired *mandibles* and *maxillae* and the fused *labium*. Orthopteroids have primitive mouthparts: strongly toothed mandibles for biting and maxillae for chewing, and long, sensitive palps on the maxillae and labium which are used in food testing and handling.

Thorax

The thorax is formed of three segments, each of which carries a pair of legs ventrally: the second and third (meso- and meta-thoracic) segments having a pair of wings dorsally. The tergite (or dorsal sclerite) of the first (or prothoracic) segment – termed the *pronotum* – may extend backwards, covering at least the wing bases. In the Dictyoptera and Dermaptera the pronotum is disc-like, but in the Orthoptera Saltatoria (except the Gryllotalpidae, see p. 98), the pronotum is a characteristic saddle-shape.

In all orthopteroids the hindlegs are slightly larger than the other two pairs, but in the Saltatoria they are much enlarged with powerful muscles for jumping. The number of tarsal segments varies between groups. In the Tettigonioidea and Grylloidea, the forelegs bear the hearing organs (or *tympana*). In the Gryllotalpidae, the forelegs are modified for digging. In the Acrididae, subfamily Gomphocerinae, the hindlegs bear a row of stridulatory pegs on the inner side of the femora. These are absent in the Acrididae, subfamily Oedipodinae.

The forewings (or *elytra*) are toughened and protective – at rest covering the delicate, fan-folded hindwings (or *alae*). The venation of the wings (text fig. 4d) differs between species and may be useful for establishing relationships within families and for identification. In the Tettigoniidae, Gryllidae and Gryllotalpidae, the male elytra are modified for sound production; in the Acrididae, stridulatory sounds are produced using the hindlegs and elytra (see p. 41).

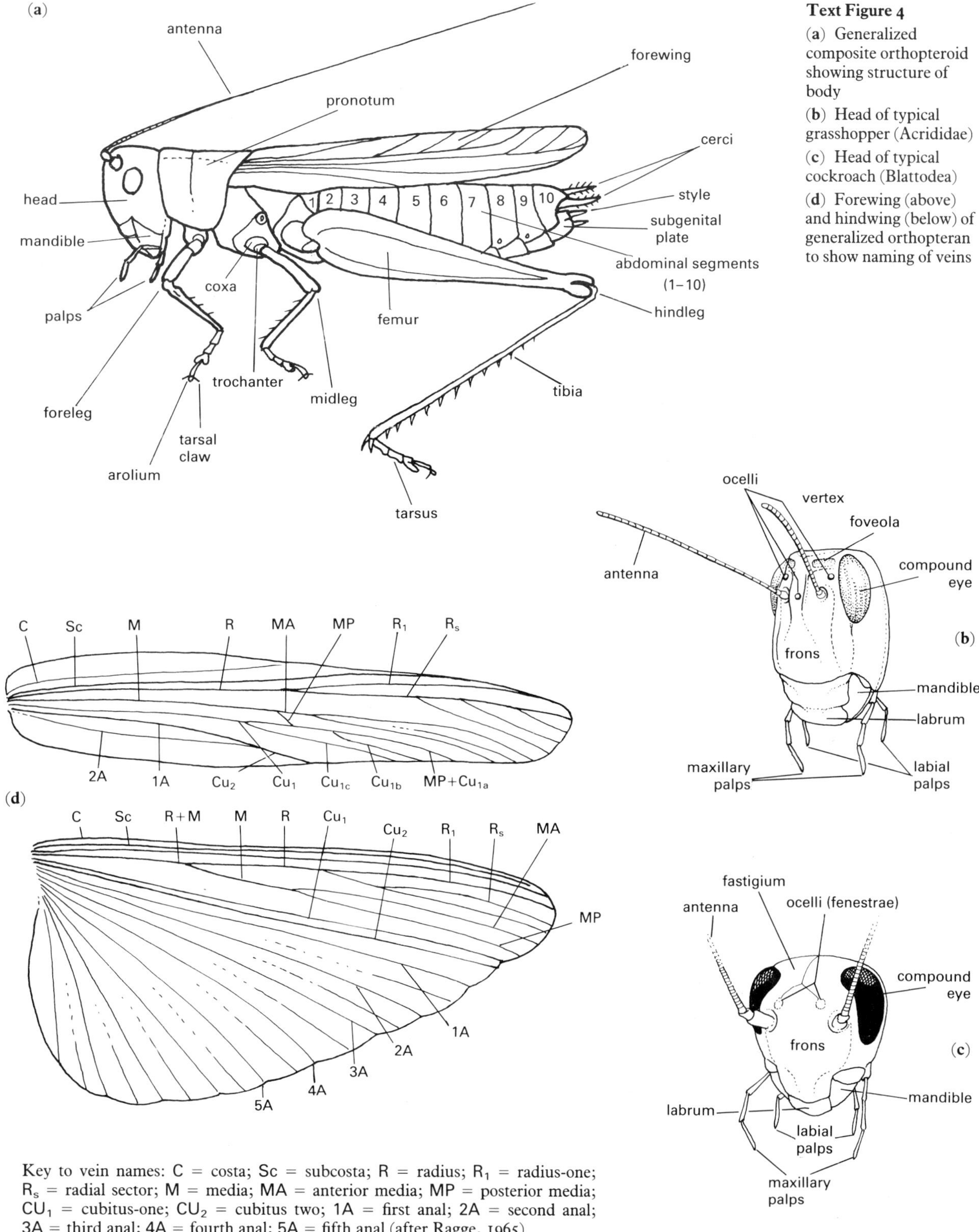

Text Figure 4

(**a**) Generalized composite orthopteroid showing structure of body

(**b**) Head of typical grasshopper (Acrididae)

(**c**) Head of typical cockroach (Blattodea)

(**d**) Forewing (above) and hindwing (below) of generalized orthopteran to show naming of veins

Key to vein names: C = costa; Sc = subcosta; R = radius; R_1 = radius-one; R_s = radial sector; M = media; MA = anterior media; MP = posterior media; CU_1 = cubitus-one; CU_2 = cubitus two; 1A = first anal; 2A = second anal; 3A = third anal; 4A = fourth anal; 5A = fifth anal (after Ragge, 1965)

Abdomen

The abdomen is formed of eleven *segments* – though not all are visible, as the last few segments are modified in different ways, for reproduction.

In Acrididae, the hearing organs (or *tympana*) are at the base of the abdomen.

Both sexes bear a pair of *cerci*, which in males, particularly Tettigoniidae, may be highly modified into grasping organs to assist in copulation.

In the Dermaptera, the cerci have become modified into forceps in both sexes, and a *pygidium* may be visible between the forceps. Females have three pairs of *ovipositor valves* (though only two may be visible) which may form a highly specialized ovipositor to enable oviposition in a wide variety of substrates.

The male *subgenital plate* may also be highly modified and characteristic for each species and may bear a pair of *styles*.

Further morphological details are given in the introductions to each group, under Life History and Development below, Song and Courtship (p.40) and in the descriptions of the species.

8. Life History and Development

All orthopteroid insects hatch from eggs, in some cases as nymphs – smaller, wingless versions of the adults. The Dermaptera and Phasmida both hatch in this manner but the Saltatoria and Dictyoptera initially hatch from the egg as a vermiform larva (text fig. 5), a pre-nymphal stage from which the first true nymphal stage, or instar, emerges. This vermiform or 'worm-like' larva has its legs enclosed within its cuticular covering and so can move only by wriggling. When eggs are laid below soil level, the vermiform larva wriggles to the surface before shedding the cuticle to become a first-instar nymph, and from this stage its development is as all other orthopteroids.

The nymphs grow by moulting, or ecdysis, until the adult stage is reached. The wings of adults develop during the nymphal stages as wing-buds or wing-pads. The number of ecdyses or moults undergone during development varies from four to ten or more in the British species, and a wide range of breeding rhythms is seen. Most orthopteroids complete their life-cycle within one year, passing the winter in the egg stage.

Because of their incomplete metamorphosis they are referred to as hemimetabolous or exopterygote insects – they do not have the complete metamorphosis or marked changes in life-cycle seen in the holometabolous or endopterygote insects. In full metamorphosis a larval grub or caterpillar hatches from the egg and grows by moulting until it forms a pupa or chrysalis, inside which develops the winged adult beetle, butterfly or other holometabolous insect.

Gradual development permits orthopteroids the capacity of regeneration. When part of a limb or antenna is lost as a young nymph, this part may be regenerated or regrown during successive moults, but once the adult stage is reached no further regrowth is possible. This feature is combined with the ability to shed limbs if they are grasped, as by predators, when the limb breaks off – usually near the base at the junction of femur and coxa. The process of limb-shedding is called autotomy, and is similar to the mechanism of tail-shedding and subsequent regrowth possessed by lizards. Dictyoptera and Phasmida are particularly adept at regeneration, and regrown limbs may often be recognized by being slightly smaller than usual, sometimes with fewer tarsal segments than normal.

Much research is currently being undertaken into the biology of orthopterans and what follows summarizes the results of these investigations. Brief details about the life histories of the Dictyoptera, Dermaptera and Phasmida are included in the introductions to each order in Part II, the Systematic Section.

The Tettigoniidae all lay their eggs singly, the shape of the egg and the ovipositor being related to the manner and place in which the eggs are deposited (text figs 6a–c). As the majority of species are omnivorous and require insect food in their diet, were many eggs to be laid together the possibility of sibling cannibalism occurring after hatching would be high. A newly-moulted insect is very pale in colour, (sometimes with dark eyes), and gradually darkens as the skin or cuticle hardens. When fully hardened, the omnivorous species – bush-crickets, crickets and cockroaches – eat their own cast skins, as also do the stick-insects. If an insect is disturbed it may move away before eating the cast skin.

Tettigonia viridissima and *Decticus verrucivorus* both have long sword-like ovipositors and lay their eggs in the ground, the other species laying their eggs above the ground, usually in a particular form of vegetation. *Meconema thalassinum* lays in crevices in the bark of oak trees, *Pholidoptera griseoaptera* also in bark but often softer, rotting wood or crevices, first palpating the bark and chewing a shallow notch, then laying the eggs parallel to the grain of the bark (Marrable, 1980). *Conocephalus* species lay in stems of rushes, reeds and sedges, first chewing a hole in the stem before inserting the ovipositor. *Metrioptera* species also oviposit in or among the stems of plants, *M. roeselii* showing a preference for dry *Juncus* stems, laying only one egg in stems under 1.7mm wide but as many as seven in a stem over 2.3mm wide (Marrable, *loc.cit.*). *Platycleis albopunctata* lays in similar crevices, in or among stems. *Leptophyes punctatissima* is the one British tettigoniid with a distinctive short, flat, very upcurved ovipositor, and a differently-shaped egg from the other species. Where the majority have a cigar-shaped, slightly curved egg, described in detail by Hartley (1964), *L. punctatissima* has a very thin, flattened oval shaped egg; this is also laid in various crevices or plant stems. Marrable (*loc.cit*) observed that females chose oak bark from recently felled trees, and laid the eggs in cracks parallel to the

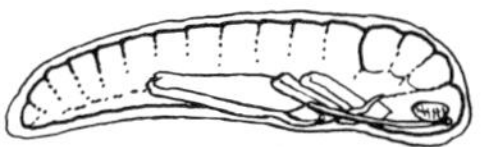

Text Figure 5 (above)
Vermiform larva, the pre-nymphal stage
(after Brown, 1983)

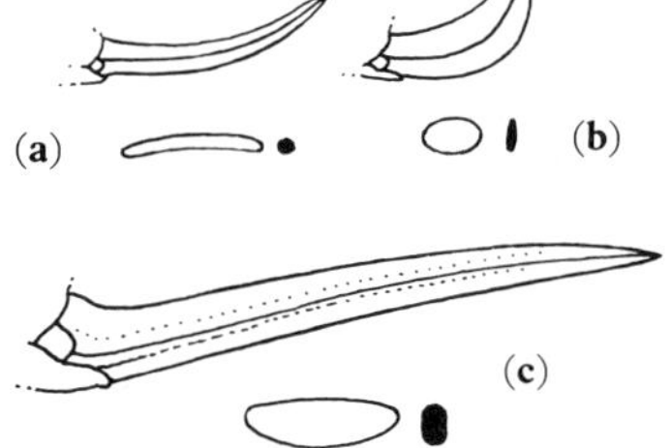

Text Figure 6 (right) Ovipositors and eggs of bush-cricket species (Tettigoniidae) showing cross-section in black.
(**a**) *Conocephalus dorsalis*; (**b**) *Leptophyes punctatissima*;
(**c**) *Tettigonia viridissima* (after Hartley, 1964)

surface of the bark. Tropical relatives are known to lay their flattened eggs in rows on the backs of leaves, along the edge or mid-rib.

The developmental biology of the egg-stages of Tettigoniidae has been described in detail for 46 European species, including the British species, by Hartley & Warne (1972b). They have shown that although *Conocephalus* species have an annual life-cycle, some Tettigoniidae are, at least, biennial, in that they cannot hatch before the spring of their second year. In *Pholidoptera griseoaptera*, most of the development in the egg-stage is in the summer of the second year, and is dependent upon at least 800 day-degrees centigrade above 11°C (Hartley & Warne, 1973). It was shown by Ragge (1973) that *M. roeselii* females introduced into a privately-owned water-meadow in 1968 did not give rise to offspring until 1970. That tettigoniid eggs may take two, three or even more seasons to develop and hatch is clearly a great advantage in poor summers, and partly explains why a poor summer with few bush-crickets about may still be followed by a very good season. The distribution of *Conocephalus dorsalis* was studied by Warne & Hartley (1975) in relation to its habitat; the eggs are laid in rush/sedge/reed-type vegetation in marshy places, and, provided the earlier stages of egg-development have been passed and diapause reached, the eggs can withstand up to several months of immersion in sea-water. Once the eggs are back in a freshwater environment, normal development can continue. This facility could explain their largely coastal and estuarine distribution, since coastal dispersion would be facilitated as eggs could withstand several weeks at sea within the plant stems where they were laid.

The newly-emerged tettigoniid nymphs, although miniature versions of the adults, may not bear too close a resemblance to their parents. Some tropical species mimic ants or beetles in their first instars, clearly useful in avoiding predation. Early instars of *Pholidoptera griseoaptera* show a striking similarity to the spider, *Pardosa lugubris* (Walckenaer) (*cf.* Pl. 2, figs 3, 4), and those of *Leptophyes punctatissima* are similar in appearance to young capsid plant bugs (*cf.* Pl. 3, figs 8,9) or even to very large aphids.

As the nymphs grow, their wings begin to develop. In macropterous species two pairs of wing-pads or buds may be clearly seen, initially lying laterally with the fore wing-pad on top of the hind wing-pad. However in Tettigoniidae and Acrididae the last two nymphal instars have the wing-pads reversed or hinged upwards, so that the hind wing-pad covers most of the fore wing-pad (text figs 7a, b). Both pairs can still be clearly seen, particularly dorsally. In some brachypterous species, *i.e.* those where the adults have very small lobe-like wings, wing reversion does not occur.

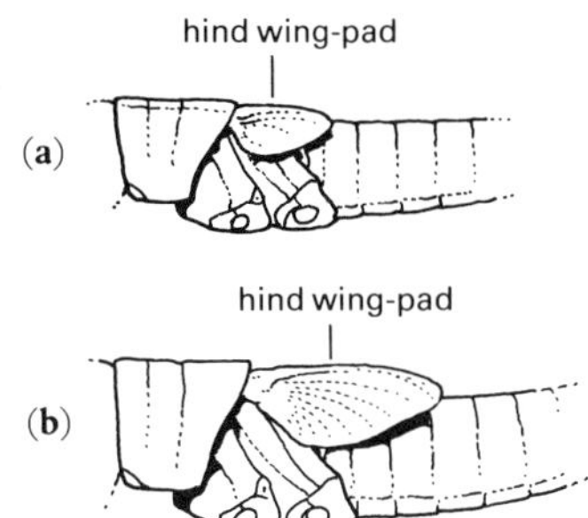

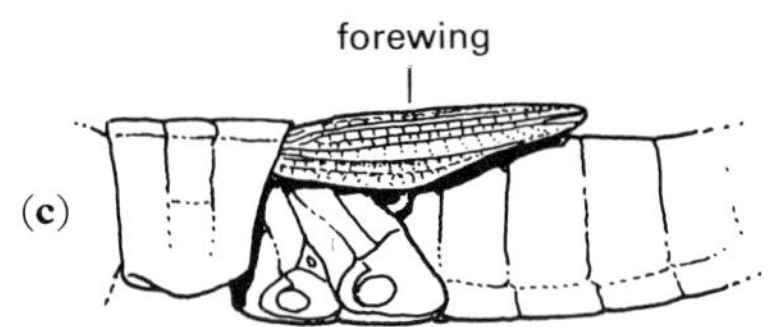

Text Figure 7 Lateral view of developing *Chorthippus* spp. ♀ showing wing development and wing-pad reversal.
(**a**, **b**) third and fourth instars of *C. brunneus*, a fully-winged species
(**c**) adult of *C. parallelus*, a brachypterous species

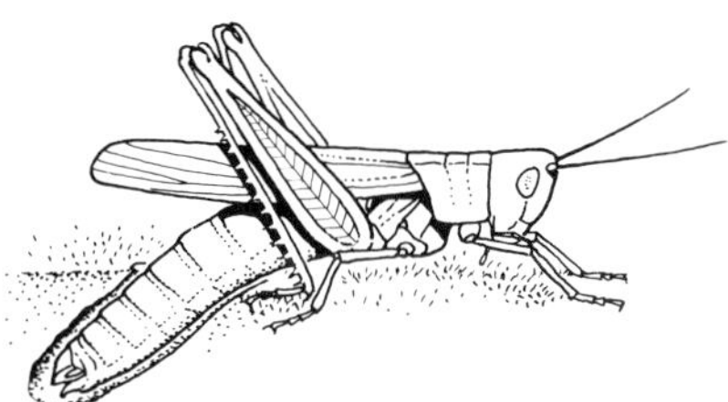

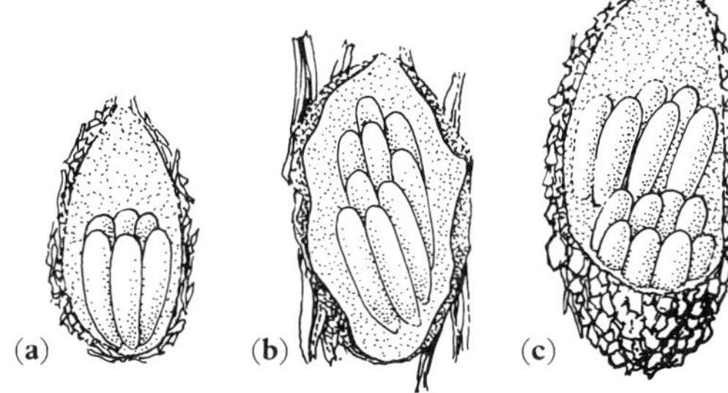

Text Figure 8 (above) Grasshoppers (Acrididae): some species oviposit in the ground, thrusting their abdomens below the surface of the soil.

Text Figure 9 (right) Grasshopper egg-pods are characteristic for each species. (**a**) *Stenobothrus lineatus*; (**b**) *Omocestus viridulus*; (**c**) *Chorthippus brunneus*. (after Waloff, 1950)

The Gryllidae lay their eggs singly in the ground, and have a range of life-cycles which may vary with climatic conditions. *Nemobius sylvestris* is at the northern end of its range in Britain and has an obligatory two-yearly life cycle here to enable it to survive the winter months. During the first season hatching occurs in late June and the nymphs develop usually to fifth instar, though third-, fourth- and sixth-instar nymphs are also found. These nymphs then overwinter deep in the woodland leaf-litter undergoing no further development until the following spring. Adults appear by early July; mating and egg-laying then occur, and the eggs undergo diapause during the winter. The eggs require a minimum period of at least twenty weeks chilling below 20°C to enable at least 50 per cent to hatch (Brown, 1978).

The Gryllotalpidae lay their eggs in batches in underground nest-chambers and have at least a two-year life-cycle (see page 98).

The British Acrididae lay their eggs in or just above the ground (text fig. 8). *Omocestus rufipes*, *Chorthippus vagans* and *Gomphocerippus rufus* oviposit in the surface soil-layer among the grass roots, whilst *C. brunneus* and *Myrmeleotettix maculatus* will use only bare soil, and *C. parallelus* prefers firm ground. For both *C. brunneus* and *C. parallelus* the ant mounds of *Lasius flavus* (Fabr.) (yellow meadow ant) form ideal oviposition sites, and at hatching time the cast skins of the vermiform larvae may be seen on the mounds. *Stenobothrus lineatus* lays just above the grassroots, whilst *Stethophyma grossum*, *O. viridulus* and *C. albomarginatus* all lay at the bases of grass blades. These three species all favour moister habitats, where oviposition beneath the soil-surface might prove too wet for the eggs. Conversely, in drier habitats the eggs are laid much deeper, and locust species in desert habitats may lay their eggs one centimetre or more below the surface. The eggs are laid in batches of up to fourteen, and are covered with a frothy secretion which hardens around them to form an egg-pod (text figs 9a–c). The number of eggs, and size and shape of the egg-pod are characteristic for each species (Waloff, 1950). Since all species are herbivorous and the eggs are laid in a suitable habitat, there is no disadvantage in siblings emerging together. There may be large numbers of grasshoppers in suitable localities, and a fairly high mortality occurs amongst the population during development, largely due to predation. In high-density populations the number of hatchlings reaching maturity may be as little as 30 per cent, although in low-density populations it may be up to 65 per cent. Males are always smaller than females, but are not at a disadvantage because of this in low-density populations; only where there are very large numbers of grasshoppers present do the males suffer a higher mortality rate (Wall & Begon, 1986).

As grasshoppers are herbivorous, their development is naturally closely linked to the composition of the habitat. In recent years *C. brunneus* has become abundant on the central reserves of motorways, often showing its highest density populations there (Monk, 1983). It has been shown that lead, sodium and nitrogen occur in high concentrations in roadside vegetation, particularly on the central reserves (Port & Thompson, 1980), as a result of pollution, and it is the high nitrogen content which seems to favour *C. brunneus*. A study of this species on calcareous grassland, heavily grazed by rabbits, (Grayson & Hassall, 1985) showed that nymphs developing within an ungrazed enclosure survived better, grew faster to adulthood and had a higher average mature weight than those developing on the rabbit-grazed grassland. In June, during nymphal development, the leaves of the ungrazed grass had a higher nitrogen content than those of the grazed grassland.

Recent research has also revealed that there is a direct link between hot weather and grasshopper abundance, in that the internal body-temperature is raised substantially in the presence of direct sunlight, increasing the rate of development and egg- production (Begon, 1983). Extra-good summers with long day-lengths also increase the rate of production of macropterous adults of normally brachypterous species, although macropterous *C. parallelus* females start mating when older than normal and are apparently less fertile (Ritchie *et al.* 1987). In common with other grasshopper species, *C. brunneus* normally has four nymphal instars, but, in two populations in the Breckland district of East Anglia, the high levels of sunshine and warm days seem to promote earlier hatching and faster growth, so that an extra nymphal instar may develop (Hassall & Grayson, 1987). This extra stage is intermediate between the normal second and third instars, without the wing-pad inversion of the third and fourth instars. The resulting adults are larger than average in size.

9. Song and Courtship

Perhaps the most acknowledged characteristic of the Orthoptera Saltatoria is their ability to make sounds in the form of recognizable songs which are distinctive for each species. These songs are produced by stridulation, or the scraping of one part of the body against another.

The sounds produced by Orthoptera are usually referred to as 'chirps', and though to the layman this may seem a perfectly suitable term to describe the song, in the world of insect acoustics 'chirp' is not a word to be used lightly, if at all! In order to describe with accuracy the songs of Orthoptera, the terms 'syllable' and 'echeme' are used. A syllable is defined as the sound produced by one complete up and down movement – of the forewings in Tettigoniidae and Gryllidae, or of the hindlegs in

Acrididae (Ragge & Reynolds, 1984). An echeme (derived from the Greek word for a sound), is defined as 'a first-order assemblage of syllables'. Thus the song or 'chirp' of *Chorthippus brunneus* may be described as 'an echeme of *c*.0.2 sec. duration, consisting of some nine syllables' (Broughton, 1976), normally formed of a sequence with an echeme repetition rate of about 1 per 2–3 seconds.

In the Tettigoniidae, Gryllidae and Gryllotalpidae, the forewings are rubbed over each other. In male bush-crickets, the base of both forewings is modified (text figs 10a, b). On the underside of the left forewing there is a tooth-bearing rib which is rubbed against the hind edge of the right wing, in which there is a clear area called the 'mirror' which serves to amplify the sound. The left forewing is thus always on top of the right forewing. In crickets (text figs 11a, b) the position of the forewings is reversed, although they are less differentiated from each other than those of bush-crickets, and there is an additional clear area of amplification called the 'harp'. In all groups, males raise their wings slightly into a characteristic position when singing. Of the British bush-crickets, only *Meconema thalassinum* does not have modified forewings but produces its recognizable song by 'drumming', that is by tapping with one hindleg on the surface on which it is standing (Currie, 1953).

Most British Acrididae sing by rubbing a row of stridulatory pegs on the inside of each hind femur against the more prominent veins, particularly the radius (R), of the flexed forewings (text figs 12a, b). In some species, part of the male forewing may be expanded to amplify the sound; *Chorthippus brunneus* has an expanded costal area for this purpose. The Oedipodinae do not have stridulatory pegs on their hind femora,

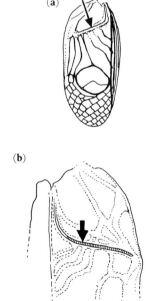

Text Figures 10–12 Different stridulatory mechanisms in Orthoptera families

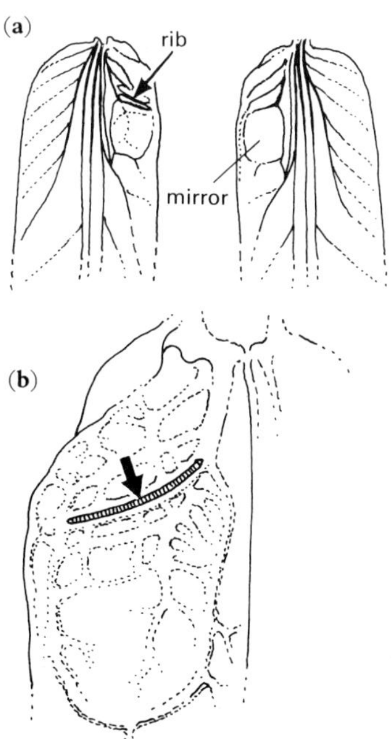

(10) Tettigoniidae: *Tettigonia viridissima* (**a**) forewings from above (**b**) left forewing from below (detail)

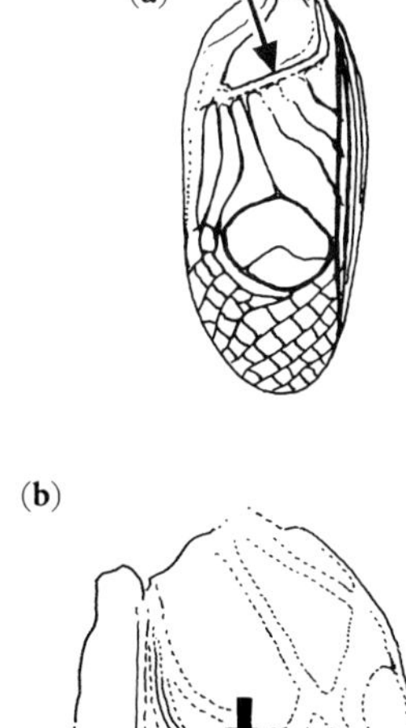

(11) Gryllidae (and Gryllotalpidae): *Gryllus campestris* (**a**) right forewing from above (**b**) right forewing from below (detail)

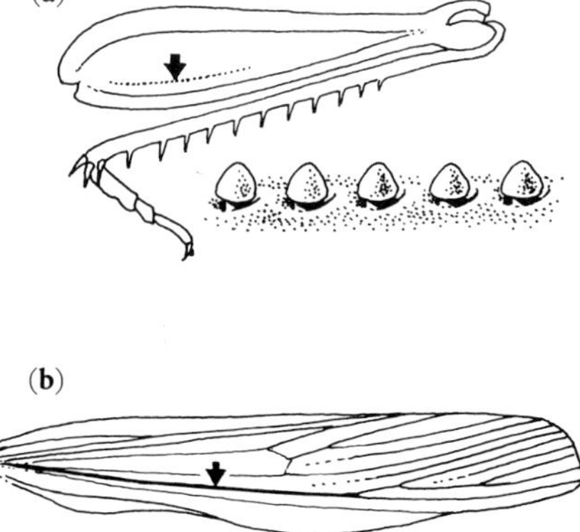

(12) Acrididae (Gomphocerinae): *Chorthippus brunneus* (**a**) inner side of right hindleg and detail of stridulatory pegs (after Pitkin, 1976) (**b**) left forewing with raised vein arrowed

merely a ridge which they rub against an intercalary vein on the forewing between the media (M) and cubitus-one (Cu_I). The song produced by the oedipodines is weak or almost non-existent, e.g. *Oedipoda caerulescens*. However, *Stethophyma grossum* does not sing in this way but produces a series of ticking sounds by flicking a hindleg against the tips of its wings.

The number of stridulatory pegs on the hind femora varies both within and between species. A study of 20 males of each of the British species by Pitkin (1976) showed that the average number of pegs varies: most species had a range varying between 80 and about 200, but *Chorthippus brunneus* had about 60–80 (the lowest number) whereas *Stenobothrus lineatus* had from about 320 to over 400 pegs. Compared with studies of European specimens, her study also showed that the hind femora are usually smaller and the files shorter in length, which correlates with the generally slightly smaller appearance of British orthopteroids compared with their Continental relatives.

Though tettigoniids and gryllids can sing whether or not they have hind legs, an acridid which has lost both hind legs cannot produce a song. The loss of one hind leg means that the song may be slightly different; it has been shown for *Chorthippus biguttulus* (L.), a European relative of *C. brunneus*, that males with one hind leg must stridulate to a very precise pattern to be recognized by the female (Helversen & Helversen, 1983).

Many species produce two distinct songs: that of an isolated male which is the recognized calling song of the species; and the often highly elaborate courtship song produced by a male when a female is nearby. There is also a variation of the calling song produced when several males are singing in competition with each other, or 'interacting'. Males of *Pholidoptera griseoaptera* produce a single short chirp when alone, but will chirp alternately when there are several together, or occasionally chirp in synchronization for 4–6 chirps, and then revert to regular alternation (Jones, 1966). A longer chirp than usual is sometimes produced in situations of conflict between males.

In most Tettigoniidae the female is attracted to the singing male and moves towards him. However in the brachypterous, flightless *Leptophyes punctatissima*, which often lives in wooded areas, the female also stridulates but does so only in response to a male chirp (Robinson, 1980). The male, on hearing response chirps, moves towards her over a distance of up to five metres (Hartley & Robinson, 1976). The wings of the female are smaller than those of the male and are without the typical male stridulatory area, but there are pegs on the dorsal side of some marginal veins with which she produces a similar high-frequency sound to that of the male.

Female Acrididae can also stridulate, but their hind femora do not have the prominent pegs of the males, nor the expanded costal area. The songs they produce are similar to those of the males, but quieter, and are produced by receptive females in response to a singing male to show that they are ready for mating. In *Chorthippus brunneus* the responding male and female then move towards each other, producing 'echemes' in alternation (Butlin, *et al.*, 1985). Stridulatory movements can also be seen in grasshopper nymphs (Ragge, 1965) in a pattern similar to those of the adults.

As in most terrestrial arthropods, internal fertilization is effected by direct copulation, or the apposition of the genital openings near the tip of the abdomen. In orthopteroids, a spermatophore or sperm package is produced by the male, and then inserted in or attached to the female's genital opening. Only when the female is mature and ready for mating will she respond to or accept the male, and in some groups copulation is preceded by a complicated pattern of courtship. Although the songs of bush-crickets and crickets may be heard frequently, because of their habitat preferences and also their more nocturnal habits, their courtship is less often observed than that of grasshoppers.

In recent years the study of orthopteroid mating behaviour and mechanisms has advanced throughout the world (Gwynne & Morris, 1983). Two forms of courtship feeding may be found in some orthopteroid insects: in one, the male may produce a glandular secretion to attract the female before mating; in the second, when the spermatophore is attached externally, as in the Tettigoniidae and Gryllidae and some Gryllacrididae (the camel-crickets), the female may eat a portion of the spermatophore after mating. The male glands producing the attractive secretion may be on the dorsal surface of the abdomen, as in the Blattodea (see also p. 77), but in *Nemobius sylvestris* they are on a small patch of the right forewing. Within the Tettigoniidae and Gryllidae particularly, the males may produce a spermatophore which contains, in addition to the sperm, a larger spermless portion called the spermatophylax; it is this part which is consumed by the female. The spermatophylax may be quite large, and represent a large proportion of the body-weight of the male. However it has been shown that its production is a worthwhile 'investment' on his part, since it both ensures successful fertilization and provides a high protein meal for the female which will assist her in egg production (Gwynne *et al.*, 1984; Gwynne, 1986). If the spermatophylax is removed artificially, the female may eat the portion of the spermatophore containing the sperm. Two differently-sized spermatophores are produced by *N. sylvestris* with a complex behaviour pattern, first described by Gabbutt (1954), in which a smaller spermatophore is produced and accepted before a larger one; and, in the event of an unsuccessful mating, the male economically eats his own spermatophore. The courtship of this species is decribed in detail by Ragge (*loc.cit*).

In other orthopteroid insects, including the Acrididae, the spermatophore is small and inserted by the male directly into the female. In the Tetrigidae, however, the spermatophore is large (up to 2mm) in comparison with the size of the adult, and consists mainly of protein which is digested inside the female (Farrow, 1963).

Details of behaviour in several British acridid species have recently been studied, and the courtship procedure found to be very elaborate. The complex courtship seen in *Myrmeleotettix maculatus*, where the male has a four-phase pattern, may serve to convert the female from semi-receptive to fully receptive, permitting the unreceptive females to continue eating whilst not being courted (Bull, 1979). Although the spermatophores produced by the Acrididae are small, multiple-mating may occur. Whilst one mating could be sufficient to fertilize the female for her lifetime, female *Chorthippus brunneus* may mate up to 25 times and this increases her fecundity (Butlin *et al.*, 1987).

The complicated patterns of song and courtship behaviour act as isolating mechanisms in preventing the interbreeding of closely related species living in the same area. A further physical factor which prevents interbreeding is the structure of the male cerci, particularly in some Tettigoniidae. During copulation, the male clasps the female with his cerci at the base of her ovipositor, his cerci gripping her subgenital plate which has lateral indentations or pockets. This mechanism has been referred to as a 'lock and key' (Rentz, 1972): the male 'key' will fit accurately only into the 'lock' of a female of the same species.

Recordings of songs of twenty-six British species are available on a companion cassette, *A Sound Guide to the Grasshoppers and allied Insects of Great Britain and Ireland*. Reference to these is made in the text.

10. Predators, Parasites and Diseases

Orthopteroid insects are a good source of food for many larger creatures, including birds, reptiles and small mammals. It is sadly not unusual to see a magazine photograph of an interesting orthopteran in the process of being eaten, particularly when the photograph has been taken under natural conditions. Heavily-contrived shots may be recognized by the prevalence of *Acheta domesticus* as the food source, as this species is reared commercially and widely sold for caged birds, lizards and tarantulas, amongst other pets.

In the wild, orthopteroids may also fall prey to other arthropods, particularly spiders. Large adult grasshoppers may have the strength to disentangle themselves from an unwary jump into a spider's web, but smaller nymphs are soon snapped up by the waiting spider. The conspicuous low-level webs of the spider, *Agelena labyrinthica* (Clerck), are frequently the last resting places for tettigoniid nymphs and even mature acridids. There are also insect predators which find orthopteroids a useful food source, such as wasps of the families Sphecidae and Vespidae, and robber-flies (Asilidae). The carnivorous bush-crickets, too, find a useful food-source in their herbivorous grasshopper cousins, and indeed even among their closer relatives, for cannibalism is not unknown.

Orthopteroids may be attacked in other ways by various groups of insects. Many grasshoppers may be parasitized by the fly *Blaesoxipha laticornis* (Meigen) (Diptera: Sarcophagidae). The female fly is viviparous, and deposits her larva on the grasshopper's body where it burrows through the cuticle and starts feeding on the host's body tissues. When fully developed, the larva chews its way out through the intersegmental membrane behind the head, emerges and drops to the ground to pupate in the soil. Usually only one larva is deposited on each grasshopper, and females are the usual subjects, perhaps because they are larger and slower than males (Richards & Waloff, 1954). A specimen may occasionally be collected which seems rather sluggish, or to have an enlarged abdomen; if kept alive the fly larva may be seen to leave the host, which will then die. An adult male *Chorthippus parallelus*, with very short wings (6.9mm) and a large abdomen, was collected in 1983 (by T. M.

Howard and J. A. Marshall); it was kept alive (separate from other specimens) and on the next day a larva of *B. laticornis* emerged.

Earwigs, notably *Forficula auricularia*, suffer similar parasitism by two flies, *Rhacodineura pallipes* Fallen and *Digonochaeta spinipennis* Meigen (both Diptera: Sarcophagidae). Females of the latter species lay eggs near to resting earwigs, the eggs hatch immediately and the larvae bore into the earwigs. Female *Rhacodineura* lay their eggs where the earwigs are feeding, so that the eggs are ingested by the earwigs and hatch in their gut, the larvae then burrowing through into the body cavities. The main brood of *F. auricularia* may suffer ten per cent or more parasitism by tachinid flies (Phillips, 1983). This may be considered to be advantageous in apple orchards, where earwigs feed on foliage, flowers and fruits and may do considerable damage to the fruit. However the earwigs themselves prey on the red spider mite, *Panonyphus ulmi* (Koch), and the codling moth, *Cydia pomonella* (L.), both pests.The Tachinidae too may suffer from hyperparasitism by Hymenoptera (Pteromalidae and Ichneumonidae), reducing their effectiveness as parasites.

Nematode worms (Mermithidae) may also live in the body cavity of orthopteroids, but little is known of their biology.

Mites (Trombidiidae) may very rarely be seen as ectoparasites on grasshoppers, attached to the intersegmental membranes; however, their occurrence is more common on the Continent.

Eggs may be parasitized by wasps: several species of *Scelio* (Hymenoptera: Scelionidae) attack grasshopper egg-pods, and another small wasp (Hymenoptera: Chalcidae) attacks the eggs of bush-crickets, *Conocephalus* spp. (Brown, 1983). Two other wasps (Hymenoptera: Evaniidae) are known to parasitize the oothecae of our native cockroaches, *Ectobius* spp. A recent study of *Brachygaster minutus* Olivier (Brown, 1973e) has shown that about ten per cent of oothecae may be parasitized. Each ootheca supports one larva, which overwinters within the ootheca, emerging in the summer to coincide with the next generation of the cockroach. The parasite, *Evania appendigaster* (L.), which attacks the domestic pest species of cockroach, has several generations each year and higher levels of parasitism may occur (Cameron, 1957).

Orthopteroids may also succumb to attacks by a fungus, *Entomophthora* spp. Dead or dying grasshoppers can be found in an unusual posture, clinging fairly high up on vegetation with their legs wrapped around the stems. The fruiting bodies of the fungus, *E. grylli* Fres., are seen emerging from the unfortunate grasshopper, which has placed itself in a good position for the dispersal of fungal spores (Bellmann, 1988), presumably induced by the presence of the fungus (Dewhurst, 1978). Another species of fungus attacks earwigs: *E. forficulae* var. *major* has been recorded as killing up to fourteen per cent of third- and fourth-instar nymphs (Phillips, *loc. cit.*). Bacteria also cause diseases.

Further hazards in the lives of orthopteroid insects are insecticide sprays – not only those used to control field-pests, but also those used in the garden and home. Although many insecticidal chemicals are very specific in their action, some are widely effective, and fly-sprays should not be used in a room where grasshoppers or stick-insects are kept.

11. Locating and Collecting Orthoptera

Locating

There are certain well-tried procedures worth following when wishing to see Orthoptera, all of which require advance planning. First, assess the terrain. Use an up to date Ordnance Survey map of the 1:50,000 scale (2cm to 1km) for a ten-kilometre square or tetrad (2 × 2km). This will indicate the physical features of the area such as sea-cliffs, dunes, steep south-facing slopes; and the nature of uncultivated areas such as downland turf, heathland or marshland, especially by ponds or in river valleys. These are the first places to search for orthopteroids. If possible, get tips from a local entomologist who is familiar with the area, or, as a refinement, use the larger scale 1:25,000 Ordnance Survey map which covers exactly one ten-kilometre square, and gives even better indication of such features as unfenced roads (shown by dotted margins) which often have unspoilt verges. In addition to the semi-natural features, note the dual carriageways and railway lines, the verges and embankments of which may support good populations of Orthoptera species in the coarse herbage to be found there, as also may urban or semi-urban wasteland. There is usually little to be gained from examining areas that are intensively farmed, densely wooded or built over.

Having noted likely places on the appropriate map, make a series of reconnaissance trips to as many potential sites as possible during the winter or early spring. Such advance visits will prove well worthwhile as they will avoid wasting time later in the season when the insects are active and every available hour will be needed for the actual recording. They may also reveal which promising areas are privately owned and so enable permission to enter the sites to be obtained well ahead of the actual survey.

To be certain of identification, field surveys are best carried out when the insects are in the adult stage. For ground-hoppers, native cockroaches and earwigs, this means searching suitable terrain in late spring or early summer (May-June). At this time it might also be possible to locate by their unmistakable stridulation the rare *Gryllus campestris* (field-cricket) or *Gryllotalpa gryllotalpa* (mole-cricket). From around the end of June, all native bush-crickets, grasshoppers and other native crickets mature and most remain active as adults throughout the summer until the first autumn frosts. Ground-hoppers may also be found in autumn as final-instar nymphs or adults, preparing for hibernation.

Weather conditions which suit butterflies are ideal also for orthopterans. In hot, sunny weather most of our native bush-crickets and grasshoppers may be located by their stridulations and identified. Crickets may also be tracked down by song, *Nemobius sylvestris* (wood-cricket) being found quite easily among the leaf-litter of its habitat. Once learned, the song alone may then be used as a reliable method of recording which can save valuable time when a large area of ground has to be covered. However certain Orthoptera, such as *Pseudomogoplistes squamiger* (scaly cricket), *Meconema thalassinum* (oak bush-cricket) and *Leptophyes punctatissima* (speckled bush-cricket), and also cockroaches and earwigs, cannot be located by ear, although a mini bat-detector will pick up some otherwise inaudible sounds. In addition, some stridulations are so high-pitched that they are beyond the range of hearing of middle-aged or older humans who must thus rely on sight! In this case, the very hottest weather is not ideal as the quarry is too active to be more than briefly glimpsed. A cool sunny or, alternatively, an overcast warm day is best as the insects are then reasonably active but considerably slower than in the blazing sun, and can usually be studied more easily. If it is necessary to search by eye in hot weather, it is advisable to work in the morning from around 09.30 hours for an hour or two, or to start in the late afternoon.

Although mainly nocturnal, most cockroaches, earwigs and the introduced phasmids (stick-insects), as well as *M. thalassinum* and *G. gryllotalpa*, may be located in daylight. Ground-hoppers, earwigs and our native cockroaches require a more nose-to-the-ground attitude by the searcher. For most species, leaf-litter must be examined by paths and at the edges of clearings. The males of *Ectobius* (cockroach) species can fly and occasionally do so when disturbed; they may also be taken in light traps, as may the female *E. pallidus* (tawny cockroach) and *Forficula auricularia* (common earwig). *Tetrix undulata* (common ground-hopper) is often found in more mossy areas, and the other *Tetrix* species on the margins of ponds and streams. When looking for stick-insects, search their foodplants for signs of chewed edges on bramble, ferns and other bushes which may indicate their presence.

The following Orthoptera species are listed in the *British Red Data Books:* 2. Insects (Shirt, 1987):

Decticus verrucivorus (Wart-biter)	Vulnerable
Gryllus campestris (Field-cricket)	Endangered
Pseudomogoplistes (as *Mogoplistes*) *squamiger* (Scaly cricket)	Endangered
Gryllotalpa gryllotalpa (Mole-cricket)	Endangered
Stethophyma grossum (Large Marsh Grasshopper)	Vulnerable
Chorthippus vagans (Heath Grasshopper)	Rare

Of these, *D. verrucivorus*, *G. campestris* and *G. gryllotalpa* are listed on Schedule 5 of the Wildlife and Countryside Act (1981). It is important that none of these species be disturbed in any way, but details of their location should be communicated to Invertebrate Zoology Branch, Nature Conservancy Council, Northminster House, Peterborough PE1 1UA and the appropriate County Naturalists' Trust as soon as possible.

Collecting

Several techniques are involved in collecting the different orthopteroid insects, but for the majority of species the most useful collecting equipment is a bag or box full of 75 × 25mm (3 × 1in.) glass tubes with cork stoppers. Polythene stoppers should not be used unless air holes are made, as large active insects in sealed tubes will rapidly suffocate. A notebook and pencil are also essential so that collection data may be recorded on site.

On a sunny day grasshoppers are relatively easy to collect, having been located by song. A glass tube may be held above the specimen and gradually moved down over it, so that even if it jumps at the last moment it is likely to leap into the tube. The cork should quickly be inserted to prevent the insect from leaping out again. On a very hot day, grasshoppers are more active and likely to take flight when disturbed though most British species fly only short distances. *Stethophyma grossum* will however fly several yards, making its collection on quaking bogs somewhat precarious; great care needs to be taken to avoid unnecessary damage to both habitat and collector. A collecting net with a short handle may be useful for grasshoppers, and also bush-crickets in grass or reeds, though a rapid sweep of the net is essential if the insect is not merely to jump aside.

The specimens collected should be temporarily stored in a shady place; they may be left in individual cork-stoppered tubes, or grasshoppers may be put in a large plastic bag with a little grass. Bush-crickets should be kept apart from each other to prevent cannibalism.

Bush-crickets may be more difficult and hazardous to collect using glass tubes as they are much more wary and tend to drop to the ground when disturbed rather than jumping. *Pholidoptera griseoaptera* (dark bush-cricket) may be found in bramble patches; *Metrioptera*-inhabited heather clumps can be very scratchy to bare arms; moreover, the carnivorous bush-crickets have powerful jaws and can give a painful bite if handled. The larger specimens should not be put in standard-sized tubes as it may be difficult to get them out again; a few larger tubes or jars should be carried ready for such use. Big bush-crickets such as *Tettigonia viridissima* (great green bush-cricket) may not be kept for long in polythene bags, as they will rapidly chew their way out. Both *Leptophyes punctatissima* and *Meconema thalassinum* are often seen in gardens, and occasionally wander indoors; *Meconema* is attracted to light, and may be found with sticky feet on sugared strips intended to attract moths. It may also be collected by beating, sharply striking the accessible branches of oak trees to dislodge them. A very effective way of recording the occurrence of *Meconema* is that of Hawkins and Baldock (Marshall, 1984): 407 of a total 468 records from one Surrey area were made by collecting squashed specimens found on country roads under overhanging trees.

If collecting at night, using a miner's lamp (obtainable from caving equipment suppliers) will leave both hands free. In dense vegetation, it may be useful to have a pair of collecting tongs, specially made from two tea-strainers and a pair of scissor-action barbecue tongs (Samways, 1974).

The large size and slowness of phasmids (stick-insects) makes them easy to collect once seen, but care must be taken to handle them by the body only as their legs are designed to be shed when grasped by a predator – a distressing event for both insect and collector!

12. Rearing and Culturing Orthopteroid Insects in Captivity

Important and useful though a collection of dead insects may be, to gain the most information possible about an insect it should be observed alive, preferably under natural conditions so that its behaviour is also natural. When collecting insects in the field, they should be observed before capture; this is comparatively easy with grasshoppers, less so with the more wary bush-crickets. If their song and courtship behaviour has not been witnessed in the field, then keeping them alive for a few days can be most rewarding, much can be learnt and positive identifications can be made.

Orthopteroids should be kept in a suitable-size of container: tall glass jars such as empty jam- or coffee-jars (well washed out) are adequate for several specimens of smaller species or for single larger specimens, though large glass or plastic sweet-jars are even better, the lid being replaced by a piece of netting or similar material. Insect breeding cylinders with perforated metal lids (as sold by entomological suppliers, see p. 54) are perhaps safer for the large bush-crickets, which are quite capable of chewing through fabric. Glass or plastic aquaria are also useful and are readily available from pet shops or aquarists, but should have a metal mesh lid or side piece to ensure adequate ventilation.

Adult female grasshoppers will want to lay eggs, and should be given either a 30mm layer of moist sharp sand in the base of the jar or a small container with a similar depth of sand. A reliable soil medium which may also be used is a mixture of half sharp sand and half prepared bulb-fibre, thoroughly mixed and kept just damp enough to feel moist but not waterlogged. The bulb-fibre contains charcoal which acts as a 'sweetener', and such a mixture will last a full season. If no suitable substrate is provided, grasshoppers will still lay eggs, usually in the grass provided as food.

Several species of grasshoppers may be kept together. All will feed on the softer grasses, so that it is easy to keep them alive. They should be given fresh grass daily. A simple way of providing this is to tie a small bunch at one end of a piece of string, so that when the bunch is placed in the jar the loose end of the string is outside the jar. It is then easy to withdraw the grass the next day and replace it without losing the inhabitants – grasshoppers have a disconcerting ability to leap out of even a narrow-necked jar! Alternatively, a clump or two of a small grass such as the ubiquitous annual meadow grass (*Poa annua*) may be planted in the container and kept trim with scissors as necessary. An analysis of the food eaten by grasshoppers from different localities (Bernays & Chapman, 1970) has shown that species are not associated with any particular species of grass so are likely to accept any grass offered.

It is often difficult to identify nymphal grasshoppers but they may easily be reared to confirm their identity. Young adult females may also pose identification problems: for example mature *Omocestus viridulus* (common green grasshopper) have long ovipositor valves which are not fully visible in newly-moulted individuals.

Ground-hoppers should be provided with small pads of freshly collected woodland moss on which they will live and feed, and which must be kept moist.

The omnivorous bush-crickets are better kept singly unless a large cage with room for vegetation is available. They will take grass, but will feed happily on lettuce and will also accept small pieces of fruit, and moist brown bread smeared with well watered-down runny honey. They should be offered small live soft-bodied insects such as non-hairy caterpillars or small nymphal grasshoppers. Aphids (except for the familiar garden blackfly (*Aphis fabae*), which seems to be distasteful) are also acceptable food, even for adult *Tettigonia viridissima*. It is also useful to provide assorted vegetation including flower-heads and grass seeds, as pollen is a high protein food-source and young bush-cricket nymphs require a diet rich in protein. When rearing *Meconema thalassinum*, an almost entirely carnivorous species, it is particularly important to feed adequately or the nymphs may not develop properly, and even the omnivorous species may moult with twisted legs. Rentz (1985) suggests that, in addition to lettuce, bush-cricket nymphs should be offered a mixture of finely ground muesli, grass seeds and flaked tropical fish-food to supplement their protein intake. Pairs of adults may be kept in the same container, though if mating is observed the male should be removed for a recovery period, and the female offered meal-worms or some similar treat. Always remove dead specimens or spent and withered vegetation to minimize the ever-present risk of disease.

Species found in more specialized habitats will clearly have different requirements. *Nemobius sylvestris* should be provided with soil and leaf-litter. *Acheta domesticus* will also require moist sand or soil in which to lay their eggs, and an escape-proof container is essential. The sounds of crickets chirping behind bookcases or in the central heating system can cause considerable distress!

Gryllotalpa gryllotalpa needs 60–100mm of moist soil as also does *Pycnoscelus surinamensis* (Surinam cockroach), both feeding on potatoes and other root vegetables, with the occasional freshly killed meal-worm or other insect.

Crickets and cockroaches are often reared in the laboratory for experimental purposes or as food for other animals, and several different food mixtures are recommended for different species (Ashby, 1972; Rochford, 1972; Brown, 1973b). Proprietary laboratory rat food may be offered, or a mixture specially made up. The essential ingredients are dry dog-biscuits (50%) and dried yeast (3–5%), with the balance made up of an assortment of the following: rolled oats (up to 45%), wheat germ (up to 40%), dried skimmed milk (up to 10%), peanuts (up to 10%), fish meal (up to 5%). The ingredients should all be finely ground and well mixed. Earwigs may be fed on a similar dry mixture, and will also eat other insects (including earwigs). When feeding a dry food such as this, it is important that it stays dry or mould may develop, or mite infestations occur.

Lettuce and pieces of fresh fruit or vegetables may be offered to crickets, cockroaches and earwigs, taking care to remove uneaten food to avoid mould. Insects also require water, which may conveniently be offered in a glass tube (such as a 75 × 25mm collecting tube) with a cotton-wool plug, through which the water will be sucked. Open water is not recommended, since dry food may become contaminated and deaths by drowning may occur.

Nocturnal cockroaches need to be able to hide during the daytime; corrugated cardboard and cardboard tubes provide suitable refuges for them. Earwigs should also be provided with hiding places.

Stick-insects may be kept in large jars, breeding cylinders or aquaria, with the appropriate food-plants provided in jars of water. It is essential that the jars are plugged with tissue so that there is no open water, since stick-insects are particularly expert at suicide by drowning. It is also essential that the cages are large enough for developing stick-insects to moult with ease; if space is cramped they may be trapped within an incompletely cast skin. Once a moult is commmenced it is vital that the insect is unhindered in its completion.

Breeding orthopteroids requires an understanding of the life-cycle of the species concerned. Grasshoppers, which lay egg-pods in soil at the base of grass tussocks in autumn to hatch the following spring, are relatively simple to rear. It is important that the eggs, in the containers in which they were laid, should be placed in a sheltered place out-of-doors to be subjected to winter temperatures in order to break the egg diapause. Ground-hoppers, which hibernate as adults or final-instar nymphs, require similar treatment, but there should be a depth of several centimetres of litter (clumps of moss, torn egg cartons, rotting twigs, etc.) to give suitable cover. Think of them as miniature hedgehogs! Bush-crickets will lay readily enough: larger species such as *Tettigonia viridissima* in soil, and most smaller species in dead plant stems. Dead, newly-dry stems of members of the lily family such as *Lilium* or *Hemerocallis* are readily utilized. However, the eggs of most species do not hatch for two or more seasons, during which time they must be subjected to natural seasonal conditions, presenting considerable practical difficulties. Most common grasshoppers, *Nemobius sylvestris*, and two of the stick-insects, *Acanthoxyla inermis* and the frost-tender *Carausius morosus*, present few problems, the last in fact being all too easy to rear!

Although it is necessary to subject the eggs of all the above-mentioned species, except the stick-insects, to outdoor conditions, it is important to avoid two common errors: the container with eggs, nymphs or adults should never be allowed to become soaked, and never be left in full sun. Direct sun on an enclosed container can quickly raise the internal temperature far above what can be endured by even the most warmth-loving grasshoppers, and the inmates will soon die or be severely damaged. Excessive wetness, even for the moisture-tolerant ground-hoppers, often results in bacterial disease. The captives become slow in movement and exude a dark fluid, with death following rapidly. A good source of light and warmth is a 60-watt pearl bulb, placed to the side of the container rather than directly above. Most orthopteroids move towards a light-source, and, if this is directly above, will crowd on to the container roof away from the provided food and cover. A 60-watt lamp, left on for eight hours or so daily, will not only prevent a container from becoming waterlogged but will also tend to desiccate the contents, so a good squirt of water from a houseplant-sprayer is essential once or twice a day, spraying until a visible dew forms. Even the nocturnal stick-insects may benefit from this treatment; they, and other species, may be seen to drink from the dew thus provided.

Laboratory rearing-techniques are very different from the natural methods described. Diapause is broken, in as short a period as possible, by refrigeration, so that several generations may be reared in one year, and the eggs are washed, separated and maintained separately in a sterile environment (Kelly-Stebbings & Hewitt, 1972; Hartley & Warne, 1972b).

13. Preservation of Orthoptera

Although large-scale collecting and killing of any insects is to be discouraged, it may occasionally be necessary to collect voucher specimens, particularly for an unusual record; or it may be useful to make a collection of local insects for identification purposes, or for assistance in teaching. Whatever the reason, if insects are to be killed it should be done rapidly and efficiently, and they should then be preserved in the best possible way. The best killing-agent for Orthoptera is, unfortunately, hydrogen cyanide gas; since this is a good killing agent for all animals (including people!) it is perhaps not to be recommended for wide usage. A properly prepared killing-jar contains potassium cyanide pellets embedded in plaster of Paris. If a professionally prepared killing-jar cannot be obtained, it is possible to make a 'cyanide' jar using finely-chopped young laurel leaves, which release cyanide gas. The great advantage of cyanide is that it does little damage to the colour of the insect and leaves it 'relaxed' after death; the muscles do not become rigid, so the insect may easily be 'set'. Other chemicals which may be used for killing Orthoptera are ethyl acetate, acetone, carbon tetrachloride, ether or chloroform; of these, ethyl acetate is a widely used insect-killing agent. Specimens may be killed in the tube in which they are captured, if this is of glass, simply by adding a drop of the killing agent to the cork, or on a piece of tissue. None of these volatile organic compounds should be used with a plastic bottle or tube, since the chemical will attack the plastic, and great care should be taken not to handle them near a naked flame because of their volatility. A permanent killing-jar may be specially prepared by putting a layer of plaster of Paris at the bottom, on to which the killing agent may be added. Although it is important that the insect should be in the vapour long enough to be sure it is dead and not merely anaesthetized, it is equally important that it should be removed as soon as possible, and should not actually be in contact with the liquid, since decolorization or distortion of the colour may occur: specimens may be turned pink or red by ethyl acetate.

When the insect is dead, it should be pinned and set. A wide variety of pins may be used, but it is recommended that for Orthoptera 'continental' stainless steel insect-pins, which are 38mm in length, should be used. Brass pins are not recommended, as a large amount of verdigris may develop around the pin, from reaction between the brass and the insect tissues. Fairly thick pins may be used for most Orthoptera; stainless steel pins range in gauge from the finest (0 and finer) to the thickest (6, and extra-long 7); usually 3, 4 or 5 are best for Orthoptera. The pronotum is the safest part through which to pin winged Orthoptera, thus leaving the wings clear for display if required. Because the wings may fold over each other, a pin through them can cause considerable damage. In the Tettigonioidea, Grylloidea, Blattodea and Dermaptera, the pin may be placed fairly centrally in the pronotum, towards the hind edge; in the Acridoidea, which have a central crest or midline, it is easier to pin to one side of this. Phasmids should be pinned through the hind part of the mesonotum, just in front of the mid-legs. Very small specimens, such as Tetrigidae, native Blattodea or nymphs, are perhaps better pinned with micropins; these are small, headless pins which again come in a variety of sizes, B3 or C3 probably being best for Orthoptera. These micropins are then mounted on small pieces of polyporus through which a large pin is placed for handling purposes and for labels.

For large Orthoptera it is often useful to eviscerate the specimen before setting. The standard procedure is to slit the membrane at the side of the abdomen, between tergites and sternites. However with larger specimens a much neater job may be accomplished by slitting the membrane dorsally between the head and pronotum and carefully removing the viscera with fine forceps. Whichever way entry is gained, paper tissue should be used to soak up the body fluids, and great care should be taken not to touch the inside surface of the sclerites, as it is possible to scrape them so clean that an almost transparent abdomen may be left! If the specimen is green, or even partly so, then it is useful to coat the inside of the cavity with boric acid crystals, which will help to preserve the green colour. A mixture of boric acid and talcum powder in a 3:1 ratio is often recommended (Rentz, 1985), but great care should be taken if using this mixture, as talc is very fine and very difficult to remove from the outside of a specimen; using plain boric acid crystals avoids a 'dusty' appearance. Larger specimens need some stuffing to restore the plumpness of the abdomen and cotton wool has a useful texture for this, though the pin should be inserted through the pronotum *before* adding the cotton wool, since it can be almost impossible to get a pin through cotton wool without damaging the insect. After stuffing, the cut edges should be placed neatly together when they will usually be moist enough to adhere without glue. The head will fit neatly back under the pronotum, showing no cut edges.

After stuffing and pinning, specimens should be dried as rapidly as possible, preferably at about 40°C. The lower the drying temperature, the poorer the colour preservation will be, and at low temperatures and high humidity the specimens will rot. Rotting insects (of any order) have a distinctive and highly disagreeable odour which it is almost impossible to eradicate even after complete drying. Drying may be accelerated with the use of anhydrous silica gel in a closed container.

If it is not possible to set the specimens immediately after they are killed, they may be preserved dry and set at a later date. They should be dried as rapidly as possible and stored on layers of tissue or cellulose wadding in suitably sturdy cartons or boxes. Cotton wool should never be used as the fibres may become dangerously entangled around fragile specimens. Dried specimens should be 'relaxed' in water vapour for setting; a suitable relaxing-box is an air-tight plastic container with a layer of moist tissue, preferably impregnated with thymol or menthol to prevent mould from forming if kept moist for any length of time. The specimens will be ready for setting after a few hours – overnight is usually long enough. If after pinning and drying it is found necessary examine the wings, it is possible to relax the wings alone using a 10 per cent ammonia solution to which a drop of washing-up liquid has been added. Using a paint brush, the wings and basal muscles are soaked with this solution, and after only a few minutes the wings may be gently spread out.

It is useful to pin specimens so that they may be handled without undue risk of damaging them, as dried Orthoptera can be quite fragile. The use of a fairly long pin means that the specimen may be placed with room above it for handling the pin with forceps or finger tips, and room beneath it for data label(s); without data, a specimen is of very little scientific value. Pinned insects are usually 'set'; the pins being pushed through the insect and then into a suitable 'setting board'. The setting board should be at least 20mm deep and the pin pushed almost through, with the body of the insect resting just above it. The legs and antennae of the specimen are then arranged neatly, using fine forceps if necessary, and held in place with 'setting pins' – usually an assortment of old insect pins, again 38mm in length. Setting boards are traditionally made of cork or moll (compressed peat-fibre) and may be obtained with a central channel in which the body is placed so that the wings may be spread out on either side. The spread wings are held in place with a setting strip – a piece of thin, semi-transparent paper. In the absence of a chanelled setting board it is still possible to display the wings neatly by inserting a small piece of cork (or something similar) between wings and setting board.

Expanded polystyrene is also useful as a setting board as it is very light-weight, but expanded polyethylene, known as 'plastazote' is an ideal medium for pinning into, and for lining insect drawers and boxes. Cork and plastazote are both used for this purpose, though cork is harder to push a pin into, and thinner pins may bend. When insects are to be transported in boxes, they should be 'cross-pinned' – spare insect pins with heads should be pushed into the box in pairs, crossing over the main part of the insect's body and touching near the heads of the pins. Should the specimen work loose it would still be held in place. In an insect collection, spare pins may also be needed as 'stay-pins', to stop a specimen from swinging round on its pin.

When an insect is collected it is important that all relevant information is noted so that, after setting, an appropriate label may be added to the pin. The essential information needed is locality and date of collection and the name of the collector, with any additional relevant information about the habitat or method of collection. Labels should be permanent – written or printed with waterproof ink on thin card. However vivid the moment of capture may seem at the time, memories may fade or disappear entirely, and any collection should be made as informative as possible.

Permanent preservation of insects can be ensured only in drawers or boxes with well-fitting lids which are proof against dermestid beetles and other pests. Naphthalene crystals in the drawer will discourage invaders, or small pieces of dichlorvos-impregnated insecticidal strip may be pinned among the specimens, though as dichlorvos is highly toxic it should be used only for long-term storage. Dried Orthoptera will travel well provided they are securely pinned into either a cork or plastazote base, with cross-pinning as described above: polystyrene should not be used as it does not grip pins firmly enough, and considerable damage could ensue in transit.

Suppliers of entomological equipment include:

Bio-Science Supplies, 4 Long Mill North, Wednesfield, Wolverhampton WV11 1JD
Marris House Nets, (nets only) 54 Richmond Park Avenue, Bournemouth BH8 9DR
Watkins and Doncaster Ltd., P.O. Box 5, Cranbrook, Kent TN18 5EZ

14. Recording Orthoptera Sounds

by J. F. Burton*

The entomologist wishing to make a collection of sound-recordings of Orthoptera for reference purposes is nowadays blessed with a wide range of portable recording equipment, not all of it prohibitively expensive and outside the pocket of a person of moderate means. It is true that the stridulations of some bush-crickets, such as the great green (*Tettigonia viridissima*), include high frequencies and harmonics which tax to the limit even those princes among tape recorders, the Kudelski range of Nagras. Nevertheless, most of the British Orthoptera can be recorded successfully not only by using Nagras and such good quality reel-to-reel recorders as the Uher and Tandberg, but also with the better cassette recorders, such as the inexpensive Sony Walkman Professional.

But, of course, not all depends upon the tape recorder: the quality of the microphone is just as important. Good quality dynamic microphones are best for recording in the field, while condenser microphones are usually the most satisfactory for studio work. Recording speeds of at least 19cm/sec. should be employed to obtain the best results.

The biggest problem normally encountered out-of-doors is the high ambient or background noise which may spoil or even 'drown' the sounds produced by the insect, especially as the quiet stridulations of some species necessitate recording at high gain (level). Nevertheless, surprisingly good results can, with patience, be obtained by placing the microphone as close to the insect as possible or by employing the directional properties of a gun microphone, or a small-diameter, funnel-shaped parabolic reflector at greater distances.

Although an orthopteran may cease stridulating when approached, it will usually begin again quite quickly if one settles down and waits patiently. While waiting, one may well spot the 'singer', if one has not already done so. Moreover, the subject may even come closer if one sits quietly and tries to merge with the environment while the disturbance caused by one's arrival dies down.

Recordings free of unwanted ambient sounds can be obtained by collecting the insect and removing it to temporary captivity in a studio or a quiet room. It can be placed in a cage constructed by stretching nylon, gauze or some other suitable fabric netting over a wire or wooden frame measuring approximately 46 × 30 × 30cm. As most orthopterans respond to warmth, a 40- or 60-watt bulb, mounted in or just outside the cage, will usually induce them to stridulate within minutes, although care should be taken not to overheat them. In the case of those species which possess a separate courtship song, this will usually be stimulated by introducing a female into the cage with the male.

With both field and studio recordings, one should try to eliminate unwanted background sounds by placing the microphone close to the subject and recording at as low a gain as is consistent with a good signal from the insect. However, recording at too low a level will result in raising the inherent tape hiss level during replay.

*BBC Natural History Unit; producer of the companion cassette of songs

15. Photographing Orthoptera

by R. & C. Foord

Bush-crickets, grasshoppers, crickets and cockroaches can all be photographed in the wild much more successfully than in a studio as the backgrounds never look contrived. Some people put insects into the refrigerator to cool them down and make them slow and dopey; however, in photographs they will always look like dopey insects when compared with natural lively ones. Photographing Orthoptera is usually a fine-weather occupation, conducted during summer in pleasant surroundings. It can be combined with the photography of wild flowers, as the varying habitats which need to be visited to obtain a wide range of Orthoptera naturally produce a wide range of wild flowers. However it is no good expecting to be able to photograph insects on a cold, miserable day because, being cold-blooded, they will be torpid and they require warm conditions to be active. In warm weather, too, adults will stridulate, which helps as it is often necessary to locate them by their song.

To make a record of each photograph as it is taken is very important in order that, when the film has been processed, details of the date, location, identification and sex of the insect can be added to it. A notebook should be used for permanent reference, but, failing this, a record in the field on the back of an envelope or similar is better than no record at all. It can be transferred to the permanent record later on. To avoid films becoming mixed up, it is advisable to give one's own film identification number to each and add this to the name and address panel when sending a film for processing.

Field notes may be as follows:

The Warren, pm July 7th. Film H1. In the ride above the Warren.

No. 6	view	No. 22	??
7 – 10	*C. brun.* M	23 – 24	Gt. Gr. F on Cr. thistle
11 – 12	” ” F	25 – 28	same as 22
13 – 14	views (farm, etc.)	29 – 36	*O. rufipes*?
17 – 21	*Myrm. mac.*? M?		also probably no. 22

It is a good practice, after taking a photograph, always to have a close look at the creature before losing sight of it in order to check on identification features which may not show in the picture, and in case the photograph does not come out well. It is also a help in learning about these insects.

When they are frightened, orthopteroids will run or jump, or, in the case of cockroaches, run and hide under the nearest stone or piece of bark. The creatures may be moving relatively fast and can move out of focus or out of the frame very rapidly. It may be necessary to pan the shot, as when taking a moving car. The same rules apply. When shooting on the move, shoot before stopping; if panning is interrupted to shoot, the subject is lost. They are also likely to be moving through grass-stems or leaves which can obscure them enough to ruin an otherwise good picture. As they are usually at, or near, ground level, it is best to lie prone with elbows on the ground to steady the camera. It is sometimes helpful to lay an ambush and get a companion to chase an insect out to an open patch where it can be photographed clearly.

Advice on camera equipment and its use is applicable here to 35mm colour-transparency film, but will, for the most part, apply equally to roll-film of larger format and to 'print' films. For satisfactory results, the camera should be a single-lens reflex. It need not be an expensive camera so long as its viewfinder permits viewing of the subject through the lens. Cameras where the viewfinder is separate and often above the lens, such as compact and Instamatic types, pose problems for this kind of photography.

The Orthoptera subjects are likely to be of any size from the 50mm length of a female *Tettigonia* down to 7mm long wood-crickets and 5mm nymphs. For the best results, close-up equipment should be used, but it is also possible to take Orthoptera photographs, using daylight, with a modern camera, perhaps assisted by dedicated flash (*i.e.*, which automatically calculates the correct exposure) or other flash and a long-focus lens which has macro facility. If the creature is near or on the ground, grass-stems may get in the way, but these can easily be moved when close-up is being used. Even so, a side view is rarely possible and a photograph will usually have to be taken with the camera lens tilted downwards. Some zoom lenses will slide out of focus at this angle. It will be necessary to use a fairly high-speed film for daylight photography to allow the lens to be stopped down and the depth of focus increased. As camera-shake can be a problem, it may be helpful to stand with legs apart and a walking-stick held under the camera to form a make-shift tripod. Close-up lenses fitted to the front of the lens will permit the use of the camera stopped down to f16 or f22. Better results will be obtained with bellows attachment or with automatic extension rings. Electronic flash is needed with these fittings. It may be found that bellow extensions, which can be used to move the lens forward of the camera to give greater magnification, will often disturb the foliage on which the subject is perched and are not easily made automatic. Extension rings, which are available singly or in sets of three, do not give these problems. All three used with a 50mm lens normally give a magnification of the image. A purpose-made macro-lens will give similar results, though at greater cost, but can be used with the rings to give higher magnification. When used with electronic flash and the smallest stop available, the depth of field is surprisingly good.

Focusing is done by moving the camera while viewing through the lens, and exposure is adjusted by moving the flashgun nearer to or farther from the subject. There is usually sufficient automatic adjustment of this because the lens being adjusted to increase magnification brings both the camera and flashgun forward and decreases lens and flashgun-to-subject distance. Normally, the flashgun cannot be used in the dedicated mode at very close distances and should, in these circumstances, be set to 'manual'.

Whatever system is used, it is best to try it out on the last three or four frames of a nearly-exposed film. Careful notes of distances, equipment and stop numbers should be taken so that conditions for the best result can be reproduced. Check for over- or under exposure by photographing an object with plenty of colour (*e.g.* a film pack).

Once the correct exposure is regularly achieved, it can be used for most of the Orthoptera. Make any other adjustments from there.

Ring-flash is not recommended as it is mounted on the lens and there is no adjustment for distance other than by the movement of the camera. However, if that is the flash equipment normally used but resulting in consistent over-exposure, the amount of flash can be modified by covering about one-third of the ring with paper on one side of the camera, holding it in place with elastic bands. It should also improve modelling, as unmodified ring-flash gives an excessively flat illumination.

A single ordinary flashgun of moderate power is ideal, mounted on a bar beside the camera and connected to the flash socket on the camera. A flashgun mounted on the hot-shoe (a mounting bracket on top of the camera with direct connections) is seldom able to angle downwards sufficiently to illuminate a subject close to the lens and is not adjustable for distance. It should, therefore, be mounted on a ball-and-socket head on the other end of the bar on which the camera is mounted by means of the tripod bush underneath. This makes the flashgun extremely adjustable. However, it is possible to manage without either of the ball-and-socket heads by using just the bar allowing movement forwards and sideways.

Sometimes two flashguns can be used – one fired by the camera and the other by a 'slave' unit, so that they both go off together. It is preferable to have one to the side of the camera, in the usual fashion, and the other at the other side or above it to illuminate some of the background and perhaps fill in some of the shadows left by the main flash. It is also useful in avoiding photographs with half the background black and unlit.

The basic system for insect photography makes use of the single-lens camera loaded with a colour-slide film of 64 ASA with one flashgun mounted so that the front of the gun is level with, or slightly forward of, the front of the camera. The lens, which is likely to be 50mm or 35mm, is fitted on an automatic extension tube, or tubes, and the shutter speed set as recommended by the manufacturer for flash photography. The lens is then set to its smallest stop of f16 or f22 after which, with the film wound on, the lens-cap off and the flash switched on, all is ready. The insect is approached slowly, if possible without showing oneself above the skyline. Any movement above the insect will be seen as danger and will encourage it to run or jump. Grasshoppers usually jump only in an emergency, and after about four or five jumps they stop and remain stationary. If there is a choice, approach should be made from a dark background. When the insect is seen to be in best focus in the viewfinder, the shutter is gently pressed and the film is wound on. There may be a wait for the flashgun to recharge before all is ready for another shot, so it is advisable to have a flashgun that recharges quickly. The flash itself does not disturb the insect as it seems to enjoy the warmth and will often settle down after the first flash as if looking forward to the next! However, should an insect on a grass-stem feel that there is danger, it will move so that the stem is between it and the cause of its alarm, thus presenting an underside view, bisected visually by the grass-stem. To counter this, one's hand should be moved gently round the side of the grass-stem and the grasshopper will move away from it and present a lateral view.

It is always helpful to have two people in the field when photographing grasshoppers; one to take the pictures while the other keeps an eye on the subject. Orthoptera seem to know when to jump which is usually when the camera is focused correctly and the shutter release is about to be squeezed! As one eye is at the viewfinder and the other closed, it is impossible to see where the subject has gone.

For the photography of small creatures such as grasshopper nymphs, which may be as small as 5mm long, it is useful to fit a lens-reversing ring to the camera and mount the lens back to front. The lenses are then no longer automatic and, to open up the lens for focusing and stopping down to take, it is necessary to move the operating lever with the fingers. With some makes of equipment, it may be necessary to obtain special fittings to do this. It is a two-handed job, with the camera usually resting on one's wrist. Practice is needed but it eventually becomes easy. A 50mm lens mounted reversed on the camera gives nearly two-times magnification, even without tubes; with a 28mm lens, three-times magnification can be achieved which is very suitable for a 5mm nymph. For even greater enlargement, tubes can be used, but this is getting very near the limit for this type of photography as the lens is very close to the subject. There is then a likelihood of the flash reflecting into the lens and causing a flare spot in the picture.

Calculations can be made to get the best results, and these may be found in the photographic literature. They are complicated and can be confusing. *The aim should be to keep as many things as possible constant*. For any given size of picture (and three sizes will cover all the Orthoptera) keep to

(i) the same type of film;
(ii) the same lens;
(iii) the same extension ring;
(iv) the same flash distance.

When photographing against a pale background such as sand, it may be found that reflection of light can cause over-exposure. The flashgun should be moved back an inch or two. When reversing the lens, it is necessary for the flash to be moved forwards an inch or so. A dedicated flashgun should be set to manual so as to prevent the camera altering the flash.

Learning from one's mistakes is important. Occasionally, when the film has been processed, a shot of habitat alone will be found without any insect at all. This usually results from the creature having jumped as the shutter was pressed and perhaps, at most, only its legs can be seen at the top of the picture. In other pictures, one discovers that limited depth of field could have been used to better advantage.

Finally, always handle the insects carefully; they are delicate creatures and legs come off easily. They have a short life and not all that many sunny days; and they do make marvellous photographs.

16. Glossary

abdomen – the third, posterior part of the body of an insect.

accessory glands – internal abdominal glands which produce a secretion during oviposition.

adult – the final (mature) stage of life of an insect during which reproduction occurs.

ala (pl. **alae**) – the membranous hindwing(s) of an insect.

anal wing veins – those in the hind part of the wing.

antenna (pl. **antennae**): the paired sensory appendages on the head of an insect, sometimes referred to as 'feelers'.

anterior – in or at the front end (*cf.* posterior).

apex (pl. **apices**; adj. **apical**) – tip.

appendage – a part or organ attached by a joint to the body.

apterous – without wings.

arolium (pl. **arolia**) – a small lobe or pad between the tarsal claws.

arthropod – one of the group of animals, including insects, spiders and crustaceans, having segmented bodies and jointed limbs.

auditory – pertaining to hearing.

autotomy – the shedding or breaking off of a damaged limb at a specialized point between trochanter and femur (*q.v.*), with subsequent regeneration (*q.v.*); a speciality of the Phasmida.

base (adj. **basal**) – that part of any appendage or structure that is nearest the body *e.g.*, of the leg or wing, that part nearest the thorax; of the thorax, that part nearest the abdomen; of the abdomen, that part nearest the thorax.

beating – the vigorous shaking of accessible branches of trees, over a footpath or spread sheet, in order to dislodge insects resting on the branches.

bilateral – with two symmetrical sides.

bilobed – having two lobes.

brachypterous – an insect having short wings (*cf.* macropterous).

brood pouch – the area within the abdomen of female Dictyoptera- Blattodea where the eggs develop inside the retracted ootheca.

calcareous – chalky.

calling song – the song produced by an isolated male bush- cricket, cricket or grasshopper.

capitulum (pl. **capitula**) – the structure attached to the operculum (*q.v.*) of the eggs of species of Phasmida.

carina (pl. **carinae**) – a keel or ridge (of the pronotum *q.v.*).

carnivorous – feeding on other animals.

cercus (pl. **cerci**) – the paired, segmented appendages at the end of the abdomen (of both sexes).

chirp – the name commonly given to the sound produced by an orthopteran insect.

chitin – the principal component of the insect cuticle or skin; a nitrogenous polysaccharide which is insoluble in water.

chitinized – hardened or horny; not flexible or membraneous.

compound eye – a large eye made up of many separate units.

cosmopolitan – having a world-wide distribution.
cosmotropical – having a tropical distribution.
costa – the first vein of the wing.
costal margin – the front margin of the wing.
courtship song – the special song produced by a male bush- cricket, cricket or grasshopper when close to a female.
coxa (pl. **coxae**) – the proximal, or basal, segment of the leg.
crepuscular – active in the half-light at dusk or dawn.
cubitus – the vein between the median and anal veins of the wing.
culture – to rear in artificial conditions in captivity.
cursorial – running (*cf.* saltatorial).
cuticle (adj. **cuticular**) – the skin of insects.
diapause – a period during the egg or nymphal stages of life in which development ceases temporarily.
discoid – shaped like a disc.
diurnal – active during daylight.
domiciliary – living in a dwelling-place.
dorsal – of or belonging to the back or upper surface (*cf.* ventral).
drumming – the sound produced by male *Meconema thalassinum* by tapping one foreleg on the surface on which it is standing.
dune slack – an area in sand-dunes where the surface dips below the normal water table to produce wet areas with marshland flora.
ecdysis (pl. **ecdyses**) – the process of moulting or shedding an entire layer of skin; the mechanism which permits growth in insects.
echeme – a first-order assemblage of syllables; a term used in insect acoustics.
ectoparasite – an external parasite.
egg-pod – a batch of grasshopper eggs covered by a hardened secretion.
egg-purse – the hardened covering around cockroach eggs (see also *ootheca*).
elytron (pl. **elytra**) – the hardened forewing of an insect (see also *tegmen*).
embryo – the developing egg stage of an insect.
endopterygote – having complete metamorphosis, including a pupal stage with wings developing internally (*cf.* exopterygote; see also *holometabolous*).
epiproct – the eleventh tergite of Dermaptera (see also *pygidium*).
exopterygote – having simple metamorphosis, without a pupal stage and with wings developing externally (*cf.* endopterygote; see also *hemimetabolous*).
fastigium – the broadened apex of the top of the head.
femur (pl. **femora**; adj. **femoral**) – the third segment and largest part or 'thigh' of the insect leg, attached at the base to the body by the trochanter and coxa.
fenestra (pl. **fenestrae**) – one of the lateral pair of ocelli (*q.v.*) in Blattodea.
foliaceous – leaf-like, or resembling a leaf.
forceps – the modified cerci of Dermaptera.
forewings – the paired outgrowths of the second thoracic segment (see also *elytron*, *tegmen*).
foveola (pl. **foveolae**) – a well-defined depression; in pairs on the top of the head of Acrididae.
frequency – the measurement of sound (in cycles per second or cps).

frons – the front of the head.
gland – a structure which produces a characteristic secretion or substance.
glandular pit – a depression on the dorsal abdominal surface of male cockroaches containing glands (*q.v.*).
gravid – pregnant.
harp – a clear area of amplification on the forewings of crickets.
hatchling – an emergent nymph.
hemimetabolous – having simple metamorphosis, without a pupal stage, and with wings developing externally (*cf.* holometabolous; see also *exopterygote*).
herbivorous – feeding only on grasses and other plants.
hindwings – the paired outgrowths of the third thoracic segment (see also *ala*).
holometabolous – having complete metamorphosis, with a pupal stage, and with wings developing internally (*cf.* hemimetabolous; see also *endopterygote*).
hyperparasitism – parasitism by one parasite upon another.
keel – (i) ridge (of pronotum); (ii) line on ootheca along which it opens to allow young to hatch.
instar – a stage between two successive moults or ecdyses in the life of an insect, before the adult stage is reached.
interacting – the singing of several males in competition with one another.
intercalary – additional or inserted between, as a wing vein or other structure.
labium (pl. **labia**; adj. **labial**) – or second maxillae, the lower or hindmost part of the insect mouth formed of fused pair of maxilla-like structures: the insect 'lower lip'.
labrum – the insect 'upper lip', partly covering the mandibles.
lateral – at or from the side.
linea scapularis – the white line or pale-coloured stripe along the anterior margin of a grasshopper forewing.
macrolabic – having large forceps or pincers (in Dermaptera).
macropterous – an insect having fully developed or long wings (*cf.* brachypterous).
mandible – the biting jaw of orthopteroid insects, paired and sharply toothed.
maxilla (pl. **maxillae**) – part of the insect mouth; paired structures behind the mandibles.
maxillary palps – the segmented structures arising from the maxillae.
median area – the central area of the wing.
media – the vein lying in the centre of the wing.
medio-cubitus – fused media and cubitus veins.
mesonotum – the dorsal surface of the second thoracic segment (*cf.* pronotum; metanotum).
mesosternum (adj. **mesosternal**) – the ventral surface of the mesothorax (*q.v.*).
mesothorax (adj. **mesothoracic**) – the second thoracic segment.
metamorphosis – growth by change of shape.
metanotum – the dorsal surface of the third thoracic segment (*cf.* mesonotum; pronotum).
metasternum (adj. **metasternal**) – the ventral surface of the metathorax (*q.v.*).
metathorax (adj. **metathoracic**) – the third segment of the thorax.
mirror – a specialized area of the forewing of male bush-crickets and crickets, formed between branches of the cubitus vein, which acts as a resonator in stridulation.

moult – to shed or cast the skin or outer covering of the body.
morph(s) – body form(s).
Nearctic – the northern New World (*cf.* Palaearctic).
Neotropical – of tropical America.
nocturnal – active during the hours of darkness.
nymph (adj. **nymphal**) – the young stage(s) between egg (or vermiform larva) and adult.
omnivorous – feeding on both animal and plant food.
ocellus (pl. **ocelli**) – a simple eye, usually occurring in small groups.
ootheca (pl. **oothecae**) – the hardened covering around cockroach eggs.
ootaxonomy – the study of the structure of eggs.
operculum (pl. **opercula**, adj. **opercular**) – (i) of female Phasmida: the subgenital plate at the end of the abdomen; (ii) of eggs of Phasmida: the 'lid' of the egg, which is pushed off by the emerging nymph when it hatches.
orthopteran – a member of the Orthoptera Saltatoria *sensu stricto*; the jumping Orthoptera with much enlarged hind legs.
orthopteroid – one of the Orthoptera *sensu lato*; i.e. including the cursorial or running Orthoptera and closely related orders without much-enlarged hind legs.
oviparity – reproduction by egg-laying.
ovipositor – the egg-laying apparatus of a female.
ovoid – having an oval shape.
ovoviviparity – reproduction by eggs which are hatched inside the body of the female.
ovum (pl. **ova**) – egg(s).
Palaearctic – the northern Old World (*cf.* Nearctic).
palps – the segmented, paired structures arising from the maxillae and the labium (*q.v.*); sensory structures used in the testing and manipulation of food.
parthenogenesis – reproduction by the development of unfertilized eggs, usually to produce only females.
pincers – the modified cerci (*q.v.*) of Dermaptera (see also *forceps*).
plantula (pl. **plantulae**) – the ventral lobes on the hind tarsi of some bush-crickets.
polyporus – strips of dried fungus material, on to which small insects may be pinned.
posterior – in or at the hind end (*cf.* anterior).
predator (adj. **predatory**) – any animal which preys on another.
process – a projection.
prognathous – having the mouthparts or jaws projecting forwards.
pronotum (adj. **pronotal**) – the dorsal surface of the first thoracic segment; in orthopteroid insects usually much enlarged and extended posteriorly to cover both the mesonotum and metanotum (*q.v.*).
prothorax (adj. **prothoracic**) – the first segment of the thorax.
prosternum (adj. **prosternal**) – the first ventral thoracic sternite (*q.v.*).
proximal – the part of an appendage nearest the body.
pubescent – covered with soft, downy hair.
punctate – pitted.
pygidium – the eleventh tergite of Dermaptera (see also *epiproct*).
quiescence – resting; non-developing.

radius – the major long vein(s) in the wing.
raptorial – predatory (*q.v.*).
regeneration – the regrowth of parts of the body lost or damaged during nymphal development.
relict – a survivor from an earlier age.
saltatorial – jumping (*cf.* cursorial).
sclerite – a hardened cuticular plate.
seasonality – pertaining to the seasons.
sibling – a member of the same egg-batch or litter; one with a parent in common with another.
siliceous – of certain rocks, such as flint and sandstone, containing silica.
song – the sound produced by stridulation.
spermatophore – a 'sperm package' produced by a male in order to fertilize the female.
spermatophylax – the portion of the spermatophore which does not contain sperm, and is normally eaten by the female.
squama (pl. **squamae**) – the chitinized (*q.v.*) portion of the Dermapteran hindwing; the only part visible when the hindwing is folded beneath the forewing.
sternite – a ventral sclerite or segment.
stigma (pl. **stigmata**) – a white or pale-coloured spot on the forewings.
stridulation – the action of rubbing two parts of the body against each other to produce sound.
stridulatory pegs – the small peg-like projections on the inner side of the hind femur of grasshoppers.
style – small unsegmented appendage on the male subgenital plate.
subcosta – the second vein of the wing.
subgenital plate – the last ventral sclerite of the abdomen.
submarginal – positioned just inside or within the margin.
sulcus – a groove.
substrate – an underlying layer.
supra-anal plate – the last dorsal sclerite of the abdomen.
syllable – the sound produced by one complete up and down movement of the hindlegs in grasshoppers, and of the forewings in crickets and bush-crickets.
tarsus (pl. **tarsi**, adj. **tarsal**) – the segmented foot of insects.
taxon (pl. **taxa**) – a division or rank, in classification.
taxonomy – classification or its principles.
tegmen (pl. **tegmina**) – the forewing(s), particularly when a hardened, leathery texture (see also *elytron*).
tergite – a dorsal sclerite or segment.
tergum (adj. **tergal**) – the dorsal surface of any body segment.
thorax (adj. **thoracic**) – the second major division of the insect body, bearing the legs and, if present, wings.
tibia (pl. **tibiae**) – the fourth segment and second long portion of the leg; the 'shin' of the insect leg.
trochanter – the second segment of the leg, articulating with the coxa and usually fixed to the femur (*q.v.*).

truncate – squared off at the end.
tubercle – a small knob.
tympanum (pl. **tympana**) – the thin membrane or 'ear-drum' of the hearing organ.
unicolorous – of one colour.
ventral – of or belonging to the underside or surface (*cf.* dorsal).
vermiform larva – the worm-like pre-nymphal stage, which emerges from the egg with legs enclosed in a cuticular covering and then hatches into the first true nymphal stage.
vertex – the crown of the head.
vestigial – apparently poorly developed, but referring to a structure which has become reduced in size until almost lost.
viscera – the internal organs of the body.
viviparity – giving birth to live young (as opposed to laying eggs).
wing-bud/wing-pad – the lobe-like, dorsal extensions of the mesothoracic and metathoracic tergites (*q.v.*) in nymphs which are the developing wings.

17. Select Bibliography

The titles listed below include important classic and modern standard works on orthopteroids and also some useful works of general entomological interest. Readers will find a more comprehensive selection of books and papers included in the References at the end of this book (pp. 218–226). Certain titles are included in both lists and the historical perspective is discussed in the 'Historical Account of the Study of Orthoptera' (see pp. 21–24).

BELLMANN, H., 1988. *A field guide to the grasshoppers and crickets of Britain and northern Europe*. Collins.

BROWN, V. K., 1983. *Grasshoppers*. Naturalist's Handbooks **2**, Cambridge University Press.

BURR, M., 1936. *British Grasshoppers and their Allies*. Philip Allan & Co. *or* Janson & Sons.

CHAPMAN, R. F., 1976 . *A Biology of Locusts*. Edward Arnold.

CHINERY, M., 1973. *A Field Guide to the Insects of Britain and Northern Europe*. Collins.

———, 1986. *Collins Guide to the Insects of Britain and Western Europe*. Collins.

CHOPARD, L., 1951. *Faune de France* **56**: *Orthoptéroïdes*. Paul Lechevalier, Paris.

HARZ, K., 1969. *The Orthoptera of Europe*. Vol. 1. W. Junk, The Hague.

———, 1975. *The Orthoptera of Europe*. Vol. 2. W. Junk.

——— & Kaltenbach, A., 1976. *The Orthoptera of Europe*. Vol. 3. W. Junk.

HOLST, K. T., 1986. *The Saltatoria (Bush-crickets, crickets and grasshoppers) of Northern Europe*. Fauna Entomologica Scandinavica **16**, Copenhagen.

LUCAS, W. J., 1920. *A Monograph of the British Orthoptera*. The Ray Society.

PICKARD, B. C., 1954. *Grasshoppers and crickets of Great Britain and the Channel Islands*. Privately published.

RAGGE, D. R., 1965. *Grasshoppers, Crickets and Cockroaches of the British Isles.* Warne.

UVAROV, B. P., 1966. *Grasshoppers and Locusts*, Vol. 1. Cambridge University Press.

———, 1977. *Grasshoppers and Locusts*, Vol. 2. Centre for Overseas Pest Research, London.

General Entomology

IMMS, A. D., 1964. *A General Textbook of Entomology* (9th edn).Methuen.

RYAN, J. G., O'CONNOR, J. P. & BEIRNE, B. P., 1984. *A Bibliography of Irish Entomology.* The Fly Leaf Press, Glenageary, Co. Dublin.

SMITH, K. G. V. & SMITH, V., 1983. *A Bibliography of the Entomology of the Smaller British Offshore Islands.* E. W. Classey, Faringdon.

TORRE-BUENO, J. R. DE LA, 1978 (5th printing). *A Glossary of Entomology.* Lubrecht & Cramer, New York.

PART II: SYSTEMATIC SECTION

Orthoptera and allied Insects

Grasshoppers and their relatives are collectively referred to as orthopteroid insects or orthopteroids. The name of the order Orthoptera is derived from the Greek for 'straight-winged'. All have straight-veined, leathery-textured forewings (also referred to as elytra or tegmina) protecting the delicate, membranous, fan-shaped hindwings or alae. They all have biting mouthparts for eating a wide variety of foods, the carnivorous species often having powerful jaws or mandibles. The grasshoppers, crickets and bush-crickets have enlarged hindlegs with powerful muscles and are known as the Orthoptera Saltatoria – those that jump (p. 78). Although regarded as one order here and in many other publications, some authors prefer to divide the group into two or more orders (see p. 18).

There are several other groups of insects which are regarded as related to the Orthoptera Saltatoria and sometimes referred to as Orthoptera Cursoria (those that run) as their hindlegs are not specially enlarged for jumping. These are the order Dictyoptera (p. 121), which includes the cockroaches (suborder Blattodea) and praying mantises or mantids (suborder Mantodea) [both given ordinal status by some authors], and order Phasmida (p. 140), the stick and leaf insects. One other closely related group, the order Grylloblattodea, consists of very odd wingless orthopteroids, known by only a few species and found in North America, Russia and Japan, but not represented in Britain.

The earwigs, order Dermaptera (p. 132), are slightly more distant relatives, distinguished by the presence of forceps or pincers at the end of the abdomen.

The orthopteroid population of the British Isles is small in numbers of species: only fifty-two, including fourteen known to be established aliens, compared with about 1100 in Western Europe, and a world population of about 26,000. Of the fifty-two, thirty-seven are saltatorial species which are known to breed here (including the established aliens), compared with about 900 in Western Europe, and a world population of over 17,000.

NOTE. Throughout the Systematic Section, the maps accompanying the text show the general distribution of each species on a vice-county basis. The key to vice-county numbering and an explanation of the system is given on pages 194–195. The map numbers cited against *Distribution and Status* refer to the 10km sq. dot-distribution maps which are printed together in the Atlas section on pages 164–189.

CHECK LIST

Species recorded in Great Britain and Ireland

The following list shows the complete currently valid scientific name for each of the orthopteroid insects mentioned in the text. However it is rarely necessary or even useful to quote this combination in full. For example, the full scientific name for the field grasshopper is here listed as *Chorthippus (Glyptobothrus) brunneus brunneus* (Thunberg), but elsewhere only *Chorthippus brunneus* is used.

The synonyms listed are not necessarily all which are applicable to the species in question, but are those of importance or of relevance to this work.

The classification used is a conservative form, as explained elsewhere (p. 19).

n = native
p = probable native
e = established alien
c = occasional casual introduction
m = occasional migrant

ORDER **ORTHOPTERA**

SUBORDER **Ensifera**

SUPERFAMILY **Tettigonioidea**

FAMILY RHAPHIDOPHORIDAE

e	*Tachycines asynamorus* Adelung, 1902	Greenhouse Camel-cricket
c	*Dolichopoda bormansi* Brunner, 1882	
	= *Chopardina importata* Uvarov, 1921	

FAMILY TETTIGONIIDAE

SUBFAMILY Hetrodinae

c	*Cosmoderus maculatus* (Kirby, 1896)	Prickly Bush-cricket

SUBFAMILY Pseudophyllinae

c	*Jamaicana subguttata* (Walker, 1870)	Mottle-winged Bush-cricket
c	*Jamaicana flava* Caudell, 1913	
c	*Mastophyllum scabricolle* (Serville, [1838])	Brown-winged Bush-cricket
c	*Nesonotus tricornis* (Thunberg, 1815)	
c	*Nesonotus* spp.	
c	*Arrhenotettix* spp.	

SUBFAMILY Meconematinae

n	*Meconema thalassinum* (De Geer, 1773)	Oak Bush-cricket

SUBFAMILY Tettigoniinae

n	*Tettigonia viridissima* Linnaeus, 1758	Great Green Bush-cricket

SUBFAMILY Decticinae[1]

n	*Decticus verrucivorus verrucivorus* (Linnaeus, 1758)	Wart-biter
n	*Pholidoptera griseoaptera* (De Geer, 1773)	Dark Bush-cricket
	= *Pholidoptera cinerea* (Gmelin, 1789)	
n	*Platycleis (Platycleis) albopunctata albopunctata* (Goeze, 1778)	Grey Bush-cricket
	= *Platycleis denticulata* (Panzer, 1796)	
n	subsp. *P. a. jerseyana* Zeuner, 1940	Jersey Bush-cricket

[1] Treated as a tribe (Decticini) of Tettigoniinae by Rentz, 1980.

n	*Metrioptera (Metrioptera) brachyptera* (Linnaeus, 1761)	Bog Bush-cricket
n	*Metrioptera (Roeseliana) roeselii* (Hagenbach, 1822)	Roesel's Bush-cricket
SUBFAMILY	Conocephalinae	
n	*Conocephalus (Xiphidion) discolor discolor* (Thunberg, 1815)[1] = *Conocephalus fuscus* (Fabricius, 1793)	Long-winged Cone-head
n	*Conocephalus (Xiphidion) dorsalis dorsalis* (Latreille, 1804)	Short-winged Cone-head
SUBFAMILY	Listroscelidinae	
c	*Phlugiolopsis henryi* Zeuner, 1940	
SUBFAMILY	Phaneropterinae	
m	*Phaneroptera falcata* (Poda, 1761)	Sickle-bearing Bush-cricket
n	*Leptophyes punctatissima* (Bosc, 1792)	Speckled Bush-cricket
SUPERFAMILY	**Grylloidea**	
FAMILY	GRYLLIDAE	
SUBFAMILY	Gryllinae	
e	*Acheta domesticus* (Linnaeus, 1758)	House-cricket
n	*Gryllus campestris campestris* Linnaeus, 1758	Field-cricket
c	*Gryllus bimaculatus* De Geer, 1773	Southern Field-cricket
c	*Gryllodes sigillatus* (Walker, 1869)	Tropical House-cricket
SUBFAMILY	Nemobiinae	
n	*Nemobius sylvestris* (Bosc, 1792)	Wood-cricket
SUBFAMILY	Mogoplistinae	
p	*Pseudomogoplistes squamiger* (Fischer, 1853) [previously known as *Mogoplistes squamiger*]	Scaly Cricket
FAMILY	GRYLLOTALPIDAE	
n	*Gryllotalpa gryllotalpa* (Linnaeus, 1758)	Mole-cricket
SUBORDER	**Caelifera**	
SUPERFAMILY	**Acridoidea**	
FAMILY	TETRIGIDAE	
n	*Tetrix (Tetrix) ceperoi* (Bolivar, 1887)	Cepero's Ground-hopper
n	*Tetrix (Tetrix) subulata* (Linnaeus, 1758)	Slender Ground-hopper
n	*Tetrix (Tetratettix) undulata undulata* (Sowerby, 1806)	Common Ground-hopper
FAMILY	ACRIDIDAE	
SUBFAMILY	Cyrtacanthacridinae	
c	*Anacridum aegyptium* (Linnaeus, 1764)	Egyptian Grasshopper
m	*Schistocerca gregaria* (Forskål, 1775)	Desert Locust
m	*Calliptamus italicus* (Linnaeus, 1758)	Italian Locust

[1] Valid name: Roberts, 1941.

SUBFAMILY Oedipodinae[1]

n	*Oedipoda caerulescens* (Linnaeus, 1758)	Blue-winged Grasshopper
n	*Stethophyma grossum* (Linnaeus, 1758)[2]	Large Marsh Grasshopper
m	*Locusta migratoria migratoria* (Linnaeus, 1758)	Migratory Locust
m	subsp. *L. m. gallica* (Remaudière, 1947)	

SUBFAMILY Gomphocerinae

n	*Stenobothrus (Stenobothrus) lineatus lineatus* (Panzer, 1796)	Stripe-winged Grasshopper
p	*Stenobothrus (Stenobothrus) stigmaticus* (Rambur, 1839)[3]	Lesser Mottled Grasshopper
n	*Omocestus rufipes* (Zetterstedt, 1821)[4] = *Omocestus ventralis* (Zetterstedt, 1821)	Woodland Grasshopper
n	*Omocestus viridulus* (Linnaeus, 1758)	Common Green Grasshopper
n	*Chorthippus (Glyptobothrus) brunneus brunneus* (Thunberg, 1815) = *Chorthippus bicolor* (Charpentier, 1825)	Field Grasshopper [= Common Field Grasshopper]
n	*Chorthippus (Glyptobothrus) vagans* (Eversmann, 1848)	Heath Grasshopper
n	*Chorthippus (Chorthippus) parallelus parallelus* (Zetterstedt, 1821)	Meadow Grasshopper
n	*Chorthippus (Chorthippus) albomarginatus albomarginatus* (De Geer, 1773) = *Chorthippus elegans* (Charpentier, 1825)	Lesser Marsh Grasshopper
n	*Euchorthippus pulvinatus elegantulus* Zeuner, 1825	Jersey Grasshopper
n	*Gomphocerippus rufus* (Linnaeus, 1758)[2]	Rufous Grasshopper
n	*Myrmeleotettix maculatus maculatus* (Thunberg, 1815)	Mottled Grasshopper

ORDER **DICTYOPTERA**[5]

SUBORDER **Blattodea**

FAMILY POLYPHAGIDAE

c	*Polyphaga aegyptiaca* (Linnaeus, 1758)	

FAMILY BLABERIDAE

SUBFAMILY Blaberinae

c	*Blaberus giganteus* (Linnaeus, 1758)[6]	
c	*Archimandrita marmorata* (Stoll, 1813)	
c	*Nauclidas nigra* (Brunner, 1892)	Round-backed Cockroach

SUBFAMILY Panchlorinae

c	*Panchlora nivea* (Linnaeus, 1758)	Cuban Cockroach

[1] Locustinae of Harz, 1975.
[2] Valid name: Roberts, 1941.
[3] Harz, 1975, restricted the nominate subspecies *stigmaticus* to the Iberian peninsula (with an invalid neotype designation), and proposed the subspecific name *faberi* for the population present in the rest of Europe.
[4] Valid under Article 24 of the Code.
[5] Dictuoptera is used by Kevan, 1977, 1980a.
[6] Kevan, 1980b, has pointed out that the name, 'The Drummer', is incorrectly attributed to this species.

SUBFAMILY	Pycnoscelinae	
e	*Pycnoscelus surinamensis* (Linnaeus, 1758)	Surinam Cockroach
SUBFAMILY	Oxyhaloinae[1]	
c	*Rhyparobia maderae* (Fabricius, 1781) = *Leucophaea maderae* (Fabricius, 1781)	Madeira Cockroach
c	*Nauphoeta cinerea* (Olivier, 1789)	Cinereous Cockroach
c	*Henschoutedenia flexivitta* (Walker, 1868)	Large Cinereous Cockroach
c	*Henschoutedenia tectidoma* Gurney, 1965	Short-winged Cinereous Cockroach
	Gromphadorhina portentosa (Schaum, 1853) [cultured species]	Madagascan Hissing Cockroach
FAMILY	BLATTIDAE	
SUBFAMILY	Blattinae	
e	*Blatta (Blatta) orientalis* Linnaeus, 1758	Common or Oriental Cockroach
e	*Periplaneta americana* (Linnaeus, 1758)	American or Ship Cockroach
e	*Periplaneta australasiae* (Fabricius, 1775)	Australian Cockroach
c	*Periplaneta brunnea* Burmeister, 1838	Brown Cockroach
c	*Neostylopyga rhombifolia* (Stoll, 1813)	Harlequin Cockroach
c	*Pelmatosilpha larifuga* Gurney, 1965	Vagabond Cockroach
c	*Pelmatosilpha* spp.	
FAMILY	BLATTELLIDAE	
SUBFAMILY	Nyctiborinae	
c	*Nyctibora laevigata* (Beauvois, 1805)	Smooth Cockroach
SUBFAMILY	Blattellinae	
e	*Blattella germanica* (Linnaeus, 1767)	German Cockroach
e	*Supella longipalpa* (Fabricius, 1798) = *Supella supellectilium* (Serville, 1838)	Brown-banded Cockroach
c	*Neoblattella* spp.	
c	*Cariblatta* spp.	
SUBFAMILY	Ectobiinae	
n	*Ectobius (Ectobius) lapponicus lapponicus* (Linnaeus, 1758)	Dusky Cockroach
n	*Ectobius (Ectobius) pallidus pallidus* (Olivier, 1789)	Tawny Cockroach
n	*Ectobius (Capraiellus) panzeri* Stephens, 1835	Lesser Cockroach
SUBORDER	**Mantodea**	
FAMILY	MANTIDAE	
m	*Mantis religiosa* (Linnaeus, 1758)	Praying Mantis

[1] Nauphoetidae is used by Kevan, 1980a.

ORDER	**DERMAPTERA**	
FAMILY	ANISOLABIDIDAE = CARCINOPHORIDAE[1]	
SUBFAMILY	Anisolabidinae	
e	*Euborellia annulipes* (Lucas, 1847)	Ring-legged Earwig
c	*Anisolabis maritima* (Bonelli [*in* Géné], 1832)	Maritime Earwig
FAMILY	LABIIDAE[2]	
SUBFAMILY	Labiinae	
n	*Labia minor* (Linnaeus, 1758)	Lesser Earwig
SUBFAMILY	Spongiphorinae	
e	*Marava arachidis* (Yersin, 1860)	Bone-house Earwig
FAMILY	FORFICULIDAE	
SUBFAMILY	Forficulinae	
n	*Apterygida media* (Hagenbach, 1822) = *Apterygida albipennis* (Charpentier, 1825)	Short-winged or Hop-garden Earwig
n	*Forficula auricularia* Linnaeus, 1758 = *Forficula forcipata* Stephens, 1835	Common Earwig
n	*Forficula lesnei* Finot, 1887	Lesne's Earwig
FAMILY	LABIDURIDAE	
SUBFAMILY	Labidurinae	
p or **e**	*Labidura riparia* (Pallas, 1773)	Giant or Tawny Earwig

ORDER	**PHASMIDA**	
FAMILY	PHASMATIDAE	
SUBFAMILY	Pachymorphinae	
e	*Acanthoxyla geisovii* (Kaup, 1866) [previously identified as *A. prasina* (Westwood, 1859)]	Prickly Stick-insect
e	*Acanthoxyla inermis* Salmon, 1955	Unarmed Stick-insect
e	*Clitarchus hookeri* (White, 1846) = *Clitarchus laeviusculus* Stal, 1875	Smooth Stick-insect
SUBFAMILY	Lonchodinae	
	Carausius morosus (Sinéty, 1901) [cultured species]	Laboratory or Indian Stick-insect

[1] Kevan, 1980b, Sakai, 1982. The stem '-labis' is derived from the Greek for forceps or tongs, plural 'labidos', hence family name-ending '-labididae' (see below).

[2] Spongiphoridae is used by Kevan, 1980b in preference to Labiidae which is commonly used. The name 'Labia' is derived from the Greek for lip, plural 'labii', hence the family name Labiidae (see above).

Introduction to the Key

The species are keyed out by order or family so that if this grouping is already known, *e.g.* Dermaptera or Tettigoniidae, one may go straight to it.

Sizes, both in the key and in species descriptions, are quoted to the nearest whole millimetre, unless a more exact measurement is critical, and measured from the vertex of the head to the end of the abdomen, or to the end of the folded wings, if these project beyond the abdomen.

Macropterous and brachypterous forms of the same species are keyed out separately, although macropterous forms of brachypterous species found among a population of normal individuals should be recognizable as such.

Where the lengths of cerci and hind femora are compared, the measurements should be taken independently.

Particularly in the Tettigoniidae and Acrididae, where the colour differences between live and dead insects may be extreme, great care should be taken when considering colour. The colours referred to in the key are those of living, freshly-killed or dead, rapidly dried, material having good colour preservation. Although specimens may be identified from colour photographs if key features can be seen, frequently the most vital area is not visible. Rotting or damaged dead specimens may present equal difficulties. Perhaps an ideal combination for identification purposes, in the absence of a live insect, is a colour photograph taken from life, together with a carefully dried, pinned specimen.

Key to Adults

1 Hindlegs enlarged for jumping or forelegs highly modified for digging – Orthoptera Saltatoria.................. 2

– Hindlegs not enlarged and forelegs not modified...... 38

2(1) Saltatorial or jumping hindlegs, forelegs not modified for digging.. 3

– Hindlegs slightly enlarged, forelegs short and broad with flattened claws for digging – Gryllotalpidae (text fig. 37, p. 98)......................... *Gryllotalpa gryllotalpa* (p. 98)

3(2) Long, thread-like antennae, hearing-organ (if present) near base of fore-tibiae, ovipositor long and sword-like – Ensifera.. 4

– Short antennae, hearing-organ on the side of the abdomen, ovipositor short – Caelifera.........................21

4(3) No hearing-organ; palps long, the maxillary pair longer than the fore-femora – Rhaphidophoridae .... *Tachycines asynamorus* (p. 78)

– Hearing-organ near the base of the fore-tibiae, palps short... 5

5(4) Tarsi 4-segmented, cerci short, always shorter than the hind-femora – Tettigoniidae (text fig. 34, p. 79).........6

– Tarsi 3-segmented, cerci long, about the same length as the hind-femora – Gryllidae (text fig. 36, p. 93)........18

TETTIGONIIDAE

6(5) Long wings; both fore- and hindwings at least as long as the abdomen... .7

– Short wings; forewings shorter than the abdomen, hindwings very short or absent........................... 14

7(6) Larger, mainly green, total length over 30mm...........8

– Smaller, total length under 30mm.........................9

8(7) Forewings under 30mm long, shorter than the hind-femora; eyes dark; pronotum with a median keel, hind-tarsi with long plantulae; ovipositor long, slightly upcurved.......... .... *Decticus verrucivorus* (p. 82)

– Forewings over 30mm, longer than the hind-femora; eyes pale greenish brown; pronotum without a median keel, plantulae only short, knob-like; ovipositor long, down-curved................ .*Tettigonia viridissima* (p. 81)

9(8) Mainly brown or grey, never totally green; pronotum with a median keel on the hind-part, hind-tarsi with long plantulae.. 10

– Mainly green, pronotum without a median keel, plantulae never long.. .12

10(9) Greyish brown, no pale band on the pronotum, no green or yellow markings.......... *Platycleis albopunctata* (p.85)
– Brown with green or yellow markings, a pale band on the side flaps of the pronotum; wings almost black........ 11
11(10) Abdomen ventrally yellow, the pronotal band on the hind, lower and fore-margins of the side flaps .... macropterous *Metrioptera roeselii* (p. 87)
– Abdomen ventrally green, the pronotal band on the hind-margin only of the side flaps........................... .... macropterous *Metrioptera brachyptera* (p. 86)
12(9) Pale green, with only a narrow yellow or brown dorsal stripe, never totally brown; ♂ cerci long, slender and curved.........................*Meconema thalassinum* (p. 80)
– Green with brown wings and a brown dorsal stripe; rarely all-brown.. 13
13(12) Hind-femora with a few small black spines on the underside; ♂ cerci with apex (beyond internal tooth) short, straight (text fig. 13); ♂ supra-anal plate with two small lobes separated by a small central notch; ovipositor almost straight; wing-length normally 11–15 mm: macropterous form wing-length 16–19mm ....*Conocephalus discolor* (p. 89)
– Hind-femora with no black spines on the underside, ♂ cerci with apex (beyond internal tooth) long and upturned at the tip (text fig. 14); ♂ supra-anal plate with two long lobes joined together centrally; ovipositor curved upwards; wing-length 15–18mm.................. ....macropterous *Conocephalus dorsalis* (p. 91)

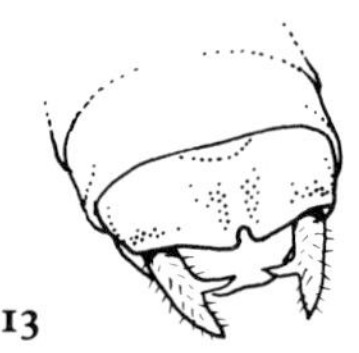

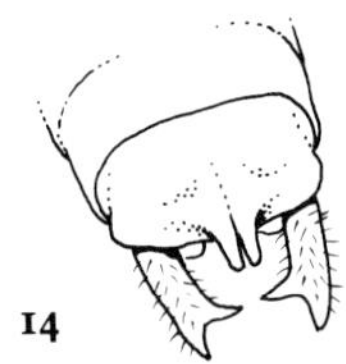

Text figures 13, 14 ♂ cerci and supra-anal plates
(**13**) *Conocephalus discolor*; (**14**) *C. dorsalis*

14(6) Forewings reduced to small, rounded lobes or tiny flaps 15
– Forewings covering about half the abdomen...........16
15(14) Bright green with minute brown spots; ovipositor short, broad and upcurved..... *Leptophyes punctatissima* (p. 92)
– Brown, abdomen yellow ventrally; ovipositor long and gently curved............ *Pholidoptera griseoaptera* (p. 84)
16(14) Slender, usually green with a brown dorsal stripe and brown wings; if brown, with no pale band on the pronotal side flaps...........*Conocephalus dorsalis* (p. 91)
– Sturdy, brown with green or yellow markings, a pale band on the side flaps of the pronotum................. 17
17(16) Abdomen ventrally yellow, the pronotal band on the hind-, lower and fore-margins of the side flaps; ♀ subgenital- plate divided into 2 lobes (text fig. 15)....... ....*Metrioptera roeselii* (p. 87)
– Abdomen ventrally green, the pronotal band on the hind-margin only of the side flaps; ♀ subgenital-plate not divided into 2 lobes (text fig. 16) .... *Metrioptera brachyptera* (p. 86)

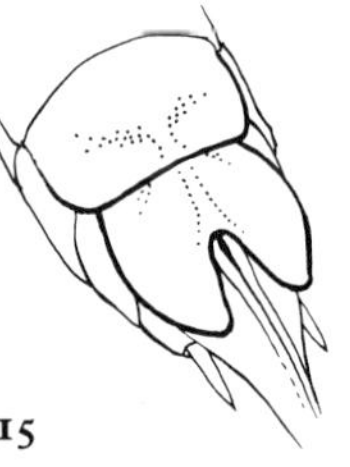

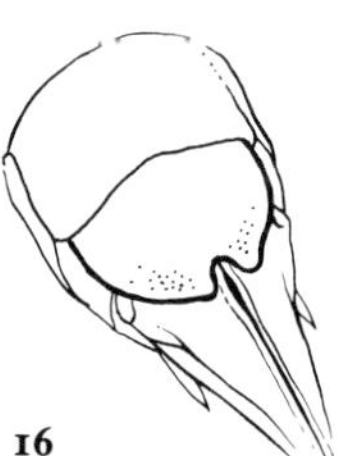

Text Figures 15, 16 ♀ subgenital plates
(**15**) *Metrioptera roeselii*; (**16**) *M. brachyptera*

GRYLLIDAE

18(5) Larger, 14–23mm, fully winged or forewings covering most of abdomen... 19
– Smaller, 7–13mm, wings reduced or absent............ 20
19(18) Dull brown; both pairs of wings fully developed, the hindwings longer, extending beyond the abdomen....... .... *Acheta domesticus* (p. 94)
– Shiny black; forewings covering most of the abdomen, the hindwings vestigial.......... *Gryllus campestris* (p. 95)
20(18) Forewings present, shorter than the abdomen; hindwings absent ....*Nemobius sylvestris* (p. 96)
– Totally wingless; body covered with minute scales .... *Pseudomogoplistes squamiger* (p. 97)
21(3) Pronotum extended backwards, covering the abdomen; 2 tarsal segments on the fore- and mid-legs, 3 on the hindlegs, no arolium present between the tarsal claws – Tetrigidae (text fig. 38a, p. 100)..........................22
– Pronotum saddle-shaped, not extending backwards over the abdomen; 3 tarsal segments on all legs, arolium present between tarsal claws – Acrididae (text fig. 40a, p. 104)...25

TETRIGIDAE

22(21) Pronotum not extending beyond the hind-knees; hindwings shorter than the pronotum........................ 23

– Pronotum extending beyond the hind-knees (text fig. 17) hindwings longer than the pronotum....................24

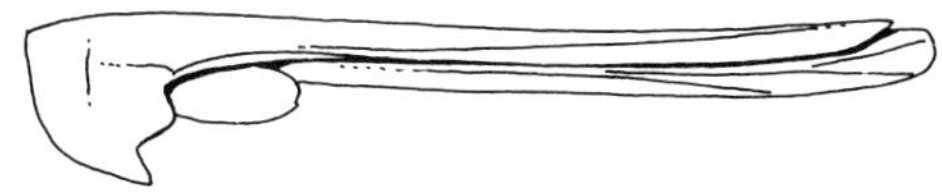

Text Figure 17 *Tetrix subulata* pronotum and hindwings

23(22) Pronotum not extending beyond the hind-knees, with a prominent median keel; hindwings much shorter than the pronotum..................... .*Tetrix undulata* (p. 103)

– Pronotum extending to about the hind-knees, with no prominent median keel; hindwings shorter than the pronotum..........brachypterous *Tetrix subulata* (p. 101)

24(22) Vertex wide, over 0.6mm in ♂ and 0.7mm in ♀, at least 1.5× eye width; mid-femur almost straight in outline .... *Tetrix subulata* (p. 101)

– Vertex narrow, under 0.6mm in ♂ and 0.7mm in ♀, never over 1.5× eye width; mid-femur wavy in outline (text fig. 39, p. 101)................ .*Tetrix ceperoi* (p. 100)

ACRIDIDAE

25(21) Hindwings pale blue with a black band (Pl. 6, fig. 1): recorded from the Channel Islands only .... *Oedipoda caerulescens* (p. 105)

– Hindwings never pale blue with a black band.......... 26

26(25) Antennae clubbed or thickened at the tip............. .27

– Antennae not clubbed or thickened at the tip.......... 28

27(26) Antennal club with a whitish tip (text fig. 18); forewings with a bulge on the costal margin .... *Gomphocerippus rufus* (p. 118)

– Antennal club without a whitish tip (text fig. 19); forewings without a costal bulge .... *Myrmeleotettix maculatus* (p. 119)

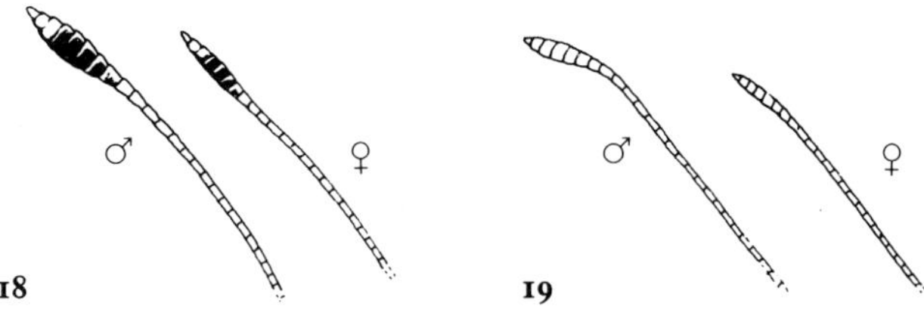

Text Figures 18, 19 Antennal clubs ♂ ♀
(**18**) *Gomphocerippus rufus*; (**19**) *Myrmeleotettix maculatus*

28(26) Side keels of the pronotum straight or slightly curved (text fig. 20)..29

– Side keels of the pronotum bent inwards in the fore-part and flared outwards towards the hind-margin......... .32

29(28) Forewings shorter than the abdomen, hindwings vestigial......................... .*Chorthippus parallelus* (p. 114)

– Both pairs of wings about as long as the abdomen..... 30

30(29) Side keels of the pronotum gently curved, not parallel (text fig. 20); the tips of the hind femora ('knees') blackish....macropterous *Chorthippus parallelus* (p. 114)

– Side keels of the pronotum straight (text fig 21); the tips of the hind femora not blackish...........................31

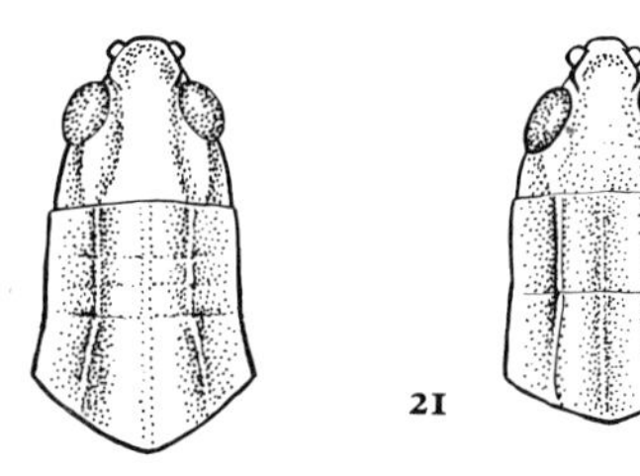

Text Figure 20, 21 Head and pronotum with straight or only slightly curved side keels, dorsal view
(**20**) *Chorthippus parallelus*; (**21**) *C. albomarginatus*

31(30) ♂ subgenital plate not pointed (text fig. 22): mainland only, not recorded from the Channel Islands ....*Chorthippus albomarginatus* (p. 115)

– ♂ subgenital plate pointed (text fig. 23): recorded from the Channel Islands only...................................... .... *Euchorthippus pulvinatus elegantulus* (p. 117)

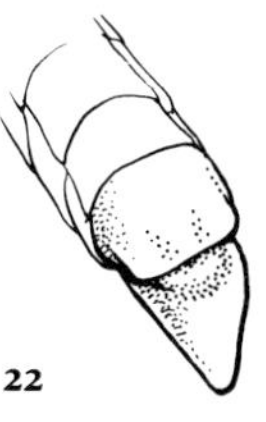

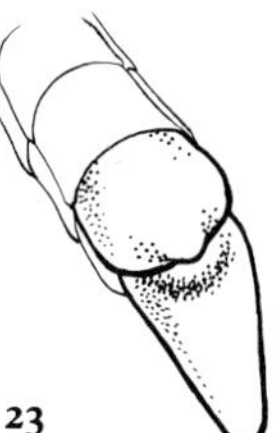

Text Figures 22, 23 ♂ subgenital plates
(**22**) *Chorthippus albomarginatus*; (**23**) *Euchorthippus pulvinatus elegantulus*

32(28) Large, ♂ over 21mm, ♀ over 28mm; hind-femora red beneath, hind-tibiae banded black and yellow............ .... *Stethophyma grossum* (p. 106)

– Smaller, ♂ under 21mm, ♀ under 28mm; hindlegs not brightly coloured... 33

33(32) Very small, ♂ under 12mm, ♀ under 15mm, (recorded only from the Isle of Man at present)........................ .... *Stenobothrus stigmaticus* (p. 108)
– Larger, ♂ over 12mm, ♀ over 15mm....................34
34(33) Forewing with a bulge on the costal margin (text fig. 24) 35
– Forewing without a bulge on the costal margin (text fig. 25)... 36

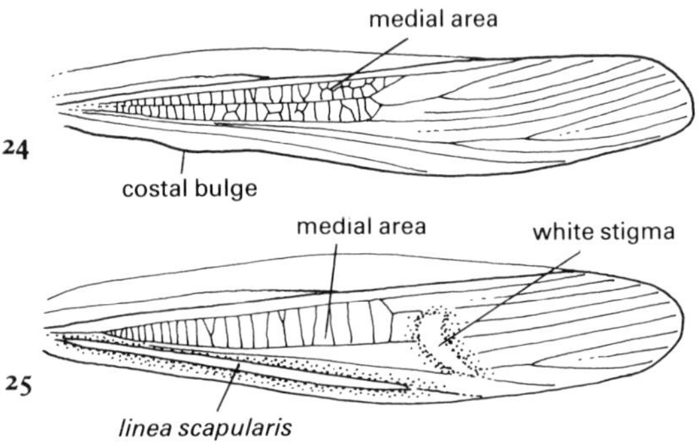

Text Figures 24, 25 Lateral view of acridid forewings showing costal bulge, stigma and *linea scapularis*

35(34) Distinctly hairy ventral thorax (text fig. 40a, p. 104); wings extending beyond the hind-knees; hind-part of the pronotum longer than the fore-part (text fig. 26), black wedge marks not reaching the hind-margin............... .... *Chorthippus brunneus* (p. 112)
– Sparsely hairy ventral thorax; wings not surpassing the hind-knees; hind-part of the pronotum the same length as, or shorter than, the fore-part, black wedge marks reaching the hind-margin (text fig. 27)..................... ....*Chorthippus vagans* (p. 113)

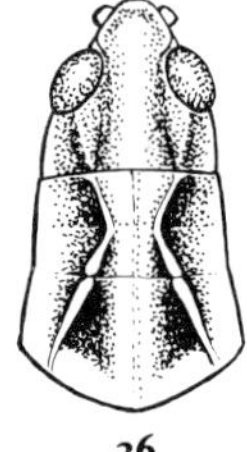

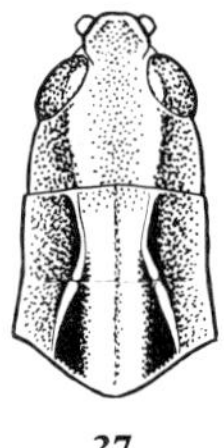

Text Figures 26, 27 Head and pronotum with black wedge marks, dorsal view
(**26**) *Chorthippus brunneus*; (**27**) *C. vagans*

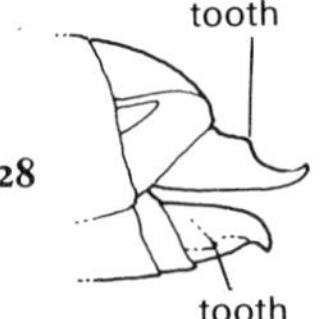

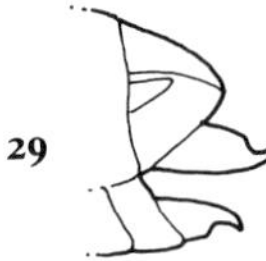

Text Figures 28–30 Ovipositor valves with and without tooth
(**28**) *Stenobothrus lineatus*, toothed; (**29**) *Omocestus rufipes* and (**30**) *O. viridulus*, untoothed

36(34) Forewing with an enlarged medial area and distinct white stigma (text fig. 25); ovipositor with toothed valves (text fig. 28)......................... *Stenobothrus lineatus* (p. 107)
– Forewing without enlarged medial area, the stigma only faintly marked; ovipositor valves untoothed (text figs. 29, 30)... 37
37(36) Darkish brown, the end of the abdomen orange or red, the tips of the palps white; ovipositor valves short (text fig. 29).............................*Omocestus rufipes* (p. 109)
– Green or olive-brown, the abdomen never orange or red, the palps not white; ovipositor valves long (text fig. 30) ....*Omocestus viridulus* (p. 110)
38(1) Total length over 45mm, generally greenish, stick-like insects – Phasmida (text fig. 54, p. 140)................ .39
– Total length under 45mm, generally brownish, beetle-like insects.. 43

PHASMIDA

39(38) Usually over 65mm long, green or brownish, inside the base of the fore-femora bright pinkish red............. 40
– Usually under 65mm long, brown, no red on the fore-femora but red on the underside of the thorax............ .... ♂ *Carausius morosus* (p. 143)
40(39) No spines on the head and/or thorax; no spine or tubercle at the base of the operculum.............................. .41
– Spines or tubercles on the head and/or thorax; a spine or tubercle at the base of the operculum.................... 42
41(40) Green or brown, the thorax dorsally with no central black line; cerci very small....... . ♀ *Carausius morosus* (p. 143)
– Bright green, the thorax dorsally with an interrupted black line; cerci distinctive pointed lobes.................. ....*Clitarchus hookeri* (p. 143)
42(40) Head, thorax and sometimes abdomen with many spines or tubercles; no black line on the thorax; the opercular spine long (2mm), pointed. *Acanthoxyla geisovii* (p. 140)
– Head and thorax with a few tubercles, not spines; a black line dorsally on the thorax near the head; the opercular spine short and blunt........ *Acanthoxyla inermis* (p. 142)
43(38) Cerci simple, not modified in any way – Blattodea (text fig. 48, p. 121)..44
– Cerci modified into forceps or pincers – Dermaptera (text fig. 53, p. 132)..55

BLATTODEA

44(43) Large, over 17mm 45
– Small, under 17mm 48

45(44) Pronotum uniformly dark brown to black, with no lighter bands or colour pattern; wings shorter than the abdomen or vestigial .... *Blatta orientalis* (p. 124)
– Pronotum reddish or dark brown, with lighter bands or patterning; wings at least as long as the abdomen 45

46(45) Total length 20–25mm, pronotum darkish brown with a pale band on the fore-edge; wings yellowish grey; burrowing, usually found in greenhouses .... *Pycnoscelus surinamensis* (p. 123)
– Total length above 25mm, pronotum reddish brown with a pale bilateral pattern; wings reddish brown; domiciliary pest species 47

47(46) Pronotum dark brown with a distinct yellow submarginal ring; forewing with a short yellow stripe basally on the fore-edge .... *Periplaneta australasiae* (p. 126)
– Pronotum reddish brown, with an indistinct lighter pattern and pale dorsal line; forewings unicolorous reddish brown .... *Periplaneta americana* (p. 125)

48(44) Domiciliary pest species 49
– Native cockroaches, found only out-of-doors 50

49(48) Pronotum light brown with 2 dark longitudinal lines; wings uniformly light brown .... *Blattella germanica* (p. 127)
– Pronotum with clear lateral margins, no dark lines; wings longer than the abdomen in ♂, shorter in ♀, with light and dark brown bands .. *Supella longipalpa* (p. 128)

50(48) ♂♂ – abdomen slender, tapering, with a dorsal glandular pit on the 7th segment (see text fig. 31) 51
– ♀♀ – abdomen wider, rounded, with no dorsal pit ... 53

51(50) Total length under 9mm; dorsal glandular pit with a hairy tubercle .... ♂ *Ectobius panzeri* (p. 131)
– Total length usually over 9mm; dorsal glandular pit without hairs 52

52(51) Wing length usually under 8mm; dorsal glandular pit empty .... ♂ *Ectobius pallidus* (p. 130)
– Wing length usually over 8mm; dorsal glandular pit with a bilobed tubercle (text fig. 31) .... ♂ *Ectobius lapponicus* (p. 129)

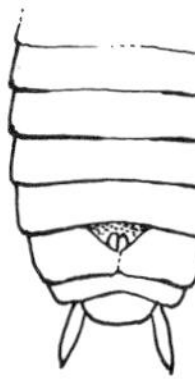

31

Text Figure 31 Dorsal glandular pit on abdominal segment 7 with bilobed tubercle. *Ectobius lapponicus* ♂

53(50) Forewings short and truncate, covering less than half the abdomen; hindwings absent .... ♀ *Ectobius panzeri* (p. 131)
– Forewings longer, not truncate, almost reaching or surpassing the end of the abdomen; hindwings present 54

54(53) Forewings almost reaching the end of the abdomen; abdomen ventrally mainly dark brown .... ♀ *Ectobius lapponicus* (p. 129)
– Forewings longer than the abdomen; abdomen ventrally light brown, with very little dark brown present .... ♀ *Ectobius pallidus* (p. 130)

DERMAPTERA

55(43) Completely apterous; legs pale with darker bands .... *Euborellia annulipes* (p. 134)
– At least elytra present 56

56(55) Elytra present, but no visible hindwings 57
– Folded hindwings present, projecting beyond elytra .. 59

32  33

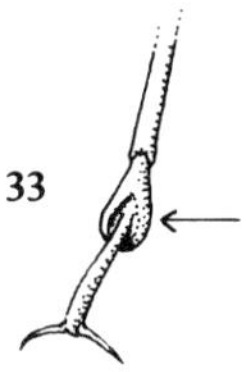

Text Figures 32, 33 Tarsal segments of Dermaptera
(**32**) Anisolabididae, Labiidae, Labiduridae spp.: second tarsal segment simple; (**33**) Forficulidae spp.: second tarsal segment broad and heart-shaped

57(56) Second tarsal segment simple (text fig. 32); ♂ forceps not broadened at base, large pentagonal pygidium present .... *Marava arachidis* (p. 135)
– Second tarsal segment broad and flattened (text fig. 33) 58

58(57) Pronotum widened posteriorly; ♂ forceps not broadened at base, pygidium large .. *Apterygida media* (p. 136)
– Pronotum not widened posteriorly; ♂ forceps with a long broadened basal part, pygidium small .... *Forficula lesnei* (p. 138)

59(56) Total length under 7mm .... *Labia minor* (p. 135)
– Total length over 8mm 60

60(59) Body brown; ♂ forceps with a broadened basal part .... *Forficula auricularia* (p. 137)
– Body yellowish, with dark brown markings; ♂ forceps not broadened at base, with 2 spines on the hind margin of the abdomen between the forceps .... *Labidura riparia* (p. 139)

Order ORTHOPTERA

There are two main subdivisions or suborders of the saltatorial Orthoptera. The Ensifera, including the Tettigonioidea and the Grylloidea, have long, sword-like ovipositors, long slender antennae, elytral stridulation and hearing organs on their fore tibiae. The Caelifera, including the Acridoidea and the Tridactyloidea (pygmy mole-crickets – not found in northern Europe), have short ovipositors, short antennae, stridulation by hind legs and elytra, and abdominal hearing organs.

Suborder Ensifera

Superfamily Tettigonioidea

RHAPHIDOPHORIDAE

The Rhaphidophoridae or wingless camel-crickets have long thread-like antennae and four-segmented tarsi, like their close relatives the Tettigoniidae or bush-crickets. However, the Rhaphidophoridae are always completely wingless and have no hearing organ on the fore tibiae. The pronotum is smoothly rounded, with no median keel. The antennae, palps and also the cerci are much longer in the Rhaphidophoridae than is usual in the Tettigoniidae – indeed the cerci are closer in appearance to those of the Gryllidae; the male cerci are unmodified. As they have no wings, songs are not produced in the usual way, but many Rhaphidophoridae can produce a variety of sounds by rubbing one part of the body against another; some species have stridulatory pegs on the abdomen against which the hind femora are scraped.

There may be ten or more nymphal instars. As there are no developing wings, it is difficult to recognize adults except by the increasing length of the ovipositor (which is formed of three pairs of valves as in the Tettigoniidae) and the fact that eventually they cease moulting. They survive here only in artificially heated conditions under which development is continuous with no diapause. This family is nocturnal, many species living in caves.

Tachycines asynamorus

Tachycines asynamorus Adelung

The Greenhouse Camel-cricket

Description (Pl. 1, fig. 1)

A medium-sized camel-cricket with dark brown patterns on a lighter background, pinkish beige in life but yellowing in dried specimens.

Both sexes completely wingless, with **very long thread-like antennae, long palps and cerci** and **legs with particularly long laterally compressed tarsi; no tympanal hearing organ** in fore tibiae. Ovipositor slightly upcurved.

Total length	♂ 11–14mm, ♀ 12–15mm
Ovipositor	10–12mm

Life History and Behaviour

The life history will vary according to the temperature of the environment; eggs, 2 × 1mm, are laid in the soil singly or in small batches, taking 2–4 months to hatch and nymphs 4–7 months, through about ten instars, to become adult. As a result, adults and nymphs may be found together at almost any season and at night are extremely active and difficult to capture. Although a mainly carnivorous species, it has been suspected of damaging young plants, but, by consuming other insect pests, quite possibly does as much good as it does harm.

Song

There is no record of stridulation.

Habitat

Colonies become temporarily established in heated greenhouses, especially among ferns and orchids and amongst potted houseplants. Colonies have also been found in zoological gardens, warehouses, factories and, more rarely, in private houses.

Distribution and Status

In England, *T. asynamorus* has been recorded from Somerset, Sussex, Kent, Surrey, Middlesex, Suffolk, Cambridgeshire, Leicestershire, Cheshire and Lancashire. Since 1960, thriving new colonies have been recorded at nurseries in Canterbury, Kent during 1962–65, and Burntcommon, Send, near Woking, Surrey, during 1970–73, and also in the garage of a private house at Cleveleys, near Fleetwood, Lancashire, in 1978. In Wales, it has been recorded from Glamorgan; in Scotland, from Glasgow (Kevan, 1951), Ayr and Edinburgh (Dunn & Kevan, 1955), and Dumfries (Kevan, 1956). In Ireland, it was found in 1975 thriving in Dublin Zoological Gardens (Speight, 1976); and there is a recently discovered specimen taken in a Dublin factory in 1937 (O'Connor, 1981).

This interesting species is thought to have been introduced to Europe from southern China in the last century, and was first decribed (in 1902) from specimens found in Leningrad in imported palms. It now has a cosmopolitan distribution and is still occasionally imported from various regions with plants. It is the only member of its family (Rhaphidophoridae: wingless camel-crickets) to be established here. In consequence of damage caused to crop-plants, most colonies have been treated with insecticides, once discovered. As a result, few colonies have persisted for more than two or three years.

TETTIGONIIDAE

The Tettigoniidae or bush-crickets (text fig. 34) are often large, though not necessarily conspicuous, and may be recognized by their very long, thread-like antennae and four-segmented tarsi. Though most species are active during the day they are not solely diurnal, and it is mainly during the afternoon and evening that their songs are produced. Their pronotum is saddle-shaped, sometimes with a small or partial median keel. Tettigoniidae have their hearing organs near the base of the fore tibiae – the tympanum or hearing membrane clearly visible on each side of the tibia in some species, in others partly covered by a ventral flap. Each species produces a characteristic song from the stridulatory areas at the base of the forewings, except for *Meconema thalassinum*, *q.v.* (see p. 41). The female ovipositor is formed of three pairs of valves; the male subgenital plate may have a pair of small, unsegmented styles or posterior processes. Females have small, pointed cerci, but the male cerci are modified into structures for holding the female whilst mating (see p. 36), and may be toothed or strongly curved.

The eggs of Tettigoniidae vary in shape from long, thin and cylindrical to short, fat, ovoid or discoid structures (text fig. 6, p. 37), and in size from three to over five millimetres in length. There have been several investigations into the developmental biology of many of the European species of Tettigoniidae, from a general study (Hartley & Warne, 1972b); through the fine structure of the embryonic stages (Warne, 1972; Ingrisch, 1984b); to the varying effects of light, temperature and contact with water on the developing eggs and length of diapause (Ingrisch, 1984a, 1985, 1986a, 1986b, 1986c).

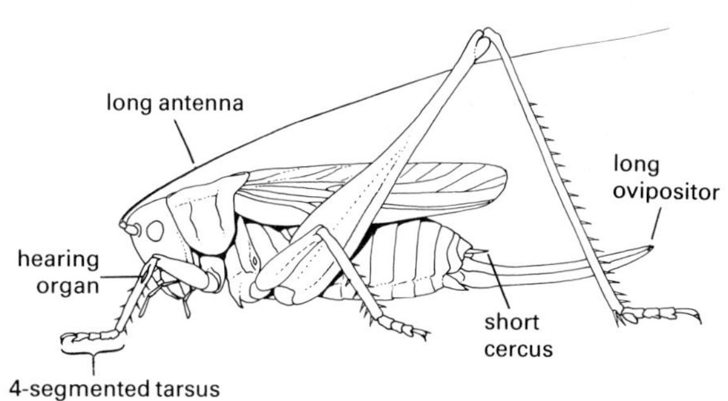

Text Figure 34 *Decticus verrucivorus* ♀ showing distinguishing characters of tettigoniid species

After the initial vermiform larval stage there are usually five or six nymphal instars, though sometimes more. Nymphal development of the British species (excluding *Decticus verrucivorus*) was studied in detail by Marrable (1980), and of three European species by Cejchan (1977). Sänger & Helfert (1976), whilst rearing continental Conocephalinae and Decticinae in the laboratory, recorded one more instar than the number normally found here. Extra instars may be recorded where there is a longer period of favourable climate for development. Wing-rudiments appear as lateral pads or lobes in the second or third instar, of species which are fully winged as adults; in brachypterous species they appear at later stages. In the last two instars the wing-pads are reversed or hinged upwards, as in all nymphs of fully-winged adult Saltatoria (see text fig. 7, p. 38). Wing venation of a fully-winged species is illustrated in text figure 35.

Hatching occurs after diapause, but in some species not until the second or even third spring after laying (see also p. 38). Development to the adult stage then takes place during the summer, egg-laying occurring through to the autumn when the adults die off.

Most species are omnivorous but *Leptophyes punctatissima* is mainly vegetarian and *Meconema thalassinum* largely carnivorous.

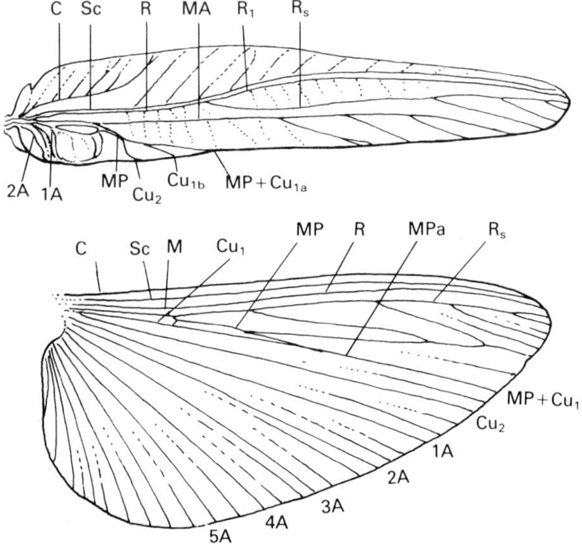

Text Figure 35 Wings of *Tettigonia viridissima* showing venation of forewing (above), hindwing (below)

Meconema thalassinum (De Geer)
The Oak Bush-cricket

Description (Pl. 1, figs 2–4)

A **small, pale green** bush-cricket, with a yellow dorsal stripe along the head, pronotum and forewings; this line may be brownish in adults, and a creamy white in nymphs.

No median keel on the pronotum. Both sexes fully winged as adults; male has no stridulatory area on forewings. Adult male with distinctive long, curved cerci (fig. 3). **Ovipositor fairly long and slightly upcurved.**

Total length	♂ 13–17mm, ♀ 14–17mm
Wing length	♂ 11–13mm, ♀ 11–13mm
Ovipositor	8–9.5mm

Life History and Behaviour

The eggs are oval, about 3 × 1mm wide, buff in colour, and are laid in crevices in bark or under lichen on trees.

Nymphs emerge during June, rarely earlier, having five nymphal instars and becoming adult during late July and August. As this is a late-maturing species adults survive into the autumn, even towards the end of November. This is the only British bush-cricket which is largely carnivorous, eating a wide variety of insects.

M. thalassinum is mainly nocturnal and attracted to light, so often encountered indoors or collected in moth traps. Females may be seen at dusk on tree-trunks where they lay their eggs in crevices in the bark. During the day it may be collected by beating from trees; however, after autumn gales, 'spent' individuals may be found wandering on the ground and squashed specimens may be found easily on roads beneath trees in wooded areas (Marshall, 1984), often providing the best way of locating the species.

Song (Cassette band 1)

Males do not have the normal stridulatory organ on the forewings but, after dark, 'drum' with one hind leg, producing short, rapid bursts of sound.

Habitat

This is the only completely arboreal species, found in oak woodland and on a wide range of broad-leaved trees as well as hedgerow and garden shrubs, particularly hazel and elder. In wet areas where tall trees are few it may be found on sallow thickets and reed beds (Haes, 1976).

Distribution and Status (Map 3, page 167)

South of a line drawn between the Dee and Humber estuaries, *M. thalassinum* is one of the most common and widely distributed bush-crickets, probably present in almost any well-wooded locality. It is scarce in such relatively treeless areas as around the Wash, the prairie-

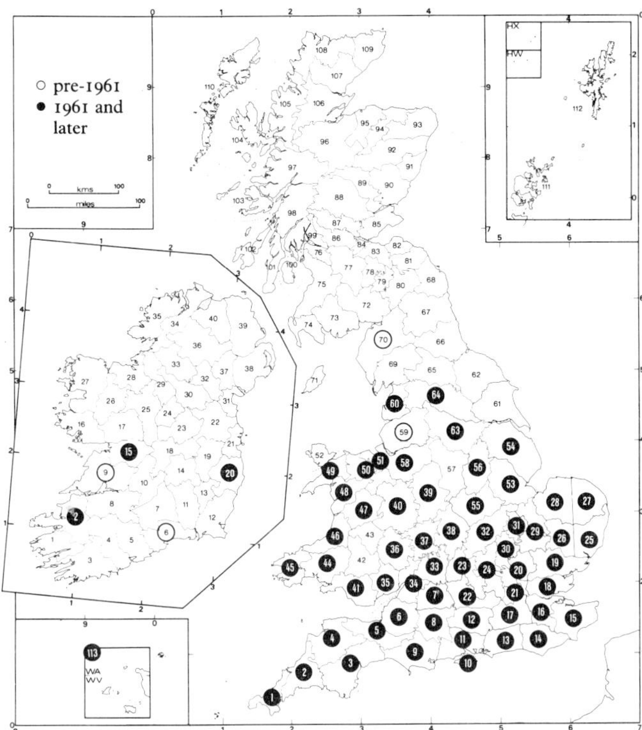

Meconema thalassinum

farmed chalklands of East Anglia, North Hampshire and in the parts of North Devon and West Cornwall exposed to westerly gales. North of the Dee-Humber line, there are several good local colonies east of the Pennines over the magnesium limestone in Yorkshire (Whiteley, 1981); west of the Pennines it has been found recently in two isolated colonies in Lancashire: near Preston in 1981 and Arnside in 1982, the most northerly recorded in the post-1960 period. In Wales, widespread but local, with records for the Gower Peninsula and around Pembroke; coastally both north and south of Aberystwyth; and from the Menai Straight to the Cheshire border. It is apparently absent from both the exposed though mild Lleyn Peninsula and Anglesey.

In Ireland, extremely local but there are recent records from four new localities (Cotton, 1980, 1982; O'Connor & O'Connor, 1988). Recorded from Jersey, Channel Islands. No records from Scotland.

M. thalassinum may have been an early post-glacial arrival as it occurs in Ireland. It probably flourished during the warm Atlantic period when most of the British Isles were tree-covered and appreciably warmer than now. Though it may have suffered during the period of woodland destruction which peaked in the eighteenth century, it is a resilient species which can survive on scrub where trees have been destroyed – for example, on elm suckers after the parent trees have died – and is likely to remain a relatively common insect in the future.

This species has a northern Palaearctic distribution, occurring from Portugal, through northern Spain, France, Italy, northern Yugoslavia through to the Crimea and the Caucasus, up to southern Sweden and central U.S.S.R. It is also found in the eastern U.S.A., possibly having been introduced with shrubs (Gurney, 1960).

Tettigonia viridissima (Linnaeus)
The Great Green Bush-cricket

Description (Pl. 1, figs 5–7)

A **large, grass-green** bush-cricket with green eyes and brown dorsal stripe on head and pronotum, continued along hind-edge of forewings; stridulatory area of male also brown.

No median keel on pronotum. Wings long, extending beyond abdomen; wingtips may become frayed in older adults. Male cerci fairly long and slender, with basal tooth on inner side; subgenital plate bears long styles. **Ovipositor very long and slightly downcurved.**

Total length	♂ 40–50mm, ♀ 42–54mm
Wing length	♂ 33–40mm, ♀ 34–44mm
Ovipositor	18–24mm

Life History and Behaviour

The eggs are dark grey, over 5mm long by about 1.5mm wide, symmetrical, tapering slightly at each end; they are laid singly in soil or suitable crevices in the ground. The bright green, green-eyed nymphs (fig. 7) emerge in May and June, having usually seven or eight nymphal instars (though six and nine have been recorded), becoming adult from late July and occasionally surviving, worn-looking, through November. They are widely omnivorous, feeding on grasses, shrubs and a variety of insects; in captivity nymphs should be kept separately to avoid cannibalism. In spite of its size, this species is not easy to locate by eye because of its good camouflage.

Song (Cassette band 2)

The song is extremely loud and far-carrying, enabling colonies to be located by the stridulation of the males which continues throughout the afternoon and into the night in late summer. The sound is loud enough to be heard even from a moving vehicle.

Habitat

In Britain, *T. viridissima* is primarily a species of wasteland where there is rough, untouched herbage with plenty of thistles, bracken and similar coarse plants, usually with brambles and other unkempt scrub, but always in warm, sunny places. In this rough vegetation it occurs over a wide range of terrain, and seems able to withstand

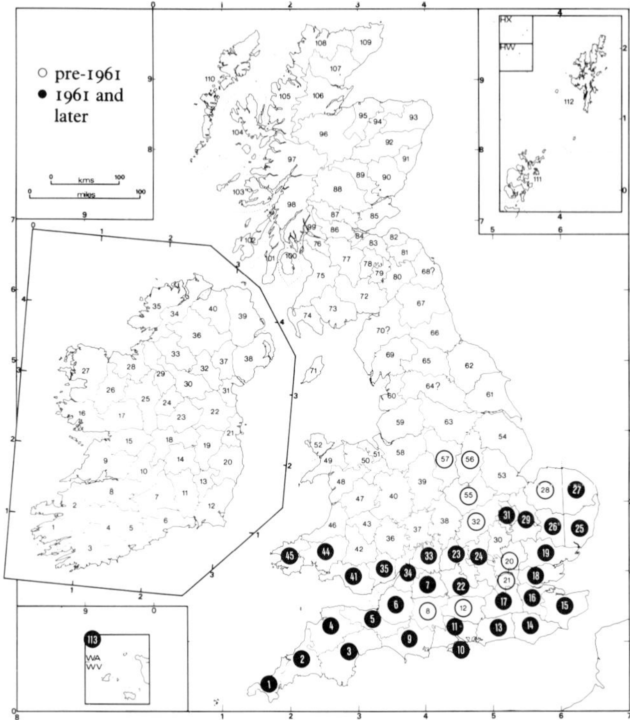

Tettigonia viridissima

considerable exposure in the mildest parts of the country, such as on the sea-cliffs of the Devonian peninsula. In some areas, it is still a familiar suburban insect, surviving on a few square metres of suitable habitat on undeveloped or neglected plots or hedgerows.

Distribution and Status (Map 4, page 167)

In England, it is generally common along the Channel coast from the Scilly Isles to Sandwich Bay, Kent, and even abounds along the Devon coast, along the Purbeck Hills, across the southern part of the Isle of Wight and around Folkestone and Dover. Formerly it was probably abundant along most of the Hampshire and Sussex coasts, but is now local becuase of extensive urbanization, to which it is very vulnerable. There are still considerable colonies around the Thames Estuary and northwards up the Essex coast, but it is probably extinct on the Norfolk coast. Inland it is now a distinctly local species. However, small colonies may persist for many years along railway embankments, in river valleys or on warm chalk or limestone hillsides. It is still present in many areas in West Cornwall, South Devon and Somerset, but most of the other post-1960 sites shown on the map seem now to have been destroyed. It still persists at one site in the Cotswolds; around Fyfield Down NNR, Wiltshire, and Abingdon, Oxon; at Wraysbury, near Staines, Middlesex, and near Tilford, in what is probably now its only Surrey locality. Inland in Sussex, there is one surviving site by the Arun at Watersfield, and it is still quite common on the South Downs between Brighton, Lewes, Polegate and the south coast. In East Anglia, it may persist by the main railway line near Huntingdon, but has probably gone from all its other once-numerous fenland sites.

In Wales, locally common along the south coast and between Newport and Chepstow, but absent farther north. Common on all larger Channel Islands. There are no recent or dependable records from Scotland and none from Ireland.

T. viridissima is probably an early post-glacial colonist since it is present in the Scilly Isles and in Guernsey, but it seems not to have been able to spread far to the north because of its need for summer warmth. Hence it has only doubtfully reached eastern Scotland and never crossed to Ireland or the Isle of Man in the milder parts of which it might well have been able to flourish.

This species occurs throughout Europe (except northern Scandinavia) to temperate Asia and the U.S.S.R.; also North Africa.

Decticus verrucivorus (Linnaeus) The Wart-biter — Red Data Book – Vulnerable

Description (Pl. 1, figs 8–10)

A **large, darkish green** bush-cricket, **usually** (especially on heath land) with **dark brown blotches** on **pronotum and wings**, although smaller, mainly green specimens, with very little spotting (as fig. 10) are found in chalkland localities. There are thus two visually distinct populations in Britain. An all-brown form, found on the Continent, is believed not to occur in Britain (see p. 23).

A **median keel on pronotum** in both sexes and wings a little longer than the body but not normally extending beyond hind-knees. Male cerci with inner tooth about midway along; subgenital plate bears quite long styles. **Ovipositor long and slightly upcurved.**

Total length	♂ 32–37mm, ♀ 31–37mm
Wing length	♂ 24–27mm, ♀ 22–27mm
Ovipositor	19–21mm

Life History and Behaviour

The eggs are greyish brown, about 5 × 2mm, blunt-ended and symmetrical, laid singly in the ground.

The dark-eyed, green or brownish nymphs (fig. 9) emerge during May, usually have six nymphal instars, and mature in July, rarely surviving later than September. Despite its large size, *D. verrucivorus* is a remarkably elusive insect, surprisingly difficult to locate. A good time to search is during warm weather in late May or early June when the nymphs are quite easily 'walked up' from coarse herbage. In late summer, the agile adults are adept at diving for cover at the slightest disturbance and are not easily observed by simply walking the ground.

This species is omnivorous, eating herbs including knapweed, nettle, woodruff and bedstraw (*Centaurea*, *Urtica*, *Asperula* and *Galium* spp.) and insects including even adult grasshoppers.

Song (Cassette band 3)

The distinctive stridulation of the males is to be heard only in hot sunny weather and is highly directional and hard to pinpoint. It consists of a series of rapidly repeated clicks, coming in short bursts which may last for several minutes.

Males also often produce a short stridulation, not unlike that of *Pholidoptera griseoaptera* (dark bush-cricket) which may easily result in the two species being confused.

Habitat

The single heathland population occupies an area of rough heather adjacent to improved grassy pasture. The other known colonies are in coarse, tussocky grass, particularly tor-grass (*Brachypodium pinnatum*) or cock's foot (*Dactylis glomerata*), in very sunny, usually well-sheltered coombs or on the banks of Iron Age fortifications, where the turf is no more than lightly grazed. All but one of these grassland colonies are, or were, over chalk, though one may have existed on gault clay close to the Lower Greensand in mid-Sussex.

Distribution and Status (Map 5, page 168)

D. verrucivorus has always been an extremely local insect, confined to southern England. Over the last two hundred years, isolated specimens or colonies have been found only in East Kent, East Sussex, Hampshire (New Forest), Isle of Wight, Dorset and Wiltshire. In East Kent, there was a substantial colony at Rochester early in the nineteenth century (Stephens, 1835) which was presumably destroyed by urban development in the late 1830s. Occasional single specimens were found in cliff-top vegetation between Deal and St. Margaret's Bay from 1886 to 1942, but, despite a careful search in the early 1970s, no further sightings have been reported in this area until an unconfirmed specimen was seen on the cliffs west of Dover in 1986. It was also found near Lydden, Kent (Burr, 1907; Lucas, 1920), but not seen after 1921. However, it was found nearby more recently (Dolling, 1968) and existed at that site until about 1975. Ironically, it may subsequently have been exterminated by the deliberate removal of coarse herbage for the purpose of encouraging choicer plants and butterflies on an extremely species-rich area of chalk downland. In East Sussex, there is one small, diffuse colony at the eastern end of the Downs where singletons were recorded in 1973 (Haes, 1976) and 1977; there are also two substantial colonies just west of the Ouse gap.

Decticus verrucivorus

Specimens were first observed in the easternmost colony here in 1945 (Payne, 1955a), and in the westernmost (now part of a National Nature Reserve) in 1967. These colonies are almost certainly part of a single population now separated by resown pasture, and constitute by far the largest population of the species known in Britain. In 1969 and again in 1973, over a hundred males were heard stridulating (Haes, 1976). It has persisted at this site in varying numbers and in 1987 a very large number of males were again heard stridulating. The non-downland colony in mid-Sussex was on ancient pasture with scattered oak trees, but this has been irreversibly damaged since conifers were planted in the early 1970s. In Hampshire, there are at present no known colonies, though there was certainly a large colony (with reputed specimens of the brown form, *bingleii* Curtis (see p. 23)), at Godwinscroft, near Christchurch, at the beginning of the nineteenth century (Curtis, 1825). Two single specimens were found in the New Forest in 1844 and 1891 (Lucas, 1920), but, despite the presence of suitable habitat, not since. A singleton captured near Ventnor, Isle of Wight, in 1951 (Marshall, 1974), and the possible sighting of a nymph in 1982, also in the Ventnor area, gives hope that this species may still be present on the island. In Wiltshire, *D. verrucivorus* was discovered during the survey of a large downland coomb (Mason, 1971) but this colony seems to have been severely affected latterly by heavy grazing and only one specimen was located in 1984 and another in 1987. In Dorset, several specimens were found in the Wareham area: near Corfe Castle in 1923 and on Slepe Heath in 1927. It was rediscovered in this area more recently (Ragge, 1955b) and a small colony persisted until 1976, since when it has not been found. However, another small colony has been found about a kilometre away and is still there. There is an unconfirmed report of a sighting on War Department land near the coast west of Tyneham in 1983. One found at Luton, Bedfordshire in 1979 is thought to have been introduced (*Orthoptera Recording Scheme Newsletters* **6** (1980) and **7** (1981)).

This species was probably one of the last of our Orthoptera to reach Britain – the heathland form perhaps crossing on the west side and the downland form on the east side of the final land connection with the Continent. In its eight thousand years or so of isolation, the tegmina of British populations appear to have become shorter; and British downland examples are distinctly smaller overall than typical Continental specimens. This fine insect is now clearly on the extreme edge of its range. Most populations are vulnerable to destruction or unsuitable management of habitat.

This species occurs throughout Europe (except the extreme south) and in temperate Asia.

Pholidoptera griseoaptera (De Geer)
[= *P. cinerea* (Gmelin)]
The Dark Bush-cricket

Description (Pl. 2, figs 1,2,4)

A medium-sized bush-cricket, **light to very dark brown** in colour, with **abdomen bright yellow or greenish yellow ventrally**, but never mainly green.

No median keel on pronotum. Forewings very small, reaching only to sound-producing area in male and reduced to tiny lobes in female; hindwings absent in both sexes. Male cerci with small inner basal tooth; subgenital plate bears styles. Ovipositor fairly long and curved upwards.

Total length	♂ 13–19mm, ♀ 13–20mm
Wing length	♂ 3–5mm
Ovipositor	9–11mm

Life History and Behaviour

The eggs are cylindrical with tapering ends, buff-coloured, over 4mm long by about 1mm wide, and are laid in soft, rotting wood or crevices in bark.

This species has a very long season. The nymphs, dark brown with broad pale longitudinal stripes dorsally, hatch from the end of April onwards, having six nymphal instars and reaching maturity during July; young nymphs, especially in the first and second instars, have a spider-like appearance (fig. 4), the possible purpose of which has been discussed by Cumming (1978). Adults may survive until late November or even early December after a fine mild autumn. Although alert and agile, this species may often be seen sunning itself, and the plump, adult females may be flushed from rough grass in late summer or early autumn.

This species is omnivorous, feeding on a wide variety of plants and insects, including small spiders (Haes, 1976).

Song (Cassette bands 4,5)

The song is a short chirp, repeated at irregular intervals (band 4) which may be heard from dense vegetation throughout the day and after dusk. Males are aggressive to each other and may interact with a rapid series of longer chirps (band 5) (see p. 42).

Habitat

P. griseoaptera frequents scrub, particularly bramble thickets, but also coarse herbage along hedgerows, woodland rides, overgrown ditches, nettle-beds and marshland vegetation. It is found both inland and on the coast, but is absent from salt-marsh, sand-dunes or shingle beaches, although it may be found in thickets bounding these habitats. In the South-West, it is also found on exposed cliffs.

Distribution and Status (Map 6, page 168)

South of the Thames, this is undoubtedly the most widespread and probably the most numerous bush-cricket, occurring wherever there is suitable habitat. North of the Thames it is more local, but present in the Cotswolds, the Forest of Dean and northwards through Herefordshire into Shropshire and the western edge of Warwickshire (Copson, 1984). It is common throughout the Chilterns, most of Bedfordshire (Rands, 1978) and most of East Anglia; and there are substantial isolated colonies as far north as Leicestershire (Evans, 1970) and the Lincolnshire Wolds. It was discovered near Robin Hood's Bay on the Yorkshire coast in the 1950s (McDermott, 1957) but this colony appears to have been destroyed by extensive clearances in the early 1970s. West of the Pennines, there are no post-1960 records from Cheshire but it was found on the southern edge of the Lake District – at Heald Wood and at Three Dubbs Crags by J. K. Bowers in 1978; at Arnside in 1984 (Paul, 1986); and at St. Bee's Head in 1987. It continues to flourish in its one known locality in the Isle of Man.

As is shown on the maps, *P. griseoaptera* appears to be absent from much of the Midland Plain and around the Wash and from almost all the North Midlands and Northern England. In southern Wales it is widespread around the coast and locally common in Monmouth, on the Gower Peninsula, and in lowland parts of Carmarthen

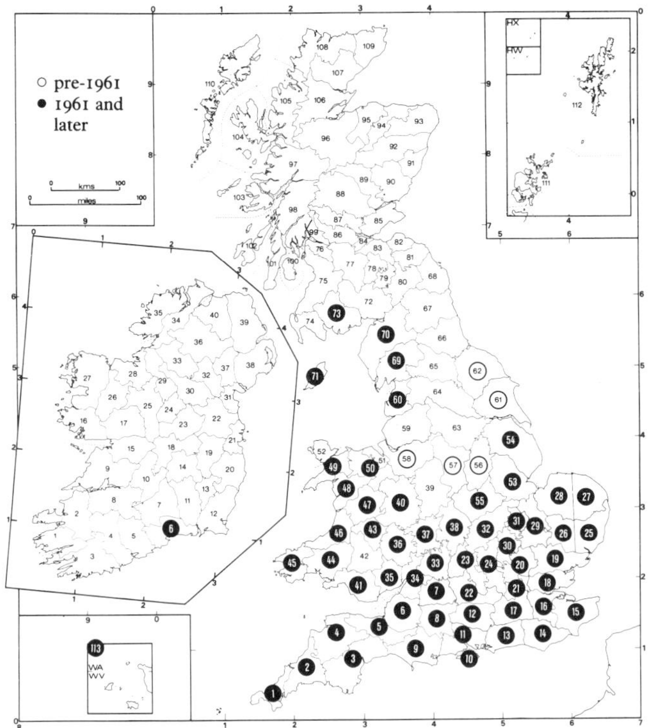

Pholidoptera griseoaptera

(Morgan, 1984) and Pembroke (J. C. Comont, pers. comm.). Northwards along the coast it is present in all the maritime counties but there are no records from Anglesey. In Scotland it is known only from Ravenshall Wood on the Galloway coast, where it has been seen regularly since its first discovery by M. J. Skelton in 1974. It was found near Waterford, Ireland, in 1983 (O'Connor & O'Connor, 1985). In the Channel Islands, known only from Jersey where it is locally common (R. Long, pers. comm.).

This species seems to tolerate a quite wide range of climatic conditions for it appears to be as numerous in the driest parts of East Anglia as in the dampest parts of the West Country. Its distribution in relation to climates in England and Wales have been considered in detail (Hartley & Warne, 1973). The isolated colonies in the North and Ireland do not seem to be recent introductions but rather relict colonies from an early invasion of a different origin. It is also possible that the extensive distribution of this bush-cricket in southern England today is the result of a fairly recent population explosion, for Wood (1872) suggested the species was quite rare at that time. At present it seems unlikely to become endangered.

This species is widely distributed from northern Spain, through central Europe as far north as Lapland and eastwards to the Caucasus.

Platycleis albopunctata (Goeze)
[= *P. denticulata* (Panzer)]
The Grey Bush-cricket

Description (Pl. 2, figs 6–8)

A medium sized bush-cricket, usually **greyish brown**, though dorsal surface of head and pronotum may be chestnut brown or even green.

A median keel on posterior part of pronotum. Both sexes **fully winged**. Male cerci with an inner tooth about midway; subgenital plate bears styles. Ovipositor fairly long and curved upwards.

Total length	♂ 20–25mm, ♀ 20–28mm
Wing length	♂ 15–19mm, ♀ 14–21mm
Ovipositor	8–11mm

Life History and Behaviour

The eggs are cylindrical, dark grey, 4 × 1mm, and are laid in dead wood, plant stems, mossy soil or any suitable crevice. Nymphs usually hatch in May, and are light brown dorsally but may be dark brown or green laterally (fig. 8), having six nymphal instars. Adults which develop from green nymphs may retain this colouring for a few days (fig. 7) before becoming greyish brown. The adults appear in July and rarely survive beyond late October. While sun-basking, they may be detected by the sharp-eyed but their camouflage is very efficient and they are easily missed. They are wary insects but often take flight when disturbed and are then briefly but clearly glimpsed before diving head first into the vegetation.

This species is omnivorous, its diet including grasshopper nymphs.

Song (Cassette band 6)

The song is a short, high-pitched chirp repeated rapidly. It is often difficult to detect against background noises of wind and sea.

Habitat

P. albopunctata appears to be restricted to the coast where it occurs in coarse grass and herbage on sand-dunes, shingle beaches or on south-facing cliffs with good vegetation. Even in the warmest districts, it does not appear to occur in salt-marsh vegetation, even though it may be numerous in the nearby sand-dunes. On sea-cliffs, it seems indifferent to the rock type and is as numerous on granites, schists or slates in the South-West as on sandstone, clay or chalk in the South and South-East.

Distribution and Status (Map 7, page 169)

This bush-cricket is present on Bryher in the Scilly Isles and in many places along the English Channel coast from Sennen Cove in West Cornwall to Sandwich Bay, East Kent. All the colonies are on the immediate coast with the

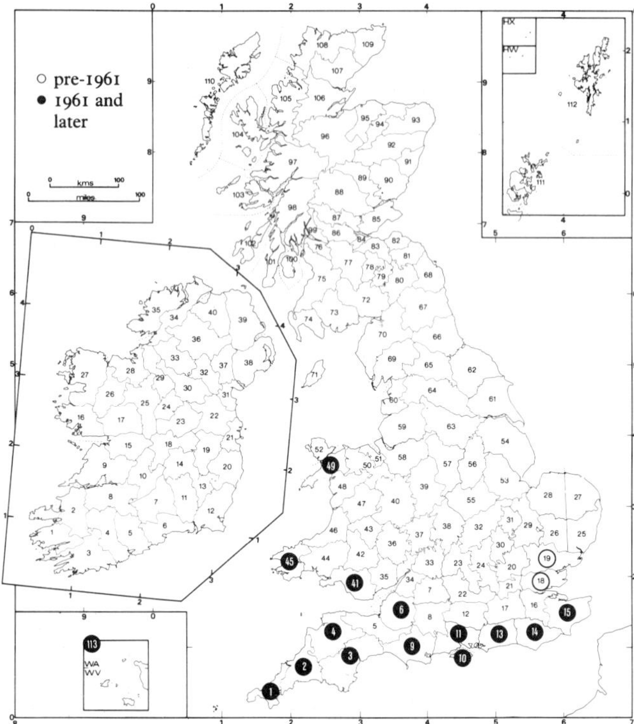

Platycleis albopunctata

exception of three: one on the south face of St. Boniface Down, Ventnor, Isle of Wight; one on Ballard Down, Swanage, Dorset; and one at Lydd, behind Dungeness, Kent, all of which are over one kilometre inland. On Pilsey Island, Chichester Harbour, Sussex, colonies occur on quite small areas of suitable habitat, whereas large populations are found on the extensive areas of dune and shingle at Dungeness and Sandwich Bay. Although one or two colonies existed on the Essex coast until early this century (Lucas, 1920), there are no post-1960 records north of the Thames Estuary. The few pre-1960 inland records are due to misidentifications (Burr, 1936) or, as with *Metrioptera roeselii* at Cheam, Surrey, in 1944, eggs may well have been taken in sand to fill wartime sandbags!

On the north coasts of the Devonian Peninsula, there are single sites at Penhale Sands, Cornwall; Braunton Burrows, Devon; and Brean Down, Somerset. There are no records from the North of England or the Isle of Man. On the South Wales coast, the species is distinctly local, although there are good populations on the Gower Peninsula and the Pembroke coast. In North Wales, a very small, isolated population was certainly present on the south side of the Lleyn Peninsula near Pwllheli up to 1973. There are no records from Scotland or Ireland.

In the Channel Islands, the form *P. albopunctata jerseyana* Zeuner, 1940, occurs on all the major islands and may be very numerous. This form is slightly smaller, with the forewings tending to be more slender and shorter than those of the mainland species.

P. albopunctata albopunctata (Goeze) is the typical form of north-western Europe (Harz, 1969) and all the English and Welsh populations are of this type. It is clearly an early post-glacial arrival, since it has reached the Scilly Isles and also the Channel Islands, where it has had time to develop its endemic form. Because of its obvious need for warmth, however, it has never been able to exploit any but the sunniest areas of the coast and has been quite unable to penetrate inland for much more than a kilometre.

This species extends from Spain through central Europe, including Scandinavia, eastwards to Poland and Rumania; also occurs in Morocco.

Metrioptera brachyptera (Linnaeus)

The Bog Bush-cricket

Description (Pl. 2, figs 9–12)

A medium-sized bush-cricket, with **pale band on hind-edge only of side flaps of pronotum** (fig. 10). **Abdomen bright green ventrally**, dark brown laterally, and may be green or brown dorsally on head, pronotum and wings; no yellowish patches on body behind pronotum.

A median keel on posterior part of pronotum. Both sexes normally brachypterous, **forewings shorter than abdomen and hindwings vestigial**; there is a rare macropterous form, *marginata* (Thunberg), with fully developed, dark brownish-black wings (fig. 12). Male cerci with inner tooth about midway; subgenital plate bears styles. Ovipositor fairly long and slightly upcurved; **female subgenital plate with small median incision** (text fig. 16, p.74).

Total length	♂ 11–18mm, ♀ 13–21mm
Wing length	♂ 5–10mm, ♀ 6–9mm
f. *marginata*	♂ ♀ 18–20mm

Life History and Behaviour

The eggs are dark brown, cylindrical with slightly tapered ends, 4 × 1mm, and are laid in or among plant stems. The nymphs emerge in May and June, and are always pale brown dorsally – the green colour not developing until some days after the final moult. There are six nymphal instars, adults appearing from July and surviving until early November in a mild autumn.

This species is omnivorous but mainly vegetarian, feeding on buds, flowers and unripe seed-heads.

Song (Cassette band 7)

The song is a short shrill chirp, repeated several times a second, more rapidly in hot weather. This scratchy stridulation is not loud but is often produced by such numbers of individuals that it is noticeable even to the casual observer, and may be heard throughout the day.

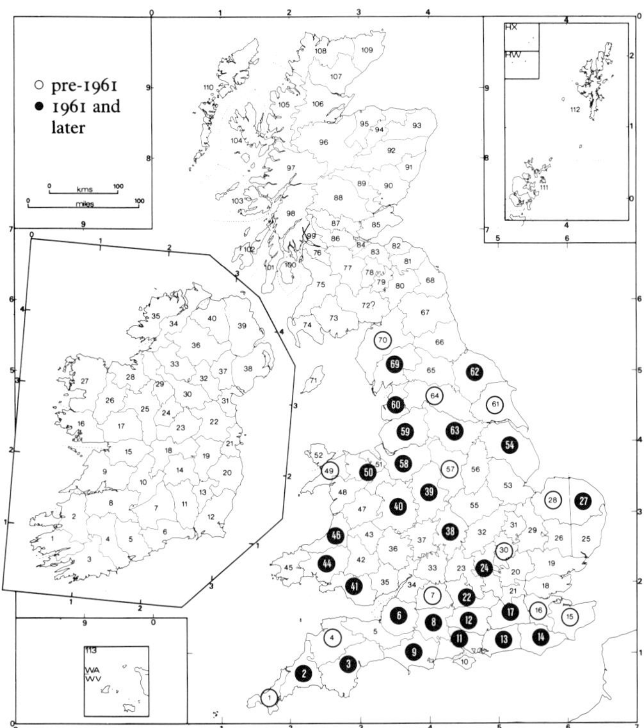

Metrioptera brachyptera

Habitat

The range of *M. brachyptera* is restricted to lowland heaths and clearings in moist, heathy woodland, where the dominant plants are cross-leaved heath (*Erica tetralix*) and purple moor-grass (*Molinia caerulea*). It is generally a low altitude insect in Britain and is absent from true moorland, even in the extreme south, though it is found up to 250m in heathy woodland at Blackdown, West Sussex and Leith Hill, Surrey.

Distribution and Status (Map 8, page 169)

In southern England, *M. brachyptera* abounds on the remaining heathlands in East Dorset and East Devon but farther west survives only in isolated colonies, such as the Tamar valley at Luckett, and has apparently gone from the Falmouth area. In Somerset, it is still present in a restricted area of the Levels at Street, Shapwick, Wedmore and Meare. It is abundant in the New Forest; throughout the 'forests' of the High Weald, on either side of the Hog's Back in Surrey, and even into the Greater London area at Addington Hills. It reaches south to the few surviving commons of West Sussex around Midhurst and north to the Thames Valley at East Burnham and Stoke Commons.

In the east of England, it has a surprisingly localized distribution. It is absent from East Kent and also from the heathlands of the Suffolk coast. However, there is an extensive population in Norfolk at Buxton Heath, Newton St. Faith, Ludham, and also at Holt Lowes. It still occurs near Horncastle, Lincolnshire on two important nature reserves, and is still present over a considerable area of Thorne Waste and Hatfield Moors, east of Doncaster. North of the Humber, there is a very strong and long-known colony on Strensall Common near York and it continues to thrive in the fascinating Fen Bog Nature Reserve near Fylingdales – now its most northerly British site. A number of isolated colonies have been discovered recently in the West Midlands, such as at Clee Hill (Paul, 1985) and on Penkridge Bank, Cannock Chase (Paul, 1986). It is also found close to the Welsh border at Whixall Moss and Wem Moss, Shropshire; Little Woolden Moss, Cheshire; and Stribers Moss, Meathop, and Nicholls Moss on the southern edge of the Lake District. There are no very recent records from its old site at Penrith but it was refound near Fleetwood in 1986. There are no records for the Isle of Man.

In Wales, the only post-1960 records are from the Gower Peninsula; Hengwrt, near Aberarth (Fowles, 1987); Borth Bog, Dyfi National Nature Reserve; and at Fenn's Moss, Denbigh, which is adjacent to Whixall Moss, Shropshire. In Scotland, the Dumfriesshire site near Carlisle (Ragge, 1965) has produced no post-1960 records. There are no records from Ireland or the Channel Islands.

This species is Palaearctic, occurring across central and northern Europe from the Pyrenees, through northern Italy, Yugoslavia and Rumania across the U.S.S.R. to Siberia.

Metrioptera roeselii (Hagenbach)

Roesel's Bush-cricket

Description (Pl. 2, figs 13–16)

A medium-sized bush-cricket with clear, **cream-coloured band around side margins of pronotum** (fig. 14). **Abdomen yellow ventrally; yellowish patches on body behind pronotum**. Brown with yellow is usual colour combination of this species, though green forms also occur, and all pale markings may show a greenish tinge.

Both sexes normally brachypterous – **forewings shorter than abdomen and hindwings being vestigial**. However, the macropterous f. *diluta* (Charpentier) (fig. 16), which has fully-developed wings, sometimes occurs in relatively high numbers in the population in very hot summers. Male cerci with an inner tooth towards apex; subgenital plate bears styles. Ovipositor curved upwards near base; **female subgenital plate divided into two lobes by deep median incision** (text fig. 15, p. 74).

Total length	♂ 13–26mm, ♀ 15–21mm
Wing length	♂ 7–10mm, ♀ 4–8mm
f. *diluta*	♂ 21–22mm, ♀ 23–25mm

Life History and Behaviour

The eggs are brown, cylindrical with slightly truncate ends, at least 4.5 × 1.0mm, laid in plant-stems, particularly rushes (*Juncus* spp.) (see also p. 37).

Nymphs emerge in late May and June, having six nymphal instars, becoming adult during late July and occasionally living until late October.

This species is omnivorous but mainly vegetarian, principally feeding on grasses.

Song (Cassette band 8)

The males produce an intensely penetrating and continuous, if high-pitched, stridulation in warm weather and often chirp far into the night if the temperature remains high. The sound has been likened to that of an electrical discharge such as is emitted by pylon-cables in damp weather.

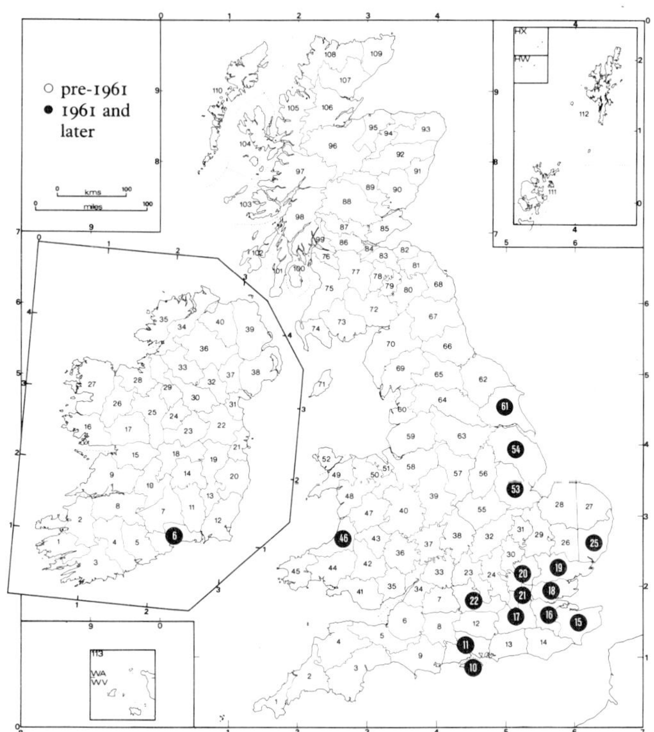

Metrioptera roeselii

Habitat

In Britain, *M. roeselii* occurs in water-meadows and in ungrazed grassland in such places as the surrounds of parks and golf-courses; beside roads and railway lines; and, near the coast, in neglected fields and on embankments right to the edge of salt-marshes. On its downland sites, it also occurs in rough, ungrazed grass, but is clearly not associated with the special flora of the chalk.

Distribution and Status (Map 9, page 170)

Until the beginning of this century, *M. roeselii* was known only from a narrow coastal belt on both sides of the Thames and northwards to the Humber. In London itself, Stephens (1835) recorded it, uncertainly, from Hampstead but it was not recorded from the area again until M. J. Skelton's Greater London Survey in 1983–84, which produced over thirty sites including Hampstead Heath. Prior to 1983 there had been odd records from Totteridge, in 1969, and from Regent's Park, in 1977 (Widgery, 1978). The most westerly record for the Thames Valley is Cox Green, near Maidenhead, Buckinghamshire, in 1982. To the south-east of London, in Kent, it is present from Greenwich to Sandwich Bay. It is found on the chalk around Chatham and at a completely new downland site discovered at Godmersham in 1982. It was also recorded from East Peckham on the Weald in 1947 but has not been seen there since. The first Hampshire record was at Lymington in 1939 and it was found there again in 1976. A separate colony was located at Needs Ore Point (Haes & Else, 1975) and in 1981 was reported to have spread about one kilometre north-west from the original site. A further population on the Hampshire coast is the result of a successful introduction of four gravid females (from Kentish stock) by B. C. Pickard in 1968 to a water-meadow he owned at Keyhaven Marshes (Ragge, 1973). Singletons have been found recently in the Isle of Wight and near Gatwick airport which could have been accidentally introduced but which may be early evidence of a further expansion in its range. In Surrey, *M. roeselii* also occurs in several sites on the North Downs in the Riddlesdown and Sanderstead areas where it has been since the late 1940s. It was first recorded in the county at Cheam (Menzies & Airy Shaw, 1947) in 1944 and then at Addington in 1948 (Collins, 1949) but both these localities have since been destroyed. North of the Thames, it is present in suitable habitat throughout the eastern half of Essex; and, in Suffolk, around Ipswich and Woodbridge with an isolated colony at Benacre Broad. There are strangely no records from Norfolk; however in Lincolnshire, although there are no post-1960 coastal records, this species continues to flourish inland in the Bardney area. Its most northerly British site is on the north shore of the Humber estuary, between Skeffling and Kilnsea.

The only known Welsh colony was discovered on the south shore of the Dovey estuary in 1970 (Ragge, 1973) and has continued to flourish over a considerable area (Fowles, 1986a). The only record from Ireland is by the

Blackwater, near Clashmore, Co. Waterford (Anderson, 1977). There are no records for Scotland or the Channel Islands.

M. roeselii is probably a comparatively late post-glacial arrival in Britain from Dogger Land before its submergence. The vicinity of the Thames seems always to have been the centre of distribution for this species, and it appears to be as numerous now as at any time in the recorded past along the Thames Estuary. However, there is no doubt that it has recently enjoyed a rapid expansion of its range in south-eastern England, which has roughly coincided with the creation of smokeless zones in London and elsewhere. A surprisingly large number of normally very rare f. *diluta* were observed in the London area and Surrey during the hot summers of 1983–84. It is quite likely that the species has spread locally by the dispersion of the free-flying form, but hardly likely that it reached Wales or Ireland in this way. It may be that these isolated colonies (as with *Pholidoptera griseoaptera*) are relicts of an earlier invasion, subsequently almost completely suppressed by the spread of woodland in the Atlantic period. The Welsh and Irish colonies certainly merit careful conservation and study.

This species occurs from Spain through central and northern Europe (though local in Scandinavia apart from southern Finland), Yugoslavia and Hungary eastwards through the U.S.S.R. to Siberia. It has been introduced into eastern Canada and the U.S.A. (Vickery, 1965).

Conocephalus discolor (Thunberg)
[= *C. fuscus* (Fabricius)]
The Long-winged Cone-head

Description (Pl. 3, figs 1–3)

A small bush-cricket, usually **green with brown dorsal stripe** on head and pronotum and brown wings. Abdomen ventrally reddish brown, and occasionally all-brown forms occur.

Pronotum without median keel. Both sexes **fully winged**, wings extending normally to just beyond abdomen, and hindwings slightly longer than forewings; there is a macropterous form with much longer wings (fig. 3). A few, usually **two or three, very small black spines on underside of hind femora. Male cerci with short, straight apex and inner tooth about midway; supra-anal plate has two small lobes separated by small central notch** (text fig. 13, p. 74); subgenital plate bears styles. **Ovipositor long and almost straight.**

Total length	♂ 16–21mm, ♀ 16–22mm
Wing length	♂ 11–15mm, ♀ 11–16mm
Macropterous form	♂ 16–18mm, ♀ 15–19mm
Ovipositor	8–9mm

Life History and Behaviour

The eggs are cylindrical and thin, 6mm long by under 1mm wide, buff-coloured, and are laid in plant stems, particularly rushes, reeds and sedges (*Juncus*, *Phragmites*, *Carex* spp.). The nymphs are bright green with a dark dorsal stripe like the adults, and emerge in May and June. They have five nymphal instars and mature during August or later, surviving until November in mild autumns. *C. discolor* is a very elusive little bush-cricket, easily overlooked, but able to build up into very large numbers in a few seasons.

This species is omnivorous; though it feeds mainly on grasses, it is also known to eat aphids and small caterpillars.

Song (Cassette band 9)

The song is a faint, high-pitched hissing sound, produced in prolonged bursts. This stridulation is, however, quite inaudible to many people.

Habitat

C. discolor occurs in coarse herbaceous vegetation in warm localities along the south coast of England: rough ungrazed downland turf; urban wasteland; coastal reed-beds and salt-marsh; wet and dry heathland and larger woodland rides and clearings. In 1983 it was found for the first time in quaking bogs – a completely new habitat for this species in Britain.

Distribution and Status (Map 10, page 170)

The outline distribution of *C. discolor*, apart from a solitary Kent record, is approximately from Lullington and Telscombe Cliffs, East Sussex westwards to the Purbeck coast of Dorset. There is no evidence of its continued presence in East Kent since the discovery of one specimen at Open Pits, Dungeness in 1953, despite careful search in a number of apparently suitable sites, including Dungeness itself. In 1931, at Chale, Isle of Wight, K. G. Blair found a number of what he assumed were *C. dorsalis* f. *burri* (macropterous short-winged cone-heads). Later, in discussion with K. H. Chapman over a genuine *C. dorsalis* f. *burri* from Norfolk, he realized that his 1931 find was, in fact, *C. discolor*, hitherto unconfirmed from this country, a conclusion he was able to substantiate by reference to Continental specimens (Blair, 1936). There appear to have been no further reports of *C. discolor* until it was discovered at Ferring, West Sussex, in 1945 (Menzies, 1946) and at several other Sussex localities during 1946–47. As H. K. Airy Shaw pointed out in a footnote to Menzies' paper, it is a remarkable coincidence that, although Stephens (1835) suggested Curtis's earlier reference to this species might have meant *C. dorsalis*, Westwood (1838) actually cited the 'Isle of Wight', where it had been found by Blair, as a locality. In 1953, A. E. Gardner discovered a second locality for the species on the island at Ladder Chine and a further new site was discovered in the St. Helens district in 1975 by E. C. M. Haes. However, during D. G. Rand's Orthoptera survey of the Isle of Wight in 1978 and 1979 (unpublished), neither of the original pre-1960 colonies could be found due to 'development'.

C. discolor was first certainly recorded from Dorset in 1953, close to Anvil Point Lighthouse, near Swanage, and again in 1955 at Chapman's Pool (Pickard, 1956a). However it was not recorded in Hampshire until 1970 at Botley Wood near Southampton (Appleton *et al.*, 1975) and subsequently, in 1976, from waste ground in Portsmouth (Janssen, 1977) and, in 1977, near East Boldre in the New Forest (Haes, 1984). Further isolated New Forest records were made in 1981 and 1982 and then in 1983, during the first year of a survey of New Forest Orthoptera on a 1km square basis, forty hitherto unknown sites were discovered in the south-east quarter of the Forest (Marshall, 1984; Welstead & Welstead, 1985). Also, during the warm summer of 1983, it was found farther north in the county at St. Catherine's Hill, Winchester, and at Stockbridge Fen (Brough *et al.* 1986). At about the same time, the insect was discovered in several heathland sites in Hampshire and Dorset, as far west as Radipole Lake, Weymouth (Haes, 1984); and, in 1985, J. Paul (1987) found the species in Wiltshire on the northern edge of the New Forest at Landford Common.

C. discolor is common on most of the larger Channel Islands, but absent from Wales, Scotland and Ireland.

Despite the nineteenth-century references to this species (Curtis, 1825; Westwood, *loc.cit.*), it is possible that *C. discolor* arrived in Britain only sometime in this century. It appears to have undergone two population explosions – one in the 1940s and again during particularly hot summers in the early 1980s. However, its fortunes seem to have fluctuated over the past quarter of a century with the destruction in the 1960s of many of the best sites. By the early 1970s the species was considered rare enough to be included in the Red Data Book of Insects but, during the latter half of the 1970s and in the hot summers of 1983 and 1984, many new colonies were found, as a result of which it was removed from the Red Data Book draft. In both 1983 and 1984, an exceptional number of macropterous individuals occurred in most sites. It has been demonstrated that this form develops in response to overcrowding (Ando & Hartley, 1982). These macropterous specimens fly readily and it is almost certain that, because of the population explosions, new colonies were started by airborne individuals making local migrations in sufficient numbers. This species merits a detailed ecological study.

With the exception of the extreme north, this species occurs throughout Europe, in temperate Asia and North Africa.

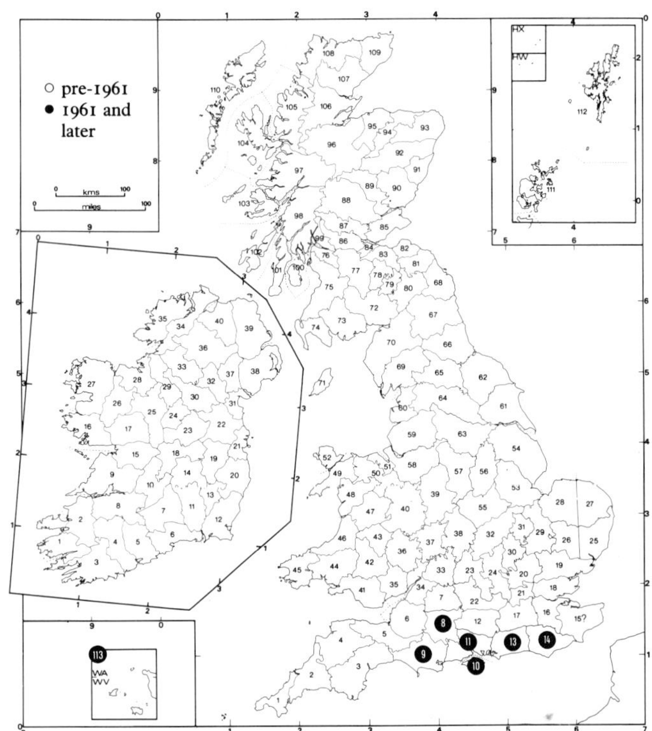

Conocephalus discolor

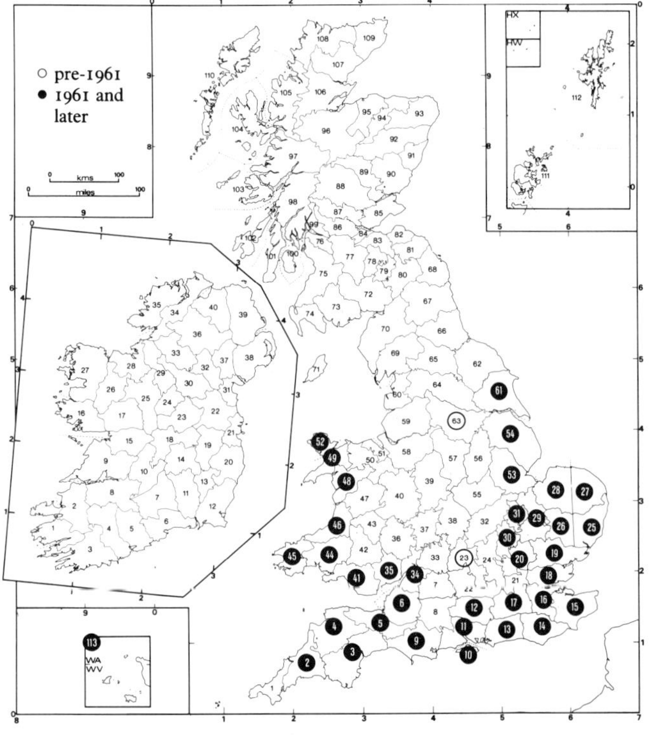

Conocephalus dorsalis

Conocephalus dorsalis (Latreille)

The Short-winged Cone-head.

Description (Pl. 3, figs 4–6)

A small bush-cricket, usually **green with brown dorsal stripe** on head and pronotum, and brown wings. Abdomen ventrally yellowish brown, and occasionally all-brown forms occur (fig. 5).

Both sexes **normally brachypterous**, with hindwings vestigial and forewings covering only part of abdomen. The macropterous form, f. *burri* Ebner, has both pairs of wings fully developed, extending well beyond abdomen (fig. 6). **No small black spines on underside of hind femora. Male cerci have long apex with upturned tip and inner tooth about midway; supra-anal plate has two long lobes joined together centrally** (text fig. 14, p. 74); subgenital plate bears styles. **Ovipositor slightly upcurved.**

Total length ♂ 11–15mm, ♀ 12–18mm
Wing length ♂ 6–10mm, ♀ 5–8mm
f. *burri* ♂ 15–17mm, ♀ 16–18mm
Ovipositor 8–9mm

Life History and Behaviour

The eggs are cylindrical and thin, 5.0–5.5mm long and under 1mm wide, buff-coloured, and laid in plant stems, particularly rushes, reeds and sedges (*Juncus, Phragmites, Carex* spp.). The nymphs are bright green with a dark dorsal stripe, and emerge in May and June, having five nymphal instars, maturing in July and August. Adults rarely survive beyond mid-October. *C. dorsalis* is adept at passing rapidly through dense vegetation and then posing lengthwise along a plant stem in the manner of a phasmid (stick-insect).

This species is omnivorous, but feeds mainly on buds, flowers and unripe seed-heads of sedges and rushes.

Song (Cassette band 10)

The long, continuous, high-pitched song is formed of two alternating sounds: a hiss like that of *C. discolor*, and a ticking sound. Although this species is more widely distributed than *C. discolor*, it is rare to find it in large numbers. There are usually only a few males stridulating together and the song is thus less easy to hear.

Habitat

C. dorsalis occupies two distinct habitats: coastally, in salt-marshes or sand-dunes, particularly in association with maritime rushes such as saltmarsh rush (*Juncus gerardii*) and sea rush (*J. maritimus*), but also sea couch (*Elymus pycnanthus*); and inland, on marshy vegetation including quaking lowland bogs, reed-beds, clumps of rushes and other coarse herbage in the flood plains of rivers or by lakes and ponds. It is normally confined to wet places; however, a specimen of f. *burri* was recently found on dry limestone near Bristol (Paul, 1986) but was presumably wind-borne or accidentally introduced.

Distribution and Status (Map 11, page 171)

In England, coastal colonies are widespread from St. Germans and Cargreen on the Tamar Estuary, East Cornwall and Bideford, North Devon, and then around the south and east coasts to the north shore of the Humber estuary.

Inland, there are several considerable colonies particularly in the Somerset Levels; and in the flood plains of the Severn in Gloucestershire, the Wey around Guildford, Surrey, and the Arun, the Adur, the Ouse, the Cuckmere and the eastern Rother in Sussex. In East Kent there is an interesting isolated colony on wet heathland at Hothfield Common near Ashford where *C. dorsalis* fills an ecological niche normally occupied by *Metrioptera brachyptera*, which has not been recorded from this district. However, on the wet heathlands of East Dorset and in the New Forest (Brown & Searle, 1974), this species is locally quite common in the company of the there far more numerous *M. brachyptera*, so it is clear that the two species can exist together in this habitat. In East Anglia there are still many widely separated colonies on the edges of the original fenlands and in the Norfolk Broads. Although quite numerous in its Humberside localities, *C. dorsalis* has never been recorded farther north and there are no records from the mosses of Cheshire or Lancashire or the very many suitable-looking coastal habitats in north-west England.

In Wales, this species is locally common from around Swansea and the Gower Peninsula westwards to Milford Haven. It is much rarer along the west coast, with isolated colonies at Newport Bay; on the Dovey estuary; at Llanbedr; and at Pwlleli, on the Lleyn Peninsula. There are two sites on Anglesey: the well-known colony at Newborough Warren National Nature Reserve and a recently-discovered one in the north of the island in Cors Goch nature reserve.

In the Channel Islands it was found in 1969 at Samarès Marsh, Jersey (Le Sueur, 1976) but the marsh has now been drained and the habitat destroyed. It has also been reported from Guernsey. There are no records from Scotland or Ireland.

The general distribution of this species does not seem to have changed substantially since the last century. It is believed to be a late post-glacial arrival since it is apparently absent from Scotland and Ireland. As an insect of wetland habitats, it is obviously vulnerable to the draining of marshes, the mechanical maintenance of river banks and recreational pressures on salt-marshes or dunes, but it is so widespread that it is hardly likely to become a threatened species in the foreseeable future. The possibility of the spread of this species in Britain by the dispersion of its eggs in sea-borne flotsam has been considered by Warne & Hartley (1975).

This species occurs throughout Europe, except the extreme south, eastwards through Yugoslavia and the U.S.S.R.

Leptophyes punctatissima (Bosc)

The Speckled Bush-cricket

Description (Pl. 3, figs 7,8,10)

A small to medium-sized bush-cricket, always **green with minute dark spots**. Abdomen with brownish stripe on dorsal surface. Male has brownish wings.

No median keel on pronotum. Both sexes brachypterous, the **hindwings absent. Male has small, rounded forewings** which are mainly stridulatory area; **female forewings reduced to short, flat lobes. Male cerci with no inner teeth,** and inwardly curved with pointed tip; **subgenital plate without styles. Ovipositor broad and upwardly curved.**

Total length	♂ 9–16mm, ♀ 11–18mm
Ovipositor	6–8mm

Life History and Behaviour

The eggs which are ovoid and flat, brown,and over 3mm long by 1.5mm wide, are inserted into plant stems and crevices, normally in oak-bark. The speckled nymphs (fig. 8) hatch during May and June and may be easily located when sunning themselves in groups on the foliage of various plants, especially stinging nettle (*Urtica dioica*), honeysuckle (*Lonicera periclymenum*), bramble (*Rubus fruticosus*) or wood sage (*Teucrium scorodonia*). They may then be confused with large aphids or juvenile capsid bugs (fig. 9). After six nymphal instars they mature during August and adults may survive until November. *L. punctatissima* is a solitary and unobtrusive bush-cricket with its shadow-masking pose and excellent camouflage. However, adults frequently ascend into taller bushes and trees, and sometimes enter houses, when they can be easily observed.

This species is largely vegetarian, feeding on all the plants mentioned above, among others.

Song (Cassette bands 11 & 12)

The male song is a high-pitched, almost inaudible chirp repeated regularly. By using a mini bat-detector, the distinctive stridulation pattern can be heard – an advantage when estimating population sizes. Receptive females have a weaker stridulation which attracts males.

Habitat

L. punctatissima frequents rough herbage and scrub in woodland rides, hedgerows, parks, mature gardens, thickets and waste ground. Of British orthopterans it is, in fact, one of the most regularly observed.

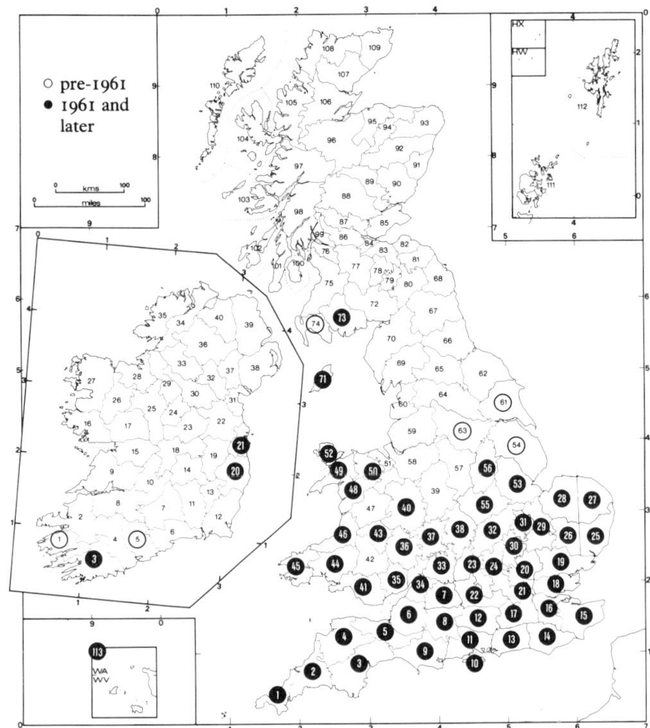

Leptophyes punctatissima

Distribution and Status (Map 12, page 171)

In England *L. punctatissima* is widespread throughout the south, except on high moorlands in the Devonian peninsula. North of the Thames, it is common in the Cotswolds, much of Herefordshire and Worcestershire (Fincher, 1965) and is widespread in Warwickshire (Copson, 1984). It is absent from large areas of the Midland Plain but is common in the Chilterns and most of eastern England as far north as Lincolnshire, where there are a very few isolated colonies, but there are no recent records from Yorkshire. It is still well-established in its single known stronghold in the Isle of Man.

In Wales, it is present in all the maritime counties except Flint, but very rare inland. In Scotland, small isolated colonies persist on the Galloway coast. In Ireland, its main distribution is around Dublin, but it is found in one or two other widely-separated localities (Cotton, 1982). In the Channel Islands, it is widespread on both Jersey and Guernsey.

The similarity in the distribution of *L. punctatissima* and *Pholidoptera griseoaptera* is probably no coincidence. Both these flightless bush-crickets seem able to tolerate a relatively wide range of conditions and both species could well be early post-glacial arrivals here. It is conceivable that they are so widespread in all but the coldest parts of Britain because their eggs are successfully transported on ornamental trees and shrubs, but there is as yet no evidence for this hypothesis. *L. punctatissima* is noteworthy for its occurrence on a number of offshore islands, which suggests a natural distribution rather than chance introductions from gardens. These isolated colonies warrant careful study and, as this species is comparatively large and flightless, monitoring of an isolated island population should not be difficult.

This species occurs in most of Europe from Spain to southern Scandinavia and eastwards to Yugoslavia and the western U.S.S.R.

Grylloidea

GRYLLIDAE

The Gryllidae have long, thread-like antennae and three-segmented tarsi. The general body shape is more compact than that of the Tettigoniidae, with a globular head which may sometimes seem disproportionately large. The pronotum is a short, squared saddle-shape (text fig. 36a). The hearing organs are on the fore-tibiae with a tympanum on each side, not covered by a ventral flap. The males of each winged species produce a characteristic song from the stridulatory areas of the forewings (see p. 41).

The life-cycles of the British crickets are more complex than those of either the Acrididae or the Tettigoniidae and are different for (and described under) each species. The eggs are elongated and cylindrical (text fig. 36b). There are from eight to eleven instars after emergence from the vermiform larval stage. As in the winged Tettigoniidae and Acrididae, the wing-pads develop first as flat lobes, then are reversed in the last two instars (see text fig. 7, p. 38). Wing venation is shown in text figure 36c.

Gryllus campestris and *Nemobius sylvestris* are active both day and night, though *N. sylvestris* avoids direct sunlight. The introduced *Acheta domesticus* is crepuscular or nocturnal, as is also *Pseudomogoplistes squamiger*.

Diet differs widely according to species, *q.v.*

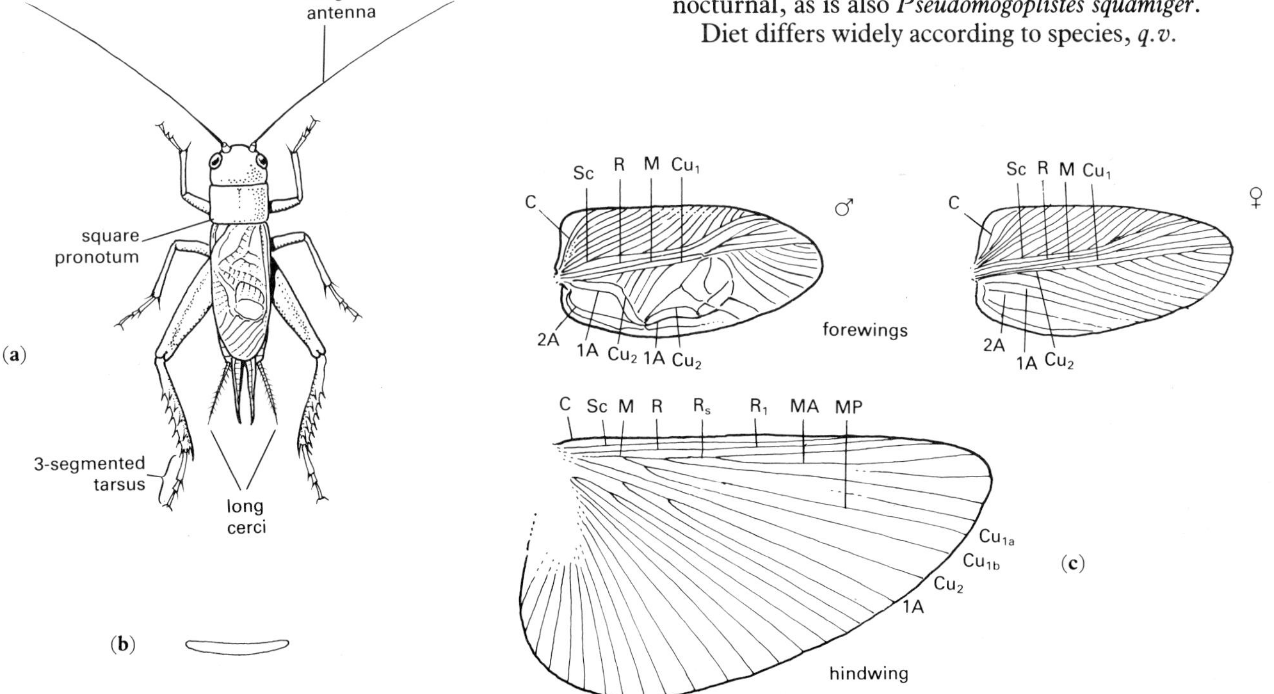

Text Figure 36 *Acheta domesticus* showing distinguishing characters of gryllid species.
(**a**) general structure, ♂; (**b**) egg; (**c**) forewings of ♂ (left) and ♀ (right), hindwing below. Note strong difference between ♂ and ♀ forewing (after Ragge, 1965)

Acheta domesticus (Linnaeus)
The House-cricket

Description (Pl. 3, figs 11, 12)

A medium-sized cricket, greyish brown in colour with darker brown markings on head and pronotum – a more yellowish colour is seen in dried specimens.

Both sexes **fully winged**: forewings covering abdomen and hindwings extending beyond body. Female has long, very slender ovipositor which extends beyond folded tips of hindwings.

Total length	♂ 14–20mm, ♀ 14–18mm
Wing length	♂, ♀ 9–12m
Ovipositor	8–13mm

Life History and Behaviour

The eggs are cylindrical, white, about 2.5mm long by under 0.5mm wide, laid singly or in groups in the soil or a similar substrate.

Development of *A. domesticus* is closely related to environmental temperature; at about 20° C eggs may hatch within two or three weeks of laying, but may take several times longer at lower temperatures. Development of the nymphs may then take between three and eight months, usually through 11 nymphal instars (though seven to thirteen are possible); with higher temperatures the nymphal development period is shorter, and so is the life of the adult. Breeding will continue as long as conditions are suitable – there is no seasonality or diapause.

This species is nocturnal and widely omnivorous.

Song (Cassette band 13)

The chirp of this cricket is repeated with a monotonous regularity over long periods, usually in the evening and at night. Although this song used to be a familiar sound, today it is to be heard widely only during long, hot summers when the crickets wander, or are carried with refuse, from their usual heated premises into the countryside.

Habitat

A. domesticus may be found in heated buildings such as private houses, hospitals, hotels and factories; and outdoors in large rubbish-tips and sewage-farms where there is constant warmth from fermenting organic matter. In warm summers, quite large numbers have been recorded out-of-doors, from road-drains, waste plots and even hedgerows and fields. In 1976 a colony with a minimum of ten singing males was located on the edge of a cornfield at Lodge Hill, near Chinnor, Oxfordshire, about 1km from the nearest farm building (D. C. F. Cotton, pers. comm.), and D. Musson (pers. comm.) has given a particularly good account of a considerable colony of *A. domesticus* in a grass field at Snitterfield, near Stratford-upon-Avon, in

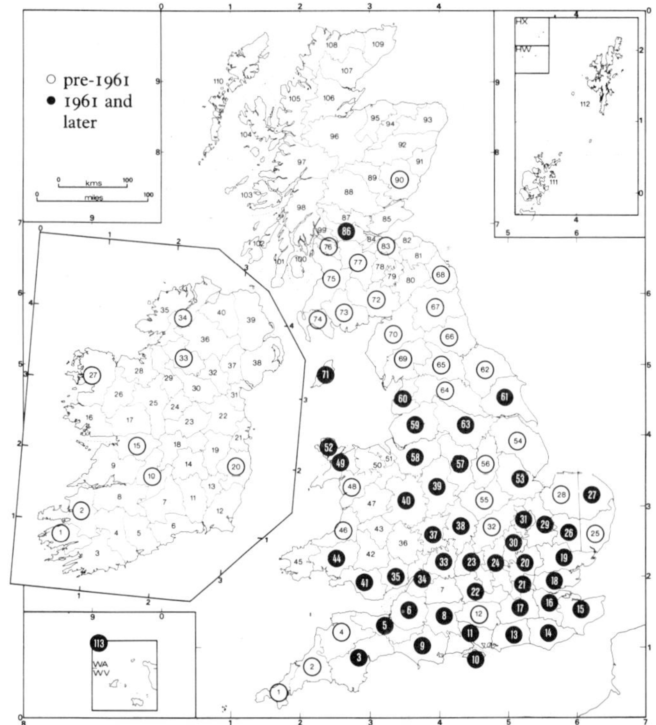

Acheta domesticus

1982. Both recorders indicated how these might easily have been misrecorded as the rare *Gryllus campestris* (field-cricket). A similar occurrence was recorded in Surrey (Hawkins, 1984).

Distribution and Status (Map 13, page 172)

This species has been recorded from almost every Watsonian vice-county in England (Ragge, 1965), but the post-1960 records are mainly from urban areas. In Wales, the few recent records are very scattered and only one is from central Wales. In Scotland, most records were from the south-west (Ragge, 1965) but the only post-1960 record is from Stirling in 1977 (M. Davies, pers. comm.).

Although recorded from several vice-counties in Ireland prior to 1961, there have been no post-1960 records, and it is now presumably very rare or absent. Its Irish status has been summarized by Cotton (1982).

The only Channel Islands from which it has been recorded are Jersey and Guernsey.

This long-established alien has certainly been present in Britain for several centuries, possibly arriving with the returning Crusaders in the thirteenth century (Kevan, 1955). Until about the 1940s most towns and even large villages had one or more bakeries which provided ideal habitats. Most hospitals, factories, larger private houses and other heated premises were then fuelled with coal, and their ash and rubbish-tips would have been very suitable sites for this cricket, as were the buildings themselves. From the 1950s many of these habitats disappeared and, at the same time, extensive use of insecticides, particularly chlorinated hydrocarbons such as DDT, exterminated many established colonies. *A. domesticus* declined rapidly during this period. Two long-standing colonies on rubbish-tips in West Sussex were destroyed in the early 1970s when the sites were bulldozed for re-development and no crickets survived on either site. Other rubbish-tip colonies have doubtless suffered a similar fate now that so much urban refuse is treated in special plants. It has never returned to many old localities but, in the last ten years, many substantial colonies have again been recorded, notably in the West Midlands and southern England.

Originally native of North Africa and the Middle East but now cosmopolitan.

Gryllus campestris Linnaeus — Red Data Book – Endangered

The Field-cricket

Description (Pl. 3, figs 13,14)

A large cricket, **shiny black** in colour, with large head (particularly in male), **yellow patches** basally on forewings, and **orange** basally on underside of hind femora.

Forewings cover abdomen in male, but are slightly shorter in female; both sexes have **vestigial hindwings**. The rare f. *caudata* Krauss, with fully developed hindwings, has not been recorded from Britain. Ovipositor is long and slender.

Total length	♂ 19–23mm, ♀ 17–22mm
Wing length	♂ 12–14mm, ♀ 10–14mm
Ovipositor	8–12mm

Life History and Behaviour

The eggs are oval, elongate, over 2.0mm long by 0.5mm wide, and are laid singly in the ground from May to July. Hatching occurs within three to four weeks, from June onwards. Nymphs reach their penultimate instar (usually the tenth) during the autumn when the sturdy nymphs dig burrows with their large mandibles and hibernate for the winter. They re-emerge during mild weather in March and undergo their last two ecdyses, becoming adult during April or early May. The mature females then lay eggs during the summer months, and adults die off by August. It is probable that only nymphs from early matings between late May and early June are robust enough to hibernate successfully in this country.

The burrows have horizontal entrances screened by tufts of uneaten vegetation and require a careful search. Grasses are the main foodstuffs of this species.

Song (Cassette bands 14–16)

The loud, penetrating song of an isolated male (band 14) is of short chirps repeated several times a second, and continuing for long periods on favourable warm, humid days. A chorus of males (band 15) may be heard up to one hundred metres away. The courtship song (band 16) is quieter than the normal song, and includes a ticking sound. Males stridulate from about the end of May until July.

Gryllus campestris

Habitat

The British race of *G. campestris* seems able to persist only in a very restricted habitat, needing short grass and a light sandy or chalk soil of the right texture for easy burrowing and to allow the hibernating nymphs to withstand our mainly wet winters. In both known sites in mainland Britain, the turf is kept suitably short by mowing.

Distribution and Status (Map 14, page 172)

In mainland Britain, there are now only two known populations – both on private land in West Sussex. There is also a recent record in Essex which may have arisen from accidentally imported stock (P. Sutton, pers. comm.).

G. campestris is now one of the rarest of British Orthoptera and was probably never a common insect, although there were isolated colonies in several counties until early this century. These pre-1961 records are from

Cornwall, Devon, Hampshire, Isle of Wight, Norfolk, Lincolnshire, Gloucestershire and Staffordshire, with doubtful records from Dorset, Wiltshire, South Essex, West Suffolk and Derbyshire (Kevan, 1961; Ragge, 1965). The record from Gloucestershire is now also considered doubtful. Some of these may have been misidentifications of *Acheta domesticus* (*q.v.*) which had wandered into open country in warm summers, or even single Continental specimens imported as pets or accidentally in camping equipment. In the Channel Islands, there are good colonies in the south and west of Jersey.

It is now very difficult to evaluate its post-glacial history as so few of the old county records gave specific localites. Gilbert White's eighteenth-century account of the cricket in the long-lost site at Selborne seems to have created an over-optimistic impression of its status in Britain, although he, like Stephens (1835), clearly considered it to be an uncommon insect. The well-known colony at Fawley, recorded by W. H. Hudson (1903) and B. C. Pickard (Ragge, 1956), was apparently completely destroyed by the construction of the oil refinery on the site. The status of this species has been summarized by Lucas (1920), Pickard (1956b) and Haes (1975). Of several attempts to introduce the native race of this cricket into new habitats between 1969 and 1973, only one proved successful, and this was on a site where the species had been recorded previously by H. Guermonprez in 1909 (Haes, 1976). It was found that artificially bred populations produced a high proportion of malformed nymphs after three or four generations, so it does appear that the native field-cricket has very limited genetic viability.

This species occurs in central and southern Europe, western Asia and North Africa.

Nemobius sylvestris (Bosc)

The Wood-cricket

Description (Pl. 4, figs 1,2)

A small **dark brown cricket with lighter markings**.

Both sexes **brachypterous – hindwings totally absent**; in male, forewings cover about half abdomen, in female, wings are shorter lateral lobes. Ovipositor long and slender.

Total length	♂ 7–9mm, ♀ 7–11mm
Wing length	♂ 3–4mm, ♀ 2–3mm
Ovipositor	5–7mm

Life History and Behaviour

N. sylvestris has an unusual two year life-cycle: eggs, which are under 2.0mm long by 0.5mm wide, hatch during June; nymphs reach their fifth or sixth instar by autumn and overwinter at this stage, though not undergoing true hibernation. In the following spring the nymphs complete their eight nymphal instars, becoming adult during June and July. Adults may survive until late November and a few will overwinter, though probably not living long into their third year. There are thus two distinct populations present every year, which rarely interbreed.

Dead leaves and perhaps associated fungi are probably the main food of this species.

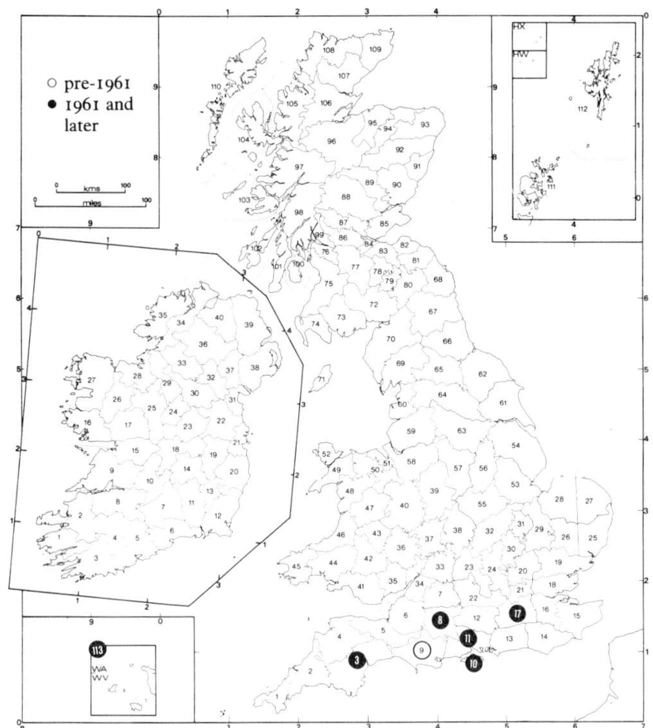

Nemobius sylvestris

Song (Cassette bands 17, 18)

The quiet, purring song of the male (band 17) is not easily heard, though a chorus of males (band 18) is a distinctive feature of woodland clearings from about the end of June until November, both by day and by night.

Habitat

N. sylvestris occurs in deep leaf-litter, mainly under oaks, holly and bracken, in warm and sunny clearings or along sunny margins of deciduous woods, often in very large populations. In some places, colonies occur in old stone walls and earthbanks, but only below scrub or on woodland margins. In the east of the Isle of Wight, there are colonies in crumbling clay sea-cliffs, but again always close to dense scrub or deciduous trees along the cliff-top. The cricket is not known from any open or exposed localities, although, in warm summers, individuals may wander some metres from dense cover.

Distribution and Status (Map 15, page 173)

N. sylvestris has a very restricted range with three separate centres of distribution: Hampshire, the Isle of Wight and South Devon. The largest population is in the New Forest where it is widespread and numerous, with colonies located from the outskirts of Christchurch and Exbury in the south through to Hamptworth Common, Bagfield Copse and Whiteparish Common in the extreme south of Wiltshire. In the Isle of Wight it is present across the north of the island from the sea-cliffs above Whitecliff Bay in the east to the vicinity of Newtown Bay in the north-west. It is also common in Parkhurst Forest and several other larger woodlands north of the central chalk (D. G. Rands, pers. comm.). In South Devon, it persists at Meadhaydown Woods, near Chudleigh and around Harpford, near Sidmouth. In addition, there is an isolated colony near the Royal Horticultural Society Garden, Wisley, Surrey (Stubbs, 1967). There is a pre-1961 record from Bere Wood, Dorset. In the Channel Islands, this species is present in wooded areas in Jersey. It is absent from Wales, Scotland and Ireland.

Mystery surrounds the origin and status of this cricket. Stephens (1835–37) recorded it from Brockenhurst, and Wood (1872) from Lyndhurst, both in the New Forest, but both clearly regarded it as a rarity. During the next hundred years, either its status changed or it was noticed more often, for it was certainly not an extreme rarity to Lucas (1920). Its distribution today is still surprising as it is apparently absent from many ostensibly suitable sites between the two large mainland populations in Devon and Hampshire. Its sea-cliff habitat in the Isle of Wight is rather different from those on the mainland and more similar to some of its habitats in northern Brittany. It is possible that it is native to the Isle of Wight but was accidentally introduced to the New Forest and South Devon on forestry trees of Continental origin about the beginning of the nineteenth century. However, its status in Britain before the beginning of the present century is so little documented that it is purposeless to speculate about its origin. One thing is certain; the few ten-kilometre squares from which it is known at present include such large populations in relatively safe habitats that its future seems assured. Moreover, the presence of the large colony in Surrey (which may have been introduced with a consignment of azaleas from Exbury in the 1960s) indicates that it can become established in a suitable area in a short space of time.

This species occurs in southern and central Europe as far north as Holland and northern Germany, eastwards through Poland to the U.S.S.R.; also in North Africa, the Azores and the Canary Islands.

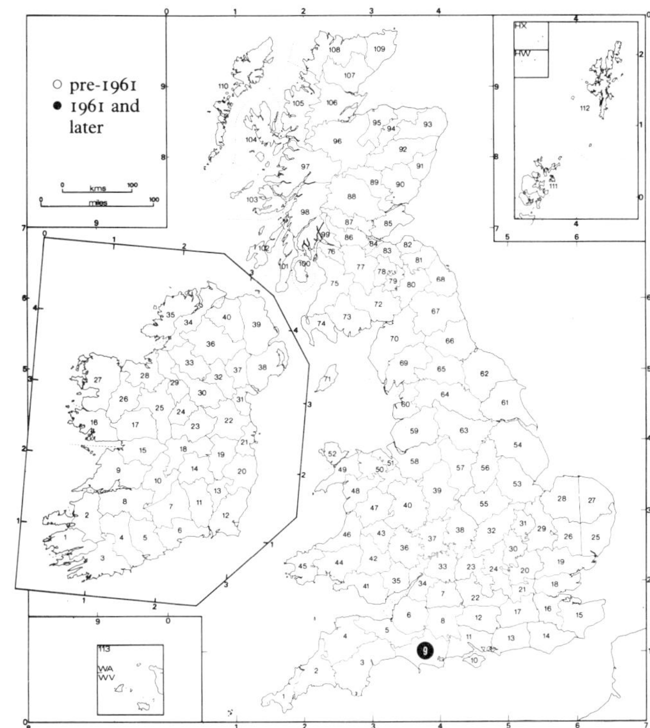

Pseudomogoplistes squamiger

Pseudomogoplistes squamiger (Fischer) Red Data Book – Endangered
The Scaly Cricket

TAXONOMIC NOTE: Previously included in *Mogoplistes*, Gorokhov (1984) separated *squamiger* from other species in the genus on the basis of the structure of the male genitalia.

Description (Pl. 4, figs 3,4)

A small cricket, greyish brown in colour, with most of body and legs **covered with minute scales**. Adults **completely apterous**. Adult male has truncate abdomen. Ovipositor slender, about the same length as cerci, and dull orange with a black tip (Paul, 1987).

Total length	♂ 8–11mm, ♀ 10–13mm
Ovipositor	5mm

Life History and Behaviour

Little is known of this insect. Eggs are a uniform dull yellow, about 1 × 3mm. A female collected in October 1985 laid eight eggs in captivity. Some of these were thrust vertically into the sand, some lay flat on the surface and others were wedged against the side of the jar (Paul, *loc.cit.*). Adults have been found from August to mid October – most recently from the last week of September to the second week of October – emerging from cover at night to forage. Probably eggs overwinter and the nymphs emerge in spring.

Song

The completely wingless male is not equipped to stridulate.

Habitat

P.squamiger is found beneath rocks and concrete rubble on the foreshore adjacent to a sheltered salt-water lagoon but protected from any direct maritime wave action by a huge but relatively recently-formed shingle beach.

Distribution and Status (Map 16, page 173)

This strange little cricket is recorded only from the eastern end of the East Fleet, behind Chesil Beach in Dorset. Only females were discovered initially, the first in 1949 (Bowen & Williamson, 1950), and males were not found until 1977.

There are no other European Orthoptera with a range comparable to that of *P. squamiger*. Chopard (1951) stated that in France it is quite rare and recorded only from a few places on the Mediterranean coast, whilst Harz (1969) has noted that it is a local insect even around the Mediterranean and that, outside that area, colonies are recorded only from the south of Portugal, Madeira, the Canary Islands and the Dorset coast. If, in fact, the Dorset colony is really native and a relict from a warmer past, then the species must have one of the most interesting distribution patterns of any European insect. However, a possible explanation for this very disjunct population is that viable eggs, nymphs or even adults were introduced, via Portland Naval Base during the Second World War, with sand of Mediterranean origin used, for example, as ballast or to fill sandbags. Even so, it is remarkable that *P. squamiger* has persisted here for nearly half a century, despite occasional sea floods. The colony merits careful study as an ecological phenomenon and should certainly be protected.

GRYLLOTALPIDAE

The Gryllotalpidae (text fig. 37) are readily distinguished from all other British orthopteroid insects by their highly modified digging forelegs, and other adaptations to their subterranean mode of life. The antennae are shorter and more sturdy than in the Gryllidae, as also are the hindlegs. The pronotum is a solidly built, oval shape with no keels. The song is characteristic.

The sole British species is among the largest in the genus, and has a life-cycle of two years, probably living longer. The females guard and care for the eggs and young nymphs (see p. 99), with a degree of maternal care similar to that shown by the Dermaptera.

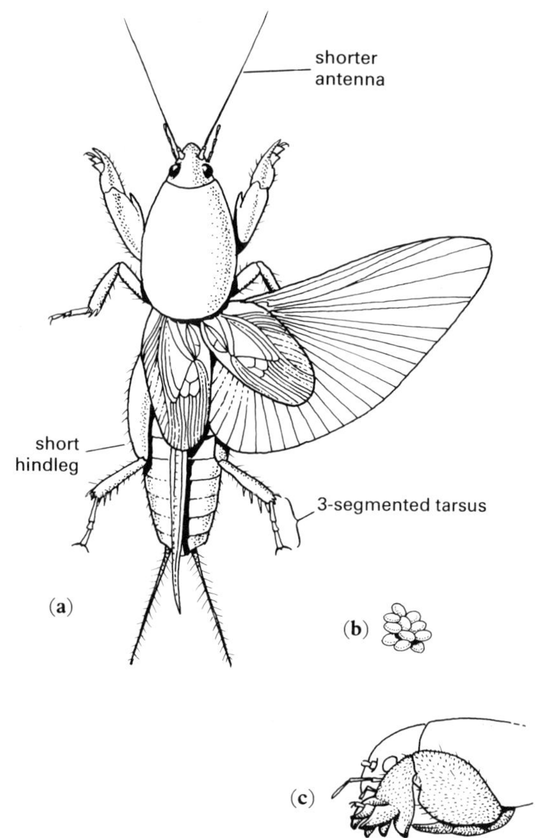

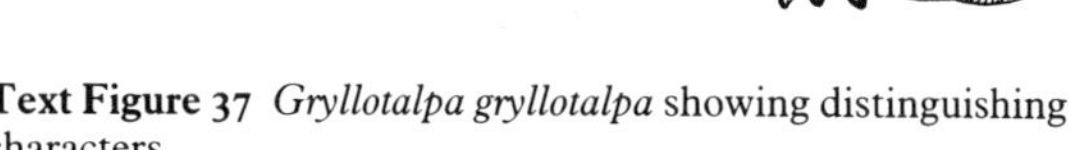

Text Figure 37 *Gryllotalpa gryllotalpa* showing distinguishing characters.

(**a**) generalized insect showing right fore- and hindwings extended; (**b**) cluster of eggs; (**c**) foreleg modified for digging, enlarged

Gryllotalpa gryllotalpa (Linnaeus) Red Data Book – The Mole-cricket Endangered

Description (Pl. 4, figs 5,6)

A large cricket, light chestnut-brown in colour, covered with velvet-like hairs.

Forelegs highly modified for digging (text fig. 37b); hindlegs comparatively small. In both sexes forewings short, about half length of abdomen, but hindwings long, extending beyond abdomen, except in the rare f. *cophta* de Haan – a brachypterous form with shorter hindwings. Ovipositor not visible externally.

Total length	♂ 35–41mm, ♀ 40–46mm
Forewing length	♂ 13–17mm, ♀ 16–18mm

Life History and Behaviour

In the spring, *G. gryllotalpa* forms underground nest-chambers in which batches of up to 300 eggs are laid. The eggs are pale, oval and large, about 3.0 × 1.5mm. The female stays with them, licking them to prevent mould until they hatch in two to four weeks, and continues to protect the young nymphs for some weeks more. Nymphs of varying instars hibernate and continue their development in the second season. Late hatchlings from the first season may not mature until their third year, thus the life-cycle may span two or three years.

G. gryllotalpa is the most elusive of our native orthopterans, spending most of its life underground, burrowing at various depths down to one metre, but on warm evenings and during the night, adults come to the surface and take to the air with a clumsy and noisy flight. Late nymphal stages and adults also swim strongly. It used to be regarded as a pest in gardens, causing considerable damage to vegetables and flowering plants such as chrysanthemums by burrowing into their roots (as Gilbert White noted in his diary); it is still considered a horticultural pest in the Channel Islands (Bryan, 1987). Despite its destructive habits, this species is largely carnivorous, feeding mainly on caterpillars and earthworms.

Song (Cassette band 19)

Males produce their distinctive nocturnal purring stridulation at the burrow entrances on warm nights in spring and early summer. In former times, when this species was widespread, it earned such evocative local vernacular names as 'eve-churr', 'jarr-worm', 'Cambridge nightingale' and, in South Wales, 'rhing y les' (Fowles, 1986a).

Habitat

G. gryllotalpa is a subterranean, wetland insect, confined in the natural state to water meadows and wet heathlands over both heavy and light soils. Urban records are likely to be casual specimens, imported from the Continent in consignments of vegetables.

Distribution and Status (Map 17, page 174)

In recent years, colonies have been located only on the northern edge of the New Forest in the extreme south of Wiltshire (Ragge, 1973); on allotments close to the Itchen at Sholing, near Southampton, where it persisted until about 1977; and around Buxted and Uckfield in East Sussex. All other post-1960 records are for individual specimens – mostly from built-up areas and thus likely to be accidentally imported examples.

The species is still numerous in the Vale district of Guernsey, Channel Islands, but there are no post-1960 records from Wales, Scotland or Ireland.

G. gryllotalpa was widespread in Britain before extensive land drainage in the seventeenth and eighteenth centuries destroyed much suitable habitat. During the last two hundred years it was recorded from many counties in England, but was always a very local insect. Finally,

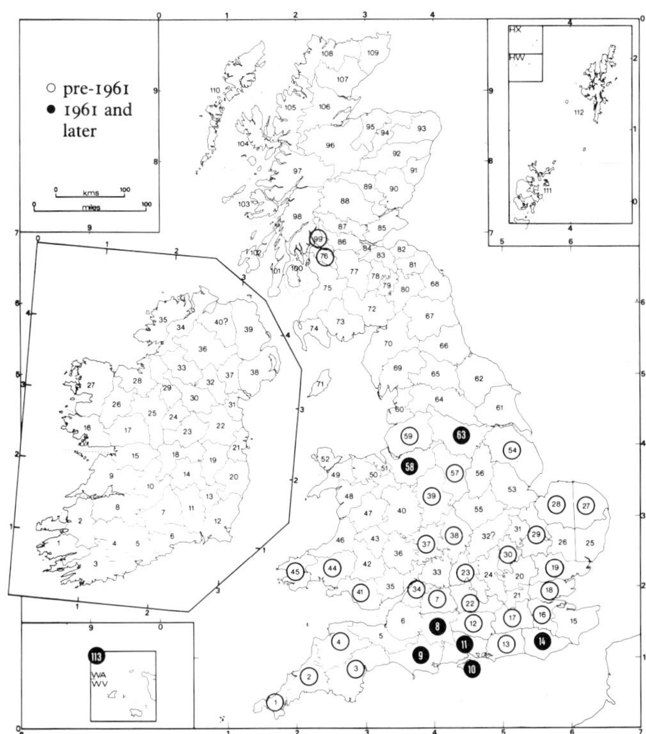

Gryllotalpa gryllotalpa

during the 1940s and 1950s, the majority of the surviving sites in Surrey, Dorset and Hampshire were destroyed by building or agricultural development. In Wales, it was known in the seventeenth century from the Carmarthenshire coast, but the only twentieth century specimen, now in the National Museum of Wales (Fowles, 1986a) was collected near Haverfordwest in 1936.

In Scotland, only one site is recorded – at Kilmacolm, Renfrewshire, at the end of the last century (King, 1901). The only Irish record is of a female collected 'on an old Irish canoe' at the outflow of the Bann at Toome, Lough Neagh, Co. Londonderry (Carpenter, 1899), but this record is regarded as unsatisfactory. The specimen itself is now in the National Museum of Ireland, but it must be considered doubtfully native (Cotton, 1982).

The species is now so rare that its British status is difficult to assess accurately and must depend on special research in its last known localities. As the species is now a scheduled insect, such investigation should be undertaken only with the authorization of the Nature Conservancy Council. All sightings, however, would be most welcome for the records, particularly from Ireland. It seems likely that this cricket will become extinct as a native species.

G. gryllotalpa occurs throughout Europe, except Norway and Finland, through to western Asia and North Africa.

Suborder Caelifera

Superfamily Acridoidea

TETRIGIDAE

The Tetrigidae or ground-hoppers are small, comparatively inconspicuous relatives of the grasshoppers. Like the grasshoppers they have short antennae but their pronotum is very long, extended backwards to cover at least the abdomen, and often extending beyond it (text fig. 38a). They have no obvious hearing organ on the abdomen, and produce no song. Their forewings are reduced to small lateral lobes; the hindwings are fan-folded, and may be shorter or longer than the extended pronotum. The fore- and mid-tarsi have only two segments, the hind tarsi have three segments; the arolium is absent from between the claws.

The eggs of Tetrigidae differ from those of the Acrididae by having an anterior horn (text fig. 38b). They are about 0.6mm wide by 3mm long including this slender anterior horn which is 0.6–0.8mm in length. Eggs are laid in groups of 10–20, not in egg-pods but simply stuck together with a glandular secretion visible where eggs are not in contact with each other. The eggs may be laid in the ground, or in crevices on the surface of the ground or in moss. The anterior horn may assist in camouflaging them when laid in moss; it has no respiratory function, though may possibly serve as an expansion area (Hartley, 1962). The eggs develop immediately without any form of diapause and hatch after 3–4 weeks. There are five instars

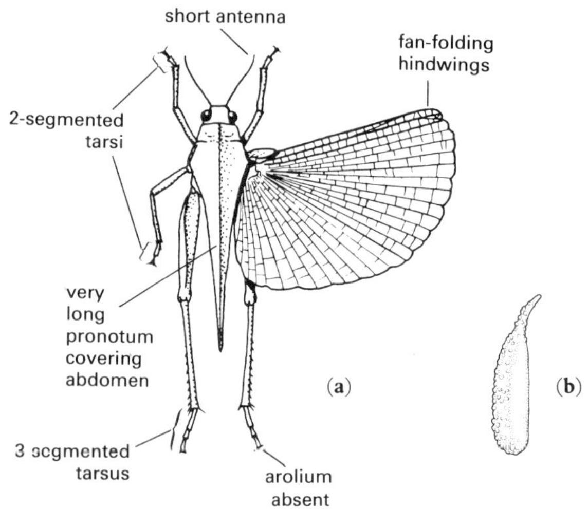

Text Figure 38 *Tetrix subulata*
(**a**) outline, dorsal view, showing general structure of *Tetrix* spp. (**b**) egg of *Tetrix* spp. with typical anterior horn

in the male and six in the female, which have been keyed out by Farrow (1963). During nymphal development the wings grow as wing-pads in the normal manner, reversing in the last two instars, although the nymphal wing-pads are not easy to see because of the long pronotum. Tetrigidae overwinter as nymphs or adults, becoming dormant during very cold weather but able to move about during very mild spells.

Like the grasshoppers, ground-hoppers are diurnal. All British species feed on mosses and algae. A surprising feature of these insects is their ability to swim: all three British species can swim on the surface of water by kicking with their hind legs, and both *Tetrix subulata* and *T. ceperoi* are also able to swim below the surface using the hind tibiae as paddles.

Tetrix ceperoi (Bolivar)

Cepero's Ground-hopper

Description (Pl. 4, figs 7–10)

A **slender** ground-hopper; colouring a wide range of subdued hues as the other two *Tetrix* species, often with a distinct greenish tint (fig. 9). There are also many variations in colour pattern, with paired dark spots and stripes, all of which are keyed out by Paul (1988a).

Pronotum extends well beyond tips of hind femora. Hindwings long, extending as far as hind-tip of pronotum. Mid-femur, in outline, appears slightly wavy (text fig. 39). Head narrow, vertex not extending far forwards so that, in lateral view, head bulges forwards below eyes (fig. 10); **width of vertex between eyes about 1.3 times eye-width in male and 1.5 times eye-width in female**.

Total length ♂ 8–10mm, ♀ 10–13mm

Life History and Behaviour

The eggs of *Tetrix* spp. are similar (text fig. 38b). Nymphs emerge from May to July, adults appearing from August although they do not mature immediately; late-instar nymphs and immature adults overwinter, maturing the following spring. Eggs are laid from late April, the adults surviving only until about July.

Habitat

T. ceperoi occurs in a variety of situations. It may be found on mud by drainage ditches or in damp areas beside gravel-pits and on shingle and the landward side of sand-dunes (as at Romney and Walland Marshes); by drainage dykes adjacent to salt-marshes (as around the Isle of Sheppey, Kent,and in Carmarthenshire); on bare peat by streams and ponds (as in the New Forest and Dorset); and by damp seepages on warm sea-cliffs or in dune-slacks (as in the majority of the coastal sites along the English and Bristol Channels).

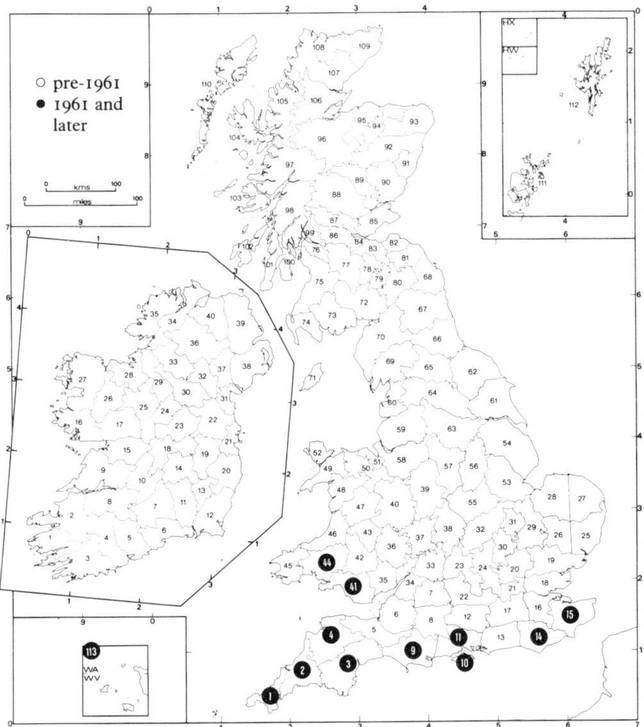

Tetrix ceperoi

Distribution and Status (Map 18, page 174)

Although very local, *T. ceperoi* may be present in large numbers in favoured sites, mainly along the coasts of southern England and South Wales. In Kent, it is known from the Canterbury area (one of its very few inland localities) and also from Elmley Island, Sheppey, and at Conyer, on the mainland side of The Swale; the earliest Kent record dates from 1935 at Minster, Sheppey (Greenslade, 1942). There is a substantial colony on the edge of the Open Pits on Dungeness, Kent and it is also found on Romney and Walland Marshes; in East Sussex, there is another large colony at Moneypenny House, north of Camber Golf Course. It still occurs in the New Forest, Hampshire, at Crockford Bridge, but has not been found since 1965 in another locality, a disused marl pit known as Marlborough Deeps in the south-west corner of the Forest (Ragge, 1965). It is numerous along the insect-rich undercliffs of the Isle of Wight between Luccombe Bay and Whale Chine and is present on the mainland coast of Hampshire at Highcliffe and Hordle Cliff near Milford-on-Sea. There are several good sites along the Dorset coast, including heathland localities at Studland and cliff-side colonies along the Purbeck coast towards Portland, but it has not yet been recorded from Portland Bill itself nor from the vicinity of the Fleet. There is, however, a cluster of colonies around Axmouth and Lyme Regis (particularly on the Undercliff, where it was first recorded in about 1963). Inland in Dorset, it was found at Iwerne Minster in 1957, and, more recently in a marshy hollow on Bere Heath near Bovington Camp. There are, surprisingly, few records from the coasts of South Devon or East Cornwall, but it occurs in West Cornwall around Porth Mellin, Hayle, Poldhu and Bude, and also on the dunes at Braunton Burrows, North Devon, where it was first recorded in 1978.

In Wales, there are several good sand-dune colonies of *T. ceperoi* on the Gower Peninsula. It has also recently been found at Tywyn Point and Witchett Pool, Laugharne Burrows, Carmarthen (Fowles, 1986a), the most northerly known sites in Britain.

In the Channel Islands, *T. ceperoi* is well established on Jersey, but there are no post-1960 records from Guernsey.

This species is clearly at the edge of its natural range in Britain, being found only in warm localities on or near the coast in the southern part of the country. Because of its close resemblance to *T. subulata* (slender ground-hopper), sight records in the field are not satisfactory and closer examination is essential for positive identification. Although a very local species, it is not endangered as some of its best-known colonies are in nature reserves or in other areas which are likely to remain undisturbed.

T. ceperoi occurs in western and southern Europe and in North Africa.

Text Figure 39 Mid-femur of *Tetrix ceperoi* illustrating wavy outline

Tetrix subulata (Linnaeus)

The Slender Ground-hopper

Description (Pl. 4, figs 11–14)

A **slim** ground-hopper; colouring a wide range of brown and grey shades, including reddish and greenish tinges. **Pronotum usually extends beyond tips of hind femora with no prominent median keel** (text fig. 17, p. 75). **Hindwings usually long, extending at least as far as hind tip of pronotum.** Mid-femur in outline appears almost straight. Head broad, with vertex extending forward (fig. 14); **width of vertex between eyes about 1.5 times eye-width in male, and 1.8 times eye-width in female.**

A short-winged form occurs, named as *bifasciata* Herbst (fig. 13), in which both pronotum and hindwings are shorter than normal, often not reaching the tips of hind femora. Pronotum and wings are still usually longer than those of *T. undulata* (common ground-hopper), from which f. *bifasciata* may easily be separated by absence of pronotal crest in *T. subulata*.

Total length ♂ 9–12mm, ♀ 11–14mm

Life History and Behaviour

The eggs of *Tetrix* spp. are similar (text fig. 38b). Nymphs emerge from May to July, adults appearing from August although they do not mature immediately; late-instar nymphs and immature adults overwinter, maturing the following spring. Eggs are laid from late April, the adults surviving only until about July.

Habitat

T. subulata is a characteristic insect of bare mud or short vegetation in marshy locations, often in large numbers and frequently in association with *Conocephalus dorsalis* and *Chorthippus albomarginatus*. This species has a marked preference for acid-free soils: it is most common in wet dune-slacks with a high lime content; on sea-cliffs, where it is usually restricted to those of limestone or serpentine or similar base-rich rocks; in the mineral-rich flood-plains of the Weald; and in the fenlands of East Anglia, Somerset and Ireland, where the ground-water is appreciably alkaline.

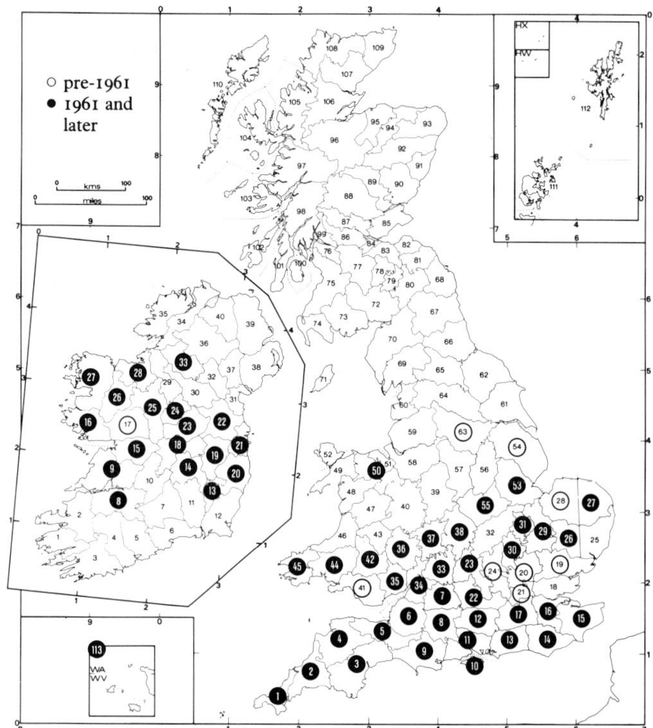

Tetrix subulata

Distribution and Status (Map 19, page 175)

T. subulata is especially widespread in central southern England, where there are many colonies in the flood-plains of the rivers Arun, Ouse and Wey. Eastwards there are increasingly scattered sites across East Sussex and Surrey and relatively few colonies in Kent east of the Medway. To the west there is a string of isolated colonies along the Thames Valley and also along the South Coast. It is widespread in surviving marshland on the Somerset Levels (Burton, 1982) and in many wetland sites on the fertile soils of South Devon, but conspicuously absent from the colder acid soils of North Devon. In West Cornwall, most of the known colonies are in wet areas on coastal dunes or by the side of streams and spring-lines in serpentine rocks, as on the Lizard.

Good localities for this species extend as far north as Herefordshire and Warwickshire, where a number of sites have been found recently (Copson, 1984), and to adjacent parts of the Midlands. There are scattered colonies around the Fens and a strong population in the Norfolk Broads. However, it has not been found since 1960 at any of its localities near Lincoln, or since the last century at Thorne Moors, its most northerly known locality (Skidmore, Limbert & Eversham, 1987).

Most of the Welsh sites are in the extreme south-east and on the coast between Llanelli and St. Bride's Bay where there are a few small colonies, but there are no records from the insect-rich Gower Peninsula. However, a very interesting and apparently totally isolated colony was found by the Dee near Overton, Clwyd, in 1983, and many specimens were found around pools by the river the following year (Paul, 1985).

T. subulata has been known from one or two sites in central Ireland since the last century, but a number of further sites have been found recently, indicating that it is much more widespread than thought formerly. Its known range includes a colony near Lough Erne in Northern Ireland and a number of other sites across central Ireland, many of which were located during the 1970s by D. C. F. Cotton who has comprehensively summarized the Irish history of this species (Cotton, 1980, 1982). In the Channel Islands, it is recorded only from the banks of streams in Jersey.

The presence of *T. subulata* in Ireland suggests an early post-glacial arrival to our islands. However, it is clear that the true distribution of this species is only now being revealed. Since 1960, it has been recorded from the additional vice-counties of East Sussex, North Hampshire, Warwickshire and Denbigh, and the majority of its Irish sites are very recent discoveries. Conversely, it seems to have disappeared from many of its pre-1960 sites in Lincolnshire and the East Midlands, presumably because the wetlands were drained for agricultural or urban developments. Its range seems to be limited by climate, for there are no records north of the line from the Dee to the Humber estuaries. Nevertheless, this unobtrusive insect is so widely distributed in marshy localities that the wholesale destruction of much suitable habitat does not yet seem to have been a serious threat to the species except perhaps in Wales, where there are very few known sites. Its existence is further safeguarded by the way quite small isolated colonies are able to persist on a few square metres of mud so long as the habitat remains unshaded and otherwise undisturbed.

This species is widespread throughout Europe (except the extreme north) to temperate Asia; also North Africa and North America.

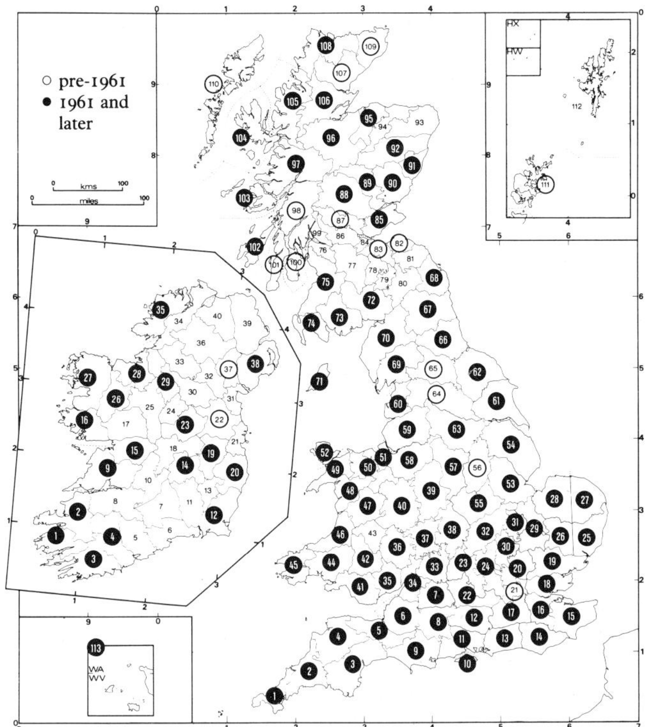

Tetrix undulata

Tetrix undulata (Sowerby)

The Common Ground-hopper

Description (Pl. 4, figs 15–18)

A **sturdy** ground-hopper; colouring a wide range of earthy hues, through sand and clay colours to grey and black; colour may be mottled, or have a dark spot on each side of pronotum, or a conspicuous pale line down centre.

Very prominent median keel on pronotum, which does not extend beyond tips of hind femora. Hindwings reduced, being considerably shorter than pronotum.

There is an extremely rare macropterous form, f. *macroptera* Haij, in which both pronotum and hindwings are much longer than normal. This form may be distinguished from the two normally macropterous *Tetrix* species by presence of prominent pronotal keel.

Total length ♂ 8–9mm, ♀ 9–11mm

Life History and Behaviour

The eggs are similar in *Tetrix* spp. (text fig. 38b). *Tetrix undulata* is the only native orthopteran species which may be found as an adult or a nymph at any time of the year. Nymphs may emerge at any time during the spring and summer and those hatching late in the year will overwinter as nymphs, many of them quite young. The next season they will become adult during the spring and early summer, when the next crop of nymphs are already hatching and growing. Since there are adults throughout the spring and summer, egg-laying and hatching will continue for as long as conditions are favourable.

Habitat

Unlike the other native ground-hoppers, *T. undulata* is equally common in wet or dry localities, so long as there is bare ground and low vegetation with a substantial moss flora. It is most familiar as an insect of woodland and plantation rides and clearings, and very large populations can build up over several years in cleared coppice and similar places with extensive moss cover. It is also often particularly common on the landward side of coastal sand-dunes and may be numerous in quite wet situations on lowland heaths. On chalk and limestone hills, it is most easily located in old quarries or on steep track-sides.

Distribution and Status (Map 20, page 175)

T. undulata is most numerous in southern England but is present over all but the most bleak and exposed parts of the country with the surprising exception of some of the entomologically rich sites along the East Coast, such as the dunes near Sandwich, Kent; the coastal heaths of Suffolk; Spurn Head on the Humber estuary; and the extensive dune-system of the Northumbrian coast. It is, however, numerous on many west-coast dunes and has been found recently on Tresco in the Isles of Scilly. In Wales, it is present on dunes in Anglesey and is widespread and locally common elsewhere, except in the most mountainous areas.

In Scotland, as in England, *T. undulata* has a very extensive distribution but is again local on the East Coast except in Fife where it has been recorded since 1980 at a number of sites. There are recent isolated records from the Hebridean islands of Islay, Colonsay, Mull, Rum, and Skye; but only pre-1960 records from Arran, Eigg, Barra and also from Hoy in the Orkneys. However, there are strong populations in the ancient pine and birch woods in several localities in the Highland zone, and it is possibly widespread in this habitat.

In Ireland it would appear to have been overlooked formerly as, since 1974, it has been recorded from many ten-kilometre squares and is probably fairly common in damp places (Cotton, 1980, 1982). In the Channel Islands it is recorded only from Jersey.

T. undulata is clearly an early post-glacial arrival, being one of the four species of Orthoptera widespread throughout the British Isles, including some of the most remote parts. It is possible, however, that the Tresco colony arrived on introduced garden plants, as it has not been found elsewhere on the Scillies. Its status is not likely to alter much in the foreseeable future.

This species occurs from northern Spain, through Europe (except northern Scandinavia and the extreme south) to the west of the U.S.S.R.

ACRIDIDAE

The Acrididae or grasshoppers are among the most conspicuous and easily recognized of diurnal insects (text fig. 40a), often occurring in large numbers in fields and pastures, jumping aside when disturbed. They have short, thickened antennae which distinguish them from the other large, jumping Orthoptera (the Tettigoniidae and Gryllidae having longer, thread-like antennae), and the tarsi all have three segments. Their pronotum is saddle-shaped, covering the thorax and wing bases, with a well-developed median keel. The pronotum also has lateral or side-keels, and a central groove or sulcus cutting across the median keel from side to side; there may be other transverse grooves in front of this. Acrididae have an abdominal hearing organ, which may be concealed by the folded wings or hindlegs; the tympanum is in a cavity sometimes partly covered by a flap. Each species produces a characteristic song; most by the use of stridulatory pegs on the hind femur (see p. 41). The female has a short ovipositor formed of two pairs of valves (text fig. 41a); the male has a smooth, upturned, subgenital plate at the end of the abdomen (text fig. 41b); both sexes have short cerci.

The eggs of Acrididae are about four millimetres in length and roughly cylindrical in shape, usually bluntly rounded at the anterior end or top, tapering at the posterior end or base (text fig. 42). They are laid in batches, and enclosed in an egg-pod formed around the eggs by the hardening of a frothy secretion produced by the female from her accessory glands. The outer wall is

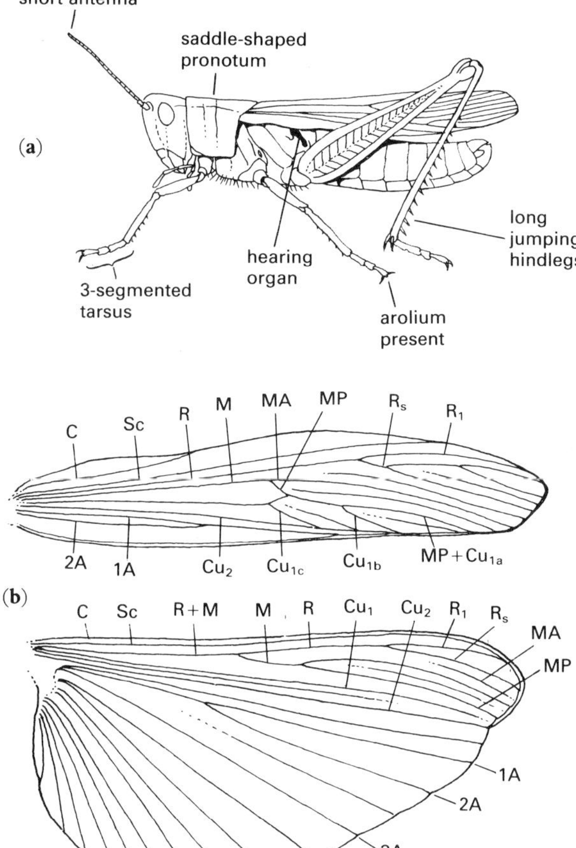

Text Figure 40 *Chorthippus brunneus* showing characters of acridid spp.
(**a**) ♂ outline, lateral view. Note also hairy ventral thorax, characteristic of *C. brunneus*. (**b**) wing venation of ♂ forewing (above) and hindwing (below) (after Ragge, 1965)

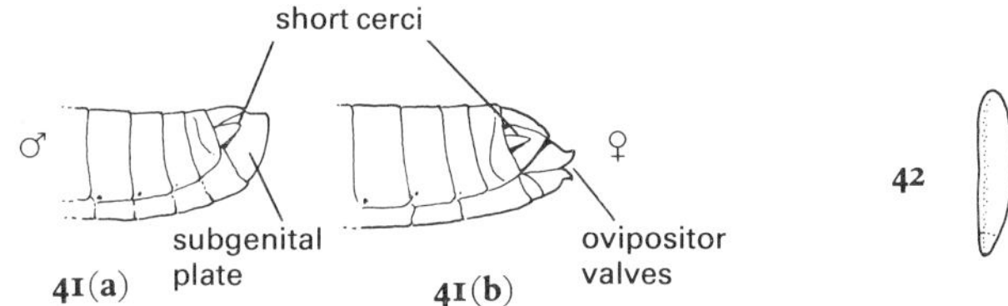

Text Figure 41 (above) Acridid abdominal features distinguishing the sexes.
(**a**) Upturned subgenital plate of ♂; (**b**) ovipositor valves of ♀ (after Ragge, 1965)

Text Figure 42 (above right) Egg of acridid spp., blunt at the top (through which the vermiform larva emerges), tapering at the base (see also text fig. 9, p. 39)

formed of this hardened secretion with cemented soil particles, or occasionally cemented plant fragments, and may have an apical lid. The shape and structure of the egg-pod (see text figs 9a–c, p. 39) is characteristic for each species (Waloff, 1950).

There are normally four nymphal instars, after the vermiform larval stage (text fig. 5, p. 37) has wriggled to the surface and emerged; though in exceptional conditions (p. 40) an extra stage may develop between the normal second and third instars. Wing rudiments appear as lateral pads in the second instar, and in the third and fourth instars are reversed or inverted (see text fig. 7, p. 38). Wing venation is shown in text figure 40b.

Acrididae have a simple one-yearly life-cycle, hatching in the spring, growing to adults during the summer, mating, egg-laying and then dying in the autumn. The eggs undergo diapause before hatching the following spring.

All British species are vegetarian, feeding mainly on grasses.

Oedipoda caerulescens (Linnaeus)

The Blue-winged Grasshopper

Description (Pl. 6, figs 1,2)

A **darkish sandy brown** grasshopper, with **darker bands on forewings and hindlegs**. At rest, difficult to detect against similarly-coloured sandy background, but, in flight, **blue hindwings with dark brown band and clear tip** distinctive (fig. 2).

Pronotum has **central keel crossed by sulcus** or groove, seen clearly when viewed laterally, and **hind femora have distinctive high crest dorsally to just beyond middle**.

O. caerulescens on Jersey is usually smaller than Continental specimens.

Total length ♂ 17–20mm, ♀ 25–26mm

Life History and Behaviour

The eggs are orange-red and laid in batches of about thirty in a curved egg-pod, widened at the base. Adults mature about late July, surviving until November.

The 'flash' coloration of the wings in flight serves to distract predators; as soon as the grasshopper lands again and conceals its hindwings, it effectively disappears into the background.

Song

The short, weak stridulation of the male is not noticeable and usually produced only in courtship. It suggests a muted version of that of *Chorthippus parallelus* (meadow grasshopper).

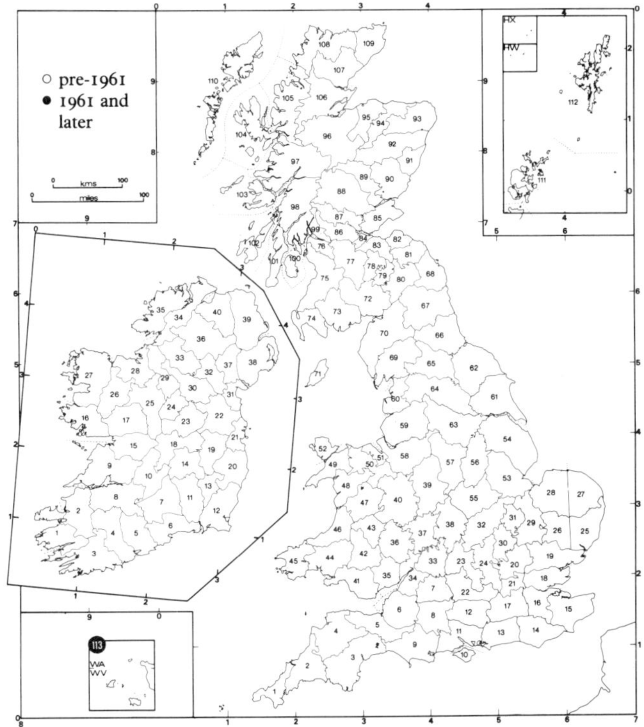

Oedipoda caerulescens

Habitat

Hot, dry areas on dunes and cliffs.

Distribution and Status (Map 21, page 176)

In the British Isles, *O. caerulescens* occurs only in the Channel Islands. It is found on sea-cliffs in the south of Guernsey, and on sand-dunes in the south and west of Jersey where, at St. Ouen's and L'Ouaisné Dunes, it was found in numbers in 1981 (J. Paul, pers. comm.).

There is one old record for St. Mary's in the Scilly Isles (Burr, 1936), but this is now regarded as dubious (Kevan, 1961). There is no evidence that this grasshopper has ever occurred naturally on mainland Britain.

This species is on the northern edge of its range and is restricted to particularly warm situations mainly on south- and west-facing coasts.

O. caerulescens is widespread across central and southern Europe, Asia Minor and eastwards to China; also occurs in North Africa.

Stethophyma grossum (Linnaeus)

The Large Marsh Grasshopper

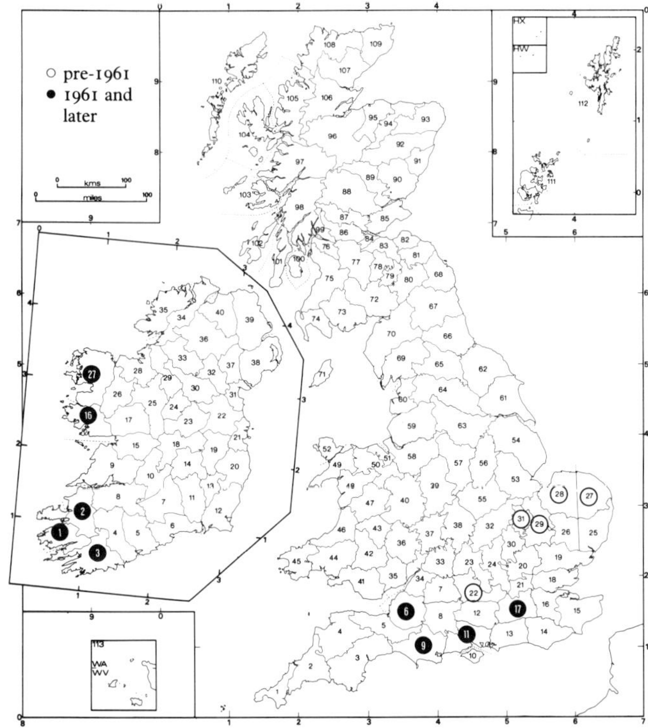

Stethophyma grossum

Description (Pl. 6, figs 3–5)

A **large** grasshopper, normally vivid greenish yellow or olive brown, with **red** underneath hind femora. Hind tibiae banded **black and yellow**. Both sexes have a greenish yellow stripe (*linea scapularis*) on the fore margin of the forewings. Female sometimes occurs in a purple colour form (fig. 5).

There are no stridulatory pegs on hind femora.

Total length	♂ 22–29mm, ♀ 29–36mm
Wing length	♂ 16–22mm, ♀ 21–26mm

Life History and Behaviour

The eggs, 6.5 × 1.5mm, are laid in batches of 11–14 in large, elongated pods without lids, about 10–16mm long, at the bases of grass blades. Nymphs emerge during late May and early June, having four nymphal instars and becoming adult only from the end of July, surviving until October in good weather.

Song (Cassette band 20)

The males have no stridulatory pegs, and they produce their ticking 'song' by flicking a hind tibia against the tips of the flexed forewings. About eight ticks are produced in 3–4 seconds, and the sound has been likened to bubbles popping. It is a most unexpected sound to be made by a grasshopper, but once learned is quite unmistakeable.

Habitat

S. grossum occurs only in very marshy places. The largest colonies in the British Isles are in quaking acid bogs with clumps of tussocky grass, especially purple moor-grass (*Molinia caerulea*), and low scrub such as bog myrtle (*Myrica gale*) and cross-leaved heath (*Erica tetralix*). In the very few fenland sites which still remain, this grasshopper occupies similar quaking terrain amongst sedges and grass tussocks. Prior to 1940, it was also recorded in riverside marshes, but has not been found in this habitat since.

Distribution and Status (Map 22, page 176)

The main English colonies are in the quaking bogs of the New Forest where there are many sites including Nomansland, close to the Wiltshire border on the northern edge of the Forest, and near Hythe on the eastern edge (Welstead & Welstead, 1985); and around Wareham in Dorset. In all of these areas strong populations persist. There is a small colony in Surrey at Thursley Common National Nature Reserve, where it was deliberately introduced in August, 1967 and a specimen was found near the Bisley ranges in 1982 which may also be the result of an (unrecorded) introduction. It is also still to be found on a nature reserve in the Somerset Levels where, since its discovery in 1942, it was locally quite abundant before the extensive habitat destruction caused by peat-cutting operations (Burton, 1981). A long-standing record from beside the Tamar in East Cornwall is now considered by D. R. Ragge (pers. comm.) to be erroneous and has been excluded from the present maps.

The history of *S. grossum* in Ireland has been discussed in detail by Cotton (1980, 1982). It still flourishes in a number of sites: in the south-west in the vicinity of Killarney, Co. Kerry, and Glengarriff, Co. Cork; and in the far west near Cashel, Connemara, and near Rosturk and also between Lough Conn and Lough Cullin, Co. Mayo, at the last of which sites it was rediscovered by D. C. F. Cotton in 1984.

There are no records from Wales, Scotland or the Channel Islands.

From its widespread distribution in western Ireland, it is likely that *S. grossum* was an early post-glacial arrival. However, its restriction to very wet localities means that it became highly vulnerable to the organized drainage schemes and peat cutting of the last two centuries and especially of the last fifty years. Early records exist for this grasshopper in the Norfolk Broads, the Cambridgeshire fenlands and the Thames Valley but there are no confirmed recent finds in these areas. Fortunately, most of the surviving English colonies are now in conservation areas where careful management should ensure the survival of what is one on our largest and most spectacular orthopterans.

Distributed locally across Europe (except the extreme south) from northern Spain through the U.S.S.R. to Siberia.

Stenobothrus lineatus (Panzer)

The Stripe-winged Grasshopper

Description (Pl. 6, figs 6–9)

A medium-sized grasshopper, usually green, sometimes with brown on legs and elsewhere; rarely purple or pinkish varieties occur, usually females (fig. 8). In mature adults, reddish orange colour appears on abdomen, particularly in males, in which hind tibiae also develop same colour. Usually white line (*linea scapularis*) present on fore-edge of wing, and whitish stigma (text fig. 25, p. 76).

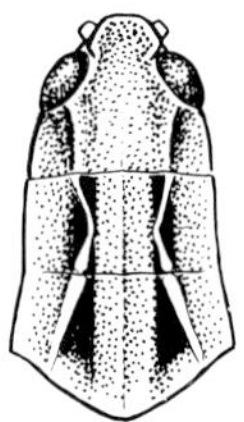

Text Figure 43 Head and pronotum of *Stenobothrus lineatus*, dorsal view

No bulge present on costal area of forewing and **medial area much enlarged** (text fig. 25). Pronotal side-keels **gently incurved** (fig. 9; text fig. 43). Male has 320–420 stridulatory pegs. **Ovipositor bears a tooth on each valve** (text fig. 28, p. 76).

Total length	♂ 15–19mm, ♀ 17–23mm
Wing length	♂ 10–14mm, ♀ 11–16mm

Life History and Behaviour

The eggs, 4 × 1mm, are laid in batches of usually six, arranged vertically in an ovoid pod about 8 × 4mm, the outer wall of which is formed of cemented plant-material fragments. Nymphs appear usually during May, having four nymphal instars and becoming adult from mid-July, few surviving until October.

Song (Cassette bands 21, 22)

The stridulatory pegs on each hind femur of the male are closely packed together. The song produced is a pulsating and rather metallic sound lasting 10–25 seconds, distinct from that of our other grasshoppers. The hindlegs of the singing male move up and down slowly, like the legs of an almost stationary cyclist, and quite unlike the brisk movements of other species. Both the sound and the slow

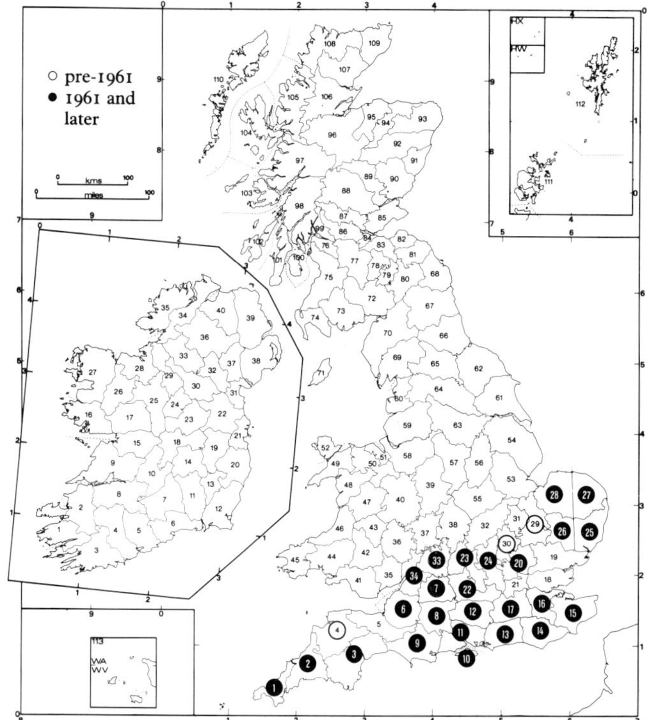

Stenobothrus lineatus

leg movements, one leg moving slightly in advance of the other, are unique among the western European Gomphocerinae (Ragge, 1987a). The fluctuations in the song pattern (band 21) correspond with the leg movements. In courtship, the male produces a longer song of up to a minute, alternating with a ticking stridulation (band 22).

Habitat

S. lineatus is restricted to warm dry places, where the turf is often broken, on chalk or limestone; more locally on heathland or dunes. It may be regarded as a good indicator of old, species-rich turf on calcareous hillsides.

Distribution and Status (Map 23, page 177)

This grasshopper is locally common along the length of the North and South Downs and widespread over the chalklands of Wiltshire, Berkshire and Hampshire. It is also present over virtually the whole of the chalk and limestone of the Purbeck Hills in Dorset and westward along the chalk to the vicinity of Admiral Hardy's Monument on Black Down. In the Isle of Wight, although apparently absent from the central chalk ridge, it is common on St. Boniface Down, Ventnor. Two interesting colonies occur on the South Coast where chalk ballast has been used in tidal barriers: at Thorney Island, West

Sussex (Haes, 1976), and on the western side of Southampton Water near Totton, Hampshire (Welstead & Welstead, 1985). *S. lineatus* has a scattered and very localized distribution on the Mendips, Somerset, but it is a rarity farther west, with one record from East Devon of a small colony north of Woodbury on dry heathland (R. S. Cropper, pers. comm., 1982), and three records from Cornwall during the 1970s. In the Cotswolds, the grasshopper is widespread in Gloucestershire, but there are no records from similar habitat in Worcestershire. In the Chilterns, north of the Thames Valley, it is very local. Its heathland populations occur mainly in central southern and eastern England with substantial populations along the western edge of The Weald in the vice-counties of North Hampshire and Surrey; in Windsor Forest and Silwood Park, Berkshire; in the Breckland (Payne, 1959; Douglas, 1973) including Wangford Warren, West Suffolk, and Weeting Heath, West Norfolk. Elsewhere in East Anglia, coastal colonies have been found recently at Winterton and Horsey, East Norfolk, and Westleton Heath, East Suffolk. Small isolated colonies also occur around Studland, Isle of Purbeck, Dorset; at Burton Common, near Christchurch, just outside the New Forest, and at Iping Common, near Midhurst, West Sussex.

S. lineatus was probably a late glacial arrival across Dogger Land. It is found only in short turf on lighter soils where its populations can build up to appreciable numbers in hot summers, but it can be noticeably scarce after two or three cooler seasons. Many of its best colonies are in protected areas either too steep for cultivation or in nature reserves. Forestry is probably the main threat to the species in unprotected areas.

This species occurs from France, through central Europe (not Scandinavia and only at higher altitude in Mediterranean countries), eastern Europe, the U.S.S.R. to Mongolia.

Stenobothrus stigmaticus (Rambur)

The Lesser Mottled Grasshopper

Description (Pl. 6, figs 10–12)

A **very small** grasshopper, usually green with brownish wings. Adult males (and sometimes females) develop orange-red coloration on tip of abdomen; females usually with white *linea scapularis*.

Both fore- and hindwings usually shorter than abdomen. Tips of **male antennae may be thickened, but not clubbed**. Pronotal side-keels **gently inflexed** (fig. 12). Ovipositor bears a tooth on each valve. The male has 80–120 stridulatory pegs.

Total length	♂ 10–12mm, ♀ 12–15mm
Wing length	♂ 7–7.5mm, ♀ 8–10mm

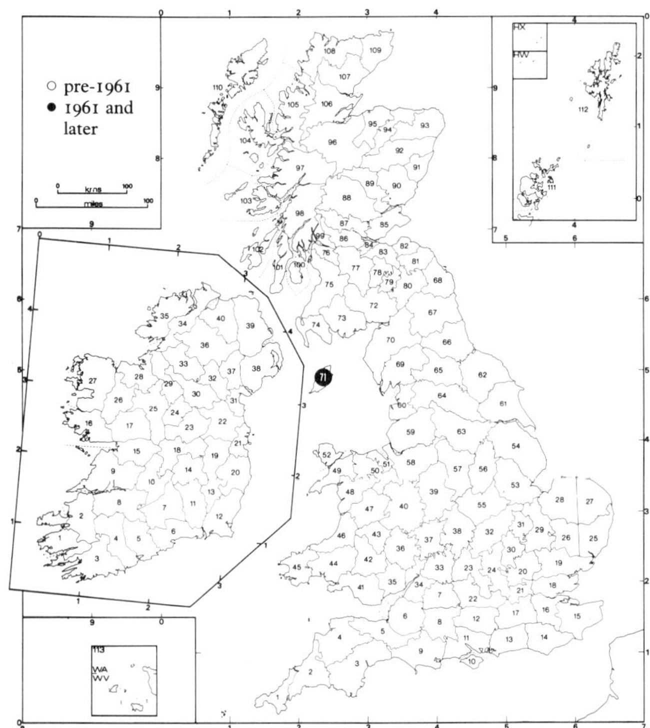

Stenobothrus stigmaticus

Life History and Behaviour

S. stigmaticus matures in July and probably survives to September, but, since its discovery in 1962 on the Isle of Man (Ragge, 1963), no detailed examination of the life history or behaviour of this colony has been made.

Song (Cassette band 23)

The song is a quiet series of chirps produced at the rate of about 15 per second, in bursts of 1–4 (usually 2) seconds. It is similar to that of *Chorthippus parallelus* (meadow grasshopper) which is absent from the Isle of Man. The courtship song is quieter and longer (3–5 seconds), and finishes with a loud sound produced by a more rapid movement of one hindleg (Ragge, 1987a).

Habitat

It occurs on thin turf and scattered clumps of heathers on sea-cliffs of Manx slate.

Distribution and Status (Map 24, page 177)

This species was discovered in 1962 on the Langness peninsula at the southern end of the Isle of Man (Ragge, 1963). It occurs at only a few sites on the eastern end of the peninsula, including Derby Haven to the north and Dreswick Point to the south.

The curious distribution of this grasshopper in the British Isles has been considered in detail by Ragge (1963,

1965) and Burton (1965). Ragge concluded that *S. stigmaticus* should be regarded tentatively as a native species. Specimens from the Manx colony are uniformly smaller in size than those from Continental populations. This further supports the view that the British population is a relict one and not the result of any recent introduction. It may yet be found to occur in Ireland.

This species is widespread in western and central Europe, but in mountains only in the Iberian and northern Balkan peninsulas, and absent from the Italian peninsula; eastwards into the U.S.S.R. and Asia Minor; also in the Rif mountains in Morocco.

Omocestus rufipes (Zetterstedt)
[= *O. ventralis* (Zetterstedt)]
The Woodland Grasshopper

Description (Pl. 6, figs 13–17)

A generally dark, greyish brown medium-sized grasshopper, with bright red or orange underside to abdomen in mature adults. **Chalk-white tips of palps** very conspicuous (fig. 17), particularly in very dark specimens where body may appear almost black. Females occur in brighter colour forms than males and are sometimes green dorsally. Red colour more distinct in male, covering ventral and dorsal surface of most of abdomen, with hindlegs also showing red tinge on at least tibiae and sometimes also femora. Ventral surface of thorax and abdominal segments 1–5 or 6 green (fig. 14).

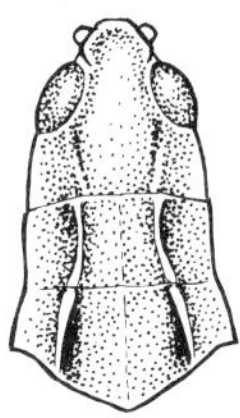

Text Figure 44 Head and pronotum of *Omocestus rufipes*, dorsal view

Side keels of pronotum **incurved** (fig. 16; text fig. 44) and **ovipositor valves short** (text fig. 29, p. 76). Both sexes fully winged, with **no costal bulge** on forewing. Male has 85–130 stridulatory pegs.

Total length	♂ 12–17mm, ♀ 18–20mm
Wing length	♂ 9–12mm, ♀ 13–16mm

Life History and Behaviour

The eggs, about 4mm long and over 1mm wide, are laid in batches of five in a short, cylindrical pod, 1 × 4mm, the outer wall formed of cemented soil particles and with a hood-like convex lid.

Nymphs may emerge in April or May, having four nymphal instars and usually becoming adult during June. As they are early to mature, adults are rarely found later than October.

Omocestus rufipes

Song (Cassette band 24)

The song begins quietly and gradually increases in loudness until it stops abruptly, after about 5–10 seconds. The song is similar to that of *O. viridulus* (common green grasshopper), but much shorter. The courtship song of the two species is also similar: after a series of normal chirps there is a different, quieter one followed by several short sharp sounds which precede attempted mating (Ragge, 1986).

Habitat

O. rufipes is usually found in grassy rides or clearings among deciduous trees, and sometimes among conifers, in warm localities. Its numbers sometimes build up rapidly after coppice is cut or trees clear-felled, only to dwindle as the site becomes over-shadowed again with the regrowth of trees. It is also found on downland turf or lowland heath but normally only close to beech or similar woodland, or gorse and birch thickets.

Distribution and Status (Map 25, page 178)

South of the Thames, this species is widespread and locally common in two main areas – the New Forest and across the western side of the Weald. Additional Hampshire sites are the Forest of Bere (Appleton *et al.*, 1975); Woolmer Forest and in several chalkland woods along the Surrey border. Sussex sites include Rewell Wood, Paine's Wood and Slindon near Arundel, with further sites along the coastal plain of West Sussex as far as Worthing. Around the Weald, it is widespread in wooded localities on the South and North Downs; around Leith Hill, and locally in St. Leonard's Forest and Ashdown Forest and elsewhere on the High Weald. There are few records for West Kent but it is locally plentiful in woodlands and plantations in the vicinities of Hamstreet, Barham, Elham and Chilham, East Kent. It is not recorded from the Isle of Wight but there are recent Dorset records from Bere Wood, Bere Regis, Cranborne Chase and Farnham Woods, Tollard Royal, and several new sites were found during surveys carried out in 1983 by J. White and R. McGibbon. In the West Country, there is one known colony in Somerset at Great Breach Wood, near Street on the Polden Hills (Burton, 1981); there are recent records from scrubby heathland in South Devon around Woodbury and Newton Abbot, but no post-1960 records from North Devon. Around the Cornish coast are several small colonies including Coombe, north of Bude; near Wadebridge; and the Lizard National Nature Reserve.

O. rufipes occurs in Windsor Great Park and on Greenham Common, Berkshire, but north of the Thames it is rare and extremely local with only a few post-1960 records: Oxfordshire in 1986 (Paul, 1988b, in press); Shabbington Wood, Buckinghamshire, in 1972 and 1987 (Paul, *loc.cit*); and Blackmore, Essex, in 1974. On this last site, however, it could not be found during a search in 1985 (A. J. Wake, pers. comm.). There are no certain records for the Cotswolds or the Forest of Dean and no post-1960 records from much of the Chilterns, despite searches; also no records since 1960 for Cambridgeshire or Suffolk, although earlier records exist (Ragge, 1965).

The only Welsh record was based on a solitary (doubtful) specimen at Kidwelly in 1952 and, failing further confirmation, this has provisionally been deleted. Not recorded from Scotland, Ireland or the Channel Islands.

From its known distribution, *O. rufipes* is clearly a late post-glacial arrival. In the past, its distribution in Britain has been obscured by a number of misidentified specimens now thought to have been dark forms of *Chorthippus brunneus* (field grasshopper) or totally brown specimens of *Omocestus viridulus*. It is now confined almost entirely to counties south of the Thames where it is locally very numerous. It seems to have benefitted from modern methods of forestry, particularly in the Weald and East Kent where its populations often outnumber those of its otherwise far commoner relative *O. viridulus*.

O. rufipes is close to the edge of its range in southern England; its few isolated populations in the West Country and north of the Thames merit special protection.

This species is found through most of central Europe from Portugal in the west, in parts of Scandinavia excluding Denmark, through eastern Europe, the Balkans, the southern U.S.S.R. to southern Siberia; also occurs in Turkey and Algeria.

Omocestus viridulus (Linnaeus)

The Common Green Grasshopper

Description (Pl. 6, figs 18–21)

A usually green, medium-sized grasshopper, mature adults **never having any red or orange colour on abdomen**. Palps may be pale, but never conspicuously chalk-white. Males may be green or olive-brown, females always green dorsally though green, brown or purple elsewhere (fig. 20).

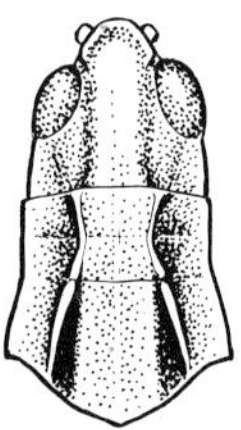

Text Figure 45 Head and pronotum of *Omocestus viridulus*, dorsal view

Pronotal side-keels **moderately incurved** (fig. 21; text fig. 45). Forewing **without bulge** on costal margin. Ovipositor valves **long, without any teeth** (text fig. 30, p. 76). Male has 90–150 stridulatory pegs.

Total length	♂ 15–19mm, ♀ 17–22mm
Wing length	♂ 10–14mm, ♀ 12–16mm

Life History and behaviour

The eggs, 4 × 1mm, are laid in batches of ten or fewer, in a large, irregular egg pod, 10 × 5mm, the outer wall formed of hardened secretion.

This is the earliest native grasshopper to reach maturity. Nymphs can hatch in April, usually May, having four nymphal instars, becoming adult from July (or even mid-June, in warm summers) and rarely surviving beyond October.

The male in this species is particularly active in warm weather, flying rapidly and well from place to place, making it difficult to spot. The bulky females fly less readily.

Song (Cassette band 25)

The song begins quietly and becomes louder, lasting 10–20 seconds or longer. Even longer songs may be produced when a female is nearby, preceding the courtship of shorter bursts of song and a series of louder sounds, followed by an attempt to mate (Ragge, 1986). Females may respond with a short subdued song. If the courtship fails at first, the male may produce a series of ticks by kicking backwards several times, as *Stethophyma grossum* does, before recommencing his normal song.

Habitat

O. viridulus prefers coarse grass in moist situations. At lower altitudes, it is often very numerous on commons, parkland, old pasture and along woodland rides but, unlike *Chorthippus parallelus*, which is frequently found with it, seems unable to colonize the coarse vegetation of wasteland or new roadside verges to any extent. It is also conspicuously absent from certain coastal habitats. At higher altitudes, it is characteristic of unimproved hillside pastures, particularly by streams that have carved sheltered valleys, and has been found up to about 1000m. It is not normally present in quaking bogs.

Distribution and Status (Map 26, page 178)

This species is present throughout Britain and Ireland with the interesting exception of a number of otherwise insect-rich localities mainly along the south-east and east coasts of England, from which it is apparently absent. These include the coastal plain of West Sussex; Dungeness; both sides of the Thames Estuary from Gravesend and Margate in Kent to the south-east of Suffolk; around the Wash; Spurn Head at the mouth of the Humber; and farther north between the Tees and Tyne estuaries. It is also apparently absent from much of south-west Cornwall but has been recorded from several places north-east of Land's End and, very recently, from the Lizard Peninsula. It is unrecorded from the Bristol Channel coast between Bude and Bideford.

O. viridulus is particularly common in cooler places where the grass is fairly tall in chalk and limestone areas such as the North and South Downs, Cotswolds, Chilterns and Wessex uplands. On lime-free soils, it is abundant in old parkland and lightly grazed common lands, as around the Malvern Hills, Dartmoor and Exmoor. In upland England, it is undoubtedly the most numerous grasshopper over large areas of the Pennines, Cheviots, Lake District, North Yorkshire Moors and Isle of Man. It is common throughout Wales, including Anglesey and the smaller offshore islands of Ramsey, Skomer and Skokholm.

In Scotland, it is locally common north to Helmsdale, East Sutherland; widespread in the mountains south of Glen More, Inverness, and at altitude around Meall nan Tarmachan and Ben Lawers in the Breadalbane mountains, Tayside (Haes, 1982). In the Inner Hebrides, present on Islay, Jura, Colonsay, Mull, Iona, Ulva, Tiree, Rum, Canna and Skye, where it is locally common, though surprisingly apparently absent from the adjacent

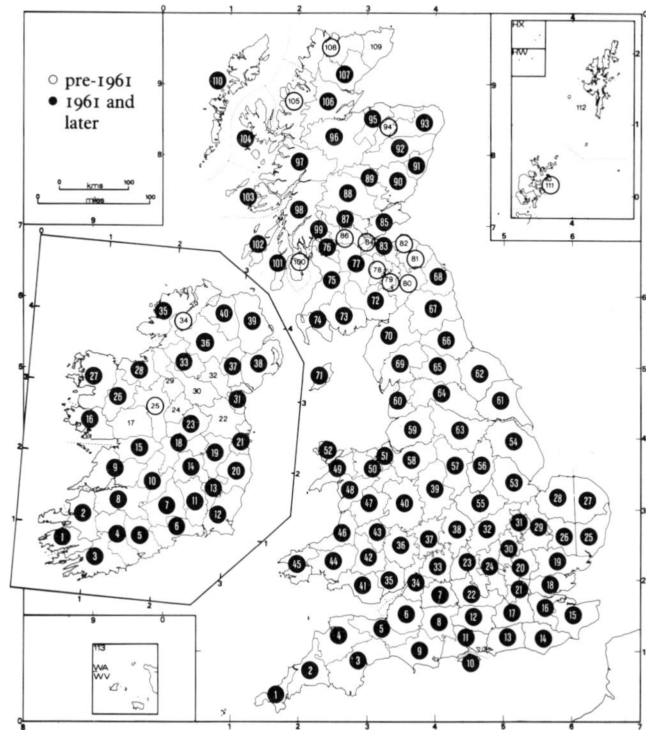

Omocestus viridulus

mainland and the whole of the north-west Highlands. There are pre-1960 records from Arran, Eigg, South Uist, the Orkneys (Burr, 1936) and Inverpolly Forest, West Sutherland. It has been recorded from Barra, Outer Hebrides (Waterston, 1981).

In Ireland, this species is the commonest and most widely distributed grasshopper (Cotton, 1982); Ragge (1965) shows it to have been recorded from all but six vice-counties. There are no records for the Channel Islands.

This is one of the four orthopterans distributed throughout almost the whole of the British Isles. It must have been an early post-glacial arrival and may be regarded as an indicator species of unimproved pasture. Its absence from considerable stretches of the south-east and east coasts of Britain may be due to the drier climate, but this would not account for its absence from coastal areas on the Devonian peninsula. It is clearly far less adaptable than *Chorthippus parallelus*, and probably unable to tolerate chemical pollution present on roadside verges and wasteland. The ecological limitations of this comparatively large and easily identified grasshopper merit investigation.

This common species occurs throughout Europe (except for the extreme north and southern parts of the Iberian, Italian and Balkan peninsulas), eastwards to Siberia and Mongolia.

Chorthippus brunneus (Thunberg)

[= *C. bicolor* (Charpentier)]
The Field Grasshopper
[= The Common Field Grasshopper]

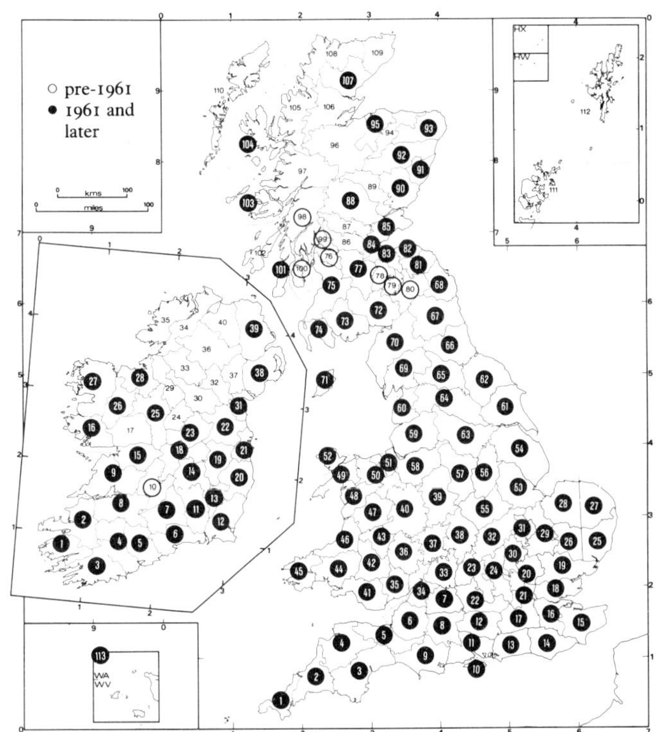

Chorthippus brunneus

Description (Pl. 7, figs 1–4)

A medium-sized grasshopper with a wide variety of colour forms, mostly of a brownish mixture; the most common colour varieties are 'striped', 'semi-mottled' and 'mottled' (Ragge, 1965). Colours of parts of body may vary from buff through orange to purple, though the green variety (fig. 3) is rare. Mature male develops orange-red colour on end of abdomen, and hind tibiae also become orange-tinged; abdomen of mature female may become yellowish, sometimes orange-pink.

Pronotal side-keels **sharply angled** and **wedge-marks do not extend to hind margin; hind part of pronotum is longer** than fore part (fig. 4; text fig. 26, p. 76). **Wings extend beyond hind knees**, and forewings have a **bulge on costal margin** (text fig. 24, p. 76). Both sexes have distinctively **hairy ventral thorax** (text fig. 40, p. 104). Male has 50–90 stridulatory pegs.

Total length	♂ 15–19mm, ♀ 19–25 mm
Wing length	♂ 11–15mm, ♀ 13–19mm

Life History and Behaviour

The eggs, about 4 × 1mm, are laid in batches of fourteen (or fewer) as two or three rows in a large, slightly curved pod, 13 × 6mm. The outer wall is formed of cemented soil particles and there is a small (2mm), thin, disc-like lid.

Hatching usually occurs in May, with four or exceptionally five nymphal instars (see page 40), adults appearing during June and July, and sometimes persisting, in very warm places, until the first week of December.

This is the only British species to exhibit swarming behaviour, although on a very small scale when compared with its relatives in warmer climates; the swarms rarely travel more than a few hundred metres (Bains, 1940; Haes, 1976).

Song (Cassette bands 26, 27)

An isolated male produces a short, brisk chirp, repeated at short intervals (band 26), but two or more males together may chirp in response to each other, often alternating rapidly (band 27). Males will actually reply to almost any chirp-like sound made to them. Receptive females chirp briefly.

Habitat

C. brunneus requires dry, sunny situations in short vegetation. It occurs in a wide range of localities in Britain, being especially numerous on downland and the coast but, where the grass becomes tall or the situation at all shaded, is outnumbered by *C. parallelus* which is usually found with it. Like *C. parallelus*, it seems readily to exploit wasteland and roadside verges (Port & Thompson, 1980) and flourishes in the often sparse vegetation of built-up areas where its ability to fly well enables it to range over small, discrete areas of grass. It is generally rare or absent on mountains, heathlands and wetlands.

Distribution and Status (Map 27, page 179)

C. brunneus is one of the four orthopterans which is widespread throughout much of the British Isles. It is very common over most of central and southern England but is distinctly local inland in the more northern counties, although commoner in urban areas such as around Sheffield and Rotherham, Yorkshire (Whiteley, 1981). It is common along the coast, particularly on the extensive sand-dunes of the Northumberland coast. It is common in many towns and cities and is even found right across London especially on south-facing railway embankments. Apart from the area of reclaimed fenland around the Wash, it is one of the few orthopterans which can be found in intensively farmed areas in much of the country.

In addition to being the commonest grasshopper in urban areas, this species is also the most frequently found on offshore islands. It is the only species recorded from the Scilly Isles and, in the post-1960 period, from Lundy; it is common on the Isle of Man and on a number of islands

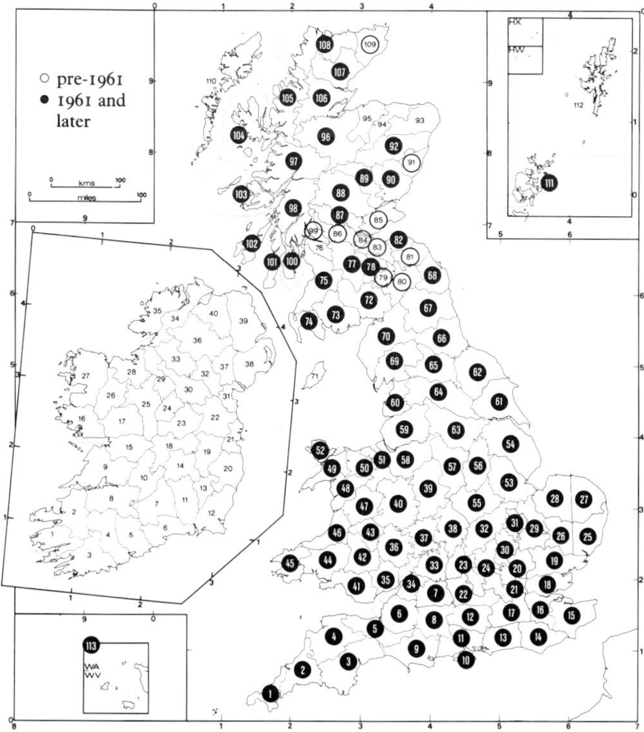

Chorthippus parallelus

number of conspicuous gaps in its distribution. It is absent from the Isle of Man, Lundy and the Scillies and even from Brownsea Island in Poole Harbour (Payne, 1972); there are no records from a large part of eastern Norfolk, from Spurn Head nor from the entire coastline of Durham and Northumberland. It is also absent from Walney Island and the adjacent portion of Furness as well as the greater part of the Lancashire mosses. In addition, it is also local or even quite scarce in several districts including the vicinity of the Wash, where *C. albomarginatus* is the commonest species; and in parts of the Midland Plain and much of the Pennines and Cheviots, where *Omocestus viridulus* predominates.

C. parallelus is generally common in Wales, except on high ground, and in Anglesey, where it is local, and it is recorded from the offshore islands of Caldey and Skomer. In Scotland, as in England, there are far fewer records from the east coast: there is one record from Fife, and between the Firth of Forth and the Moray Firth there is only one known coastal colony – at Montrose dunes. However it is common in many places, especially along the west coast and has strong colonies on many of the islands including Bute, Islay, Jura, Mull, Iona, Rum, Canna, Skye and Raasay. There are no records for the Outer Hebrides but there are colonies on Hoy in the Orkneys (Pelham-Clinton, 1971) – the most northerly known co-ordinates for any grasshopper in Britain. In the Channel Islands it is present on Jersey. It is absent from Ireland.

Although this must be a late post-glacial arrival which failed to reach Ireland, the Isle of Man, and some of the offshore islands, its adaptability has enabled it to exploit the 'grasshopper niche' in a great many localities in a wide range of habitats. The occurrence of macropterous individuals in large populations as a response to overcrowding perhaps explains how this normally flightless grasshopper has been able to become so widespread in Britain. Nevertheless, there appears to be an ecological factor limiting its spread into certain localities, mainly along the North Sea coast, which would repay investigation.

This species occurs from France, to Scandinavia, through Central Europe to Turkey, the U.S.S.R. and Mongolia.

Chorthippus albomarginatus (De Geer)
[= *C. elegans* (Charpentier)]
The Lesser Marsh Grasshopper

Description (Pl. 7, figs 13–15)

A medium-sized grasshopper, usually green or brown in colour and of more subdued tones than *C. parallelus*; pinkish colour forms may occur but never bright purple, and some populations may be nearly all of the same colour form.

Both pairs of wings rarely extend beyond end of abdomen. Forewing of female but not of male has **bulge** on costal margin; females also usually with distinctive white *linea scapularis*. Pronotal side-keels **parallel** or only slightly incurved, straighter than in *C. parallelus* (fig. 15; text fig. 21, p. 75). Male has 90–140 stridulatory pegs.

Total length	♂ 14–17mm, ♀ 17–21mm
Wing length	♂ 9–12mm, ♀ 11–15mm

Life History and Behaviour

The eggs, 4 × 1mm, are laid in batches of three to ten in two or three rows in a small, irregular pod, about 9 × 5mm. The outer wall is formed of hardened secretion, with the opening to the side of the apex.

This is a mid-season species, nymphs emerging in May, having four nymphal instars and maturing from early July, with some adults surviving until mid-November. Both sexes fly but females may fly only in hot weather.

Song (Cassette bands 30, 31)

The normal song is a gentle burr of less than one second, repeated a few times (band 30). The courtship song is a complicated sequence of several different chirps (Ragge, 1965) with the hind legs in different positions (band 31). This courtship song-cycle seems to attract other males as well as females, and groups of both sexes are often seen at this time.

Habitat

This grasshopper is found in a variety of habitats. It is a characteristic species on the swards of sea couch (*Elymus pycnanthus*) adjacent to salt-marsh; it also abounds over both wet and dry areas of coastal sand-dunes. Inland, it occurs alongside the course of many rivers, typically on sites that are flooded in winter, and in some localities is the most numerous grasshopper on grassy commons and wastes over wet soils. It also occurs locally on roadside verges, especially in East Anglia. In addition to these well-known habitats, it has recently been found well established on dry grassy hillsides in the West Midlands.

Distribution and Status (Map 30, page 180)

C. albomarginatus is a locally common insect south and east of a line between the Severn and Humber estuaries. Along the south coast, it is common, in suitable habitat, from around Abbotsbury, Dorset, eastwards to Sandwich, Kent, and is present along the lower reaches of nearly all the creeks and rivers. Inland in southern England, it is widespread on flood plains, water-meadows, and damp grassy commons in the Weald, particularly in Surrey (Baldock, pers. comm.). Farther west, it is locally common and widespread in the Somerset Levels and around the Severn estuary (Burton, 1982) but remarkably local and scarce to the south-west, where isolated colonies have been found recently but only at Porlock Weir, Minehead Warren, the Sludge Beds Nature Reserve, near Exeter, where it was recorded as numerous in 1979, and on the Camel Estuary in 1973. There are no other post-1960 records for Devon and Cornwall.

Its main centres of distribution in England are around the Thames Estuary, where it is abundant on both sides, westwards into London, where it has been found on several areas of wasteland or rough grass in parkland; and across the fenlands of East Anglia, from Bedfordshire in the south (Rands, 1978) through Huntingdon, Cambridgeshire and South Lincolnshire (Skelton, 1978). It has also been recorded from almost the entire coastline of Essex, Suffolk, Norfolk, Lincolnshire and into Yorkshire, where it is common on the north shore of the Humber estuary around Spurn Head and up the Humber and its tributary, the Don, as far as the edge of Thorne Moors (pers. obs., 1975) although not recorded from the moors themselves since the last century (Limbert, 1986).

Inland, it is found in the Severn Valley water-meadows as far upstream as Coombe Hill and Longdon Marsh near Tewkesbury; up the Thames valley system as far as the Windrush at Witney, Oxon, (Sheppard & Campbell, 1984); and by Hell Coppice Pond, Bernwood Forest, Buckinghamshire (Paul, 1988b, in press). Farther north,

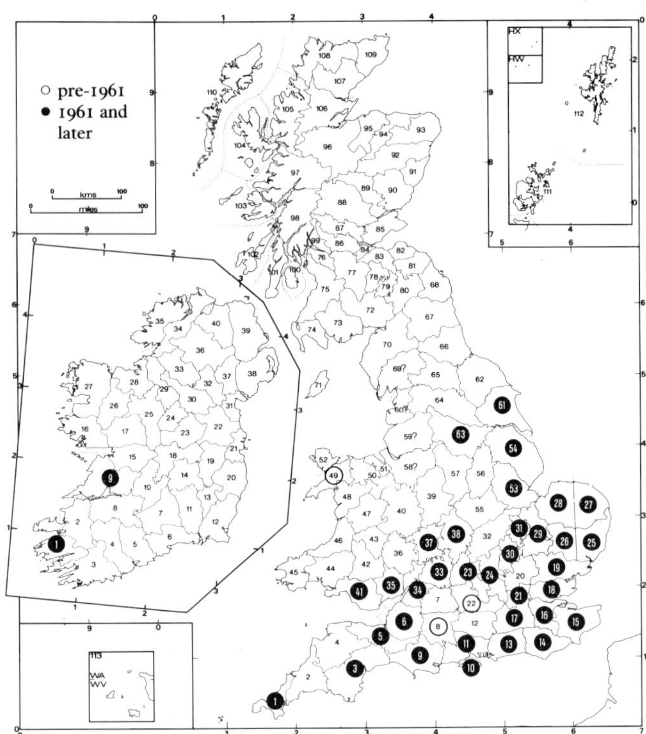

Chorthippus albomarginatus

it has been recorded, during a recent survey, from over a dozen sites in Warwickshire. Most were in damp meadows but, interestingly, it was also found in dry grassland near Edge Hill and on the Warwick bypass (Copson, pers. comm.).

There are neither current, nor reliable old, records for *C. albomarginatus* from the north-west coast of England or North Wales, but it has been recorded from Goldcliff and Magor, Monmouthshire and from the Gower Peninsula. There are two known sites in the west of Ireland – at Lough Bunny, Co. Clare (Lansbury, 1965), and Castlegregory, Co. Kerry (Baldock, 1977) – but no records from the Isle of Man, Scotland or the Channel Islands.

An interesting feature of the British distribution of this grasshopper is that it is difficult to find common factors in the various habitats in which it occurs. In some places, *C. albomarginatus* is present amongst large populations of *C. parallelus*, *C. brunneus* and *Omocestus viridulus* yet, in the East Anglian fens where it abounds, its other normally common relatives are sometimes noticeably local or even virtually absent. In coastal and water-meadow sites, it may be that its egg-pods can better survive prolonged immersion during winter or spring tidal flooding, but this cannot be the case inland. There are presumably some as yet undiscovered but potent factors which account for its curiously limited range in Britain. Its rarity in western

Britain and presence in only isolated sites in western Ireland indicate the possibility that there were two separate arrival times in the post-glacial period. However, it may be more widespread than is yet appreciated since it has clearly been overlooked or misrecorded in the past. A further thorough study of the distribution of this species is merited; careful scrutiny of the salt-marshes and sand-dunes along the west coasts of England and Wales and around the Shannon estuary in Ireland might reveal hitherto unrecorded colonies.

This species occurs throughout Europe (except the extreme south) from Spain to the U.S.S.R. and through to Central Asia.

Euchorthippus pulvinatus Fischer de Waldheim subsp. *E. pulvinatus elegantulus* Zeuner

The Jersey Grasshopper

Description (Pl. 7, figs 16–18)

A small, slender grasshopper, usually brownish or straw-coloured. Forewing usually with white *linea scapularis*.

Both pairs of wings short, almost covering abdomen but not reaching tips of hind femora. Pronotal side-keels **almost parallel** (fig. 18), similar to *Chorthippus albomarginatus*, (which does not occur on Jersey). Male with distinctive **pointed subgenital plate** (text fig. 23, p. 75). Male has 115–165 stridulatory pegs.

E. p. elegantulus is essentially a small form of *pulvinatus*, distinguished particularly by smaller head size – less than 2.4mm wide in male; less than 3.2mm wide in female.

Total length	♂ 10–13mm, ♀ 16–22mm
Wing length	♂ 7–9mm, ♀ 7–13mm

Life History and Behaviour

The eggs, about 4 × 1mm, are laid in batches of about ten in an oval pod about 12.0 × 7.5mm. This is a mid-season species, nymphs appearing in May, maturing in July after probably four nymphal instars, and surviving until the end of October.

Song (Cassette band 32)

The highly characteristic song consists of bursts of short, 'zipping' sounds, produced in long sequences; each 'zip' or echeme (see p. 40) repeated at about one per second (Ragge & Reynolds, 1984). The songs of *E. p. elegantulus* and *E. p. gallicus* (another subspecies, found in western Europe) are very similar.

Habitat

This grasshopper is found in hot, dry grassy places, especially on sand-dunes, but also along roadside verges and in unimproved pastures, often in situations fully exposed to strong Atlantic gales.

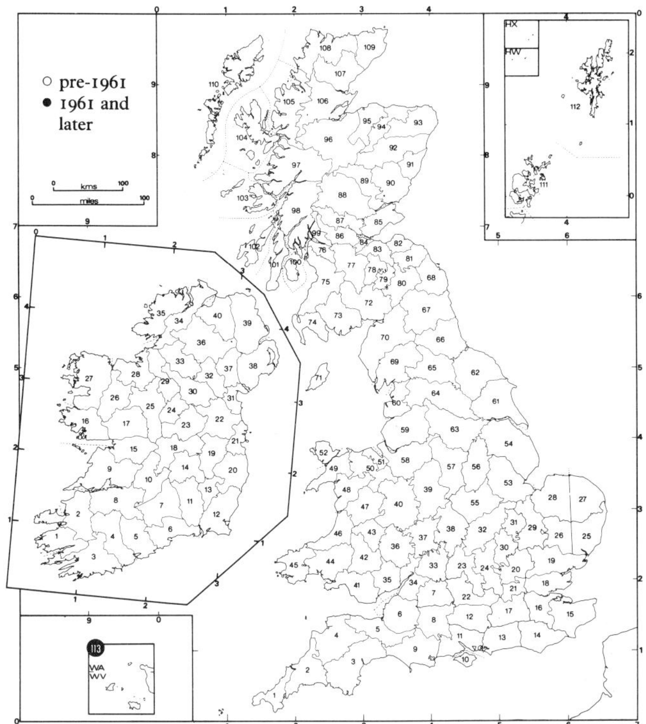

Euchorthippus pulvinatus elegantulus

Distribution and Status (Map 31, page 181)

E. pulvinatus elegantulus is confined to the southern part of Jersey, Channel Islands, where it is widespread.

It was described as a distinct species (Zeuner, 1940a) from specimens collected in 1938 at L'Ouaisné (the holotype), Quennevais and St. Ouen's Pond, and was assumed to be endemic (Le Sueur, 1976). Zeuner considered *elegantulus* to be close to the European *E. declivus* (Brisout), and Harz (1975) synonymized it with this species. However a recent study of the genus *Euchorthippus* has shown that a form closely resembling *elegantulus* occurs in southern Brittany, in the Quiberon to Le Croisic area. These two groups are now regarded as a subspecies of the Continental *Euchorthippus pulvinatus* which, in Jersey, is at the extreme north of its range (Ragge & Reynolds, 1984). The nominate subspecies, *E. pulvinatus pulvinatus*, does not occur in western Europe, but is found from Czechoslovakia eastwards to Asia. In western Europe, the principal subspecies is *E. pulvinatus gallicus* Maran, which occurs in the Iberian Peninsula, central and southern France.

Gomphocerippus rufus (Linnaeus)
The Rufous Grasshopper

Description (Pl. 7, figs 19–21)

A medium-sized, predominantly brown grasshopper, distinguished by conspicuous **pale-tipped, clubbed antennae** (text fig. 18, p. 75). In mature males tip of abdomen becomes orange tinged; less so in females. In both sexes hind tibiae also develop this colour. Green forms do not occur, and reddish purple variety seen only in females.

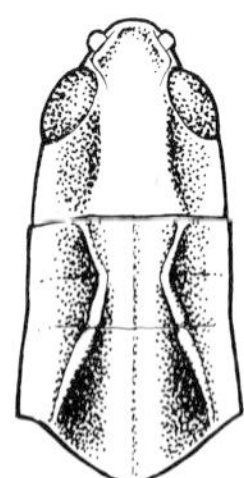

Text Figure 46 Head and pronotum of *Gomphocerippus rufus*, dorsal view

Pronotal side-keels **fairly strongly incurved** (fig. 21; text fig. 46). Wings do not usually extend beyond hind knees, and forewings have **bulge** on costal margin. Specimens lacking antennal clubs (through damage) may be distinguished from *Chorthippus brunneus* by slightly shorter wings and lack of thoracic hairs in *G. rufus*. Male has 140–240 stridulatory pegs.

Total length	♂ 14–18mm, ♀ 16–22mm
Wing length	♂ 10–13mm, ♀ 10–15mm

Life History and Behaviour

The eggs, 4 × 1mm, are laid in batches of usually ten, in a shortish, cylindrical pod about 10 × 5mm. The outer wall is formed of cemented soil particles and there is a concave lid of 2–3mm diameter.

G. rufus has a late season. Nymphs emerge only late in May, having four nymphal instars and becoming adult from late July, though young nymphs may still be seen in August. After a warm autumn, adults may be found as late as the first week of December. This ability to survive so late in the year may be the result of the insect's habit of creeping under fallen leaves at night and in cold weather.

Song (Cassette bands 33, 34)

The normal song is an urgent, slightly fluctuating buzz of sound, lasting about five seconds and dying away at the end of each burst, like a small clockwork motor running down (band 33). Occasionally shorter chirps are produced between responding males, as *Chorthippus brunneus*.

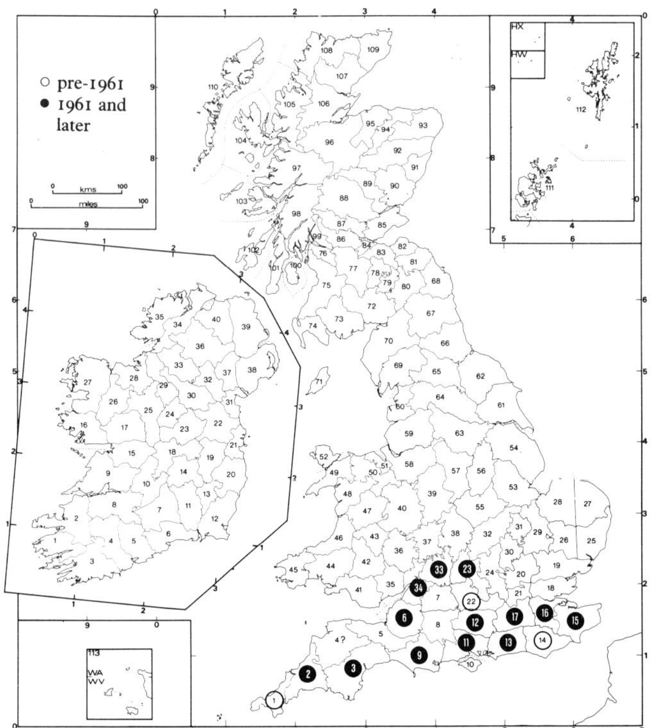

Gomphocerippus rufus

However, in courtship the song is incorporated into a remarkable 'dance' in which the clubbed antennae of the males are twirled around in a loop and the hind legs flicked with an audible click (band 34). The performance may be repeated many times before mating is attempted. Females may stridulate briefly.

Habitat

This species is restricted to rough grass in warm, sheltered localities almost always on calcareous soils. There are a few records on the landward side of calcareous sand-dunes and on chalk sea-cliffs, but most records have been made under open tree-canopy or in clearings amongst scrub over chalk or limestone. It has also been found over calcareous sandstone.

Distribution and Status (Map 32, page 181)

G. rufus is a very local species, confined to the south of England. On chalk, it occurs along the North Downs from Folkestone Warren and Wye in Kent as far west as the Hog's Back in Surrey. Along the South Downs there are a number of sites between Arundel Park (where there is a large colony) and Kingley Vale, but it has never been found east of the Arun in West Sussex. In Hampshire, there are a number of isolated colonies, including Noar

Hill Nature Reserve, near Selborne; Old Winchester Hill National Nature Reserve and Farley Mount, south of the A272 between Winchester and Stockbridge. In the limestone Cotswolds, there are strong colonies in the Nailsworth area and around Dursley, but despite extensive recording over the past twenty years, none have been found farther north than Cleeve Hill.

In the south-west, this species is known from about half-a-dozen sites on the Jurassic limestone of the Polden Hills (Burton, 1982) but is rare and extremely local on the Carboniferous limestone of the Mendips, having been found recently only at Portishead Down in 1981 and near Draycott in 1984. On the south coast, it occurs in good numbers around the Lyme Regis landslip, Dorset, and again around Beer Head and Branscombe, near Sidmouth, Devon. Farther west there is also an isolated colony on the calcareous dunes at Polzeath, North Cornwall. Some pre-1940 records from several other sites on the Devonian peninsula are doubtful. There are two records from areas of calcareous sandstone: one at East Grinstead, East Sussex, in 1925 (Kevan, 1952); and another on a roadside verge at Milford, near Godalming, Surrey, in 1976. There are, in addition, isolated colonies on chalk in the Thames Valley – the most recently recorded at Path Hill, near Pangbourne in 1986.

G. rufus is on the edge of its range in southern England. Fortunately, as many of its isolated colonies are on nature reserves, its future in Britain seems reasonably secure, although its numbers can decrease sharply after several successive poor summers, as was the case in 1977–81 and 1985–87.

This species occurs throughout Europe (except Denmark, Finland, and the extreme south) from France through the Balkans and the U.S.S.R. to Siberia.

Myrmeleotettix maculatus (Thunberg)
The Mottled Grasshopper

Description (Pl. 7, figs 22–25)

A small grasshopper with twelve described colour variations (Ragge, 1965). Forewings usually brownish or darker but never green and general coloration dark, though other parts of body may be coloured from green through to dark purple – colours blending well with their habitat. **Clubbed antennae in male and thickened antennal tips in female** (text fig. 19, p. 75) both **lack white tips** seen in *Gomphocerippus rufus* (*cf.* text fig. 18).

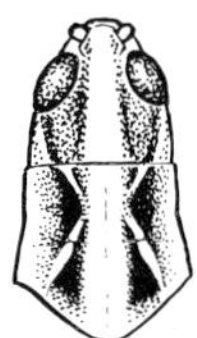

Text Figure 47 Head and pronotum of *Myrmeleotettix maculatus*

Pronotal side-keels **strongly indented** (fig. 25; text fig. 47). **No bulge** on costal margin of forewing. Brown females could be mistaken for males of *Chorthippus vagans*, though more strongly indented pronotal side-keels in *M. maculatus* should aid identification (*cf.* text figs 47; 27, p. 76). Male has 120–180 stridulatory pegs.

Total length	♂ 12–15mm, ♀ 13–19mm
Wing length	♂ 8–11mm, ♀ 9–13mm

Life History and Behaviour

The eggs, over 4 × 1mm, are laid in batches of usually six, in two rows in a sausage-shaped pod, 9 × 4mm. The outer wall is formed of cemented soil particles and there is no lid.

Nymphs may emerge from April until June, usually in May, and have four nymphal instars. Adults may be heard stridulating by mid-June. Many will have died off by early September, and few survive beyond the end of October.

Song Cassette band 35)

The song is a long series of buzzing chirps, starting quietly but becoming louder, and stopping abruptly after 10–15 seconds. As with *Gomphocerippus rufus*, males produce an elaborate courtship song in which the body sways, the hind legs jerk and the antennae are thrown backwards (Ragge, 1965). Females may also produce brief stridulation.

Habitat

M. maculatus requires the maximum amount of sun in dry localities. It is found in short turf with much bare ground

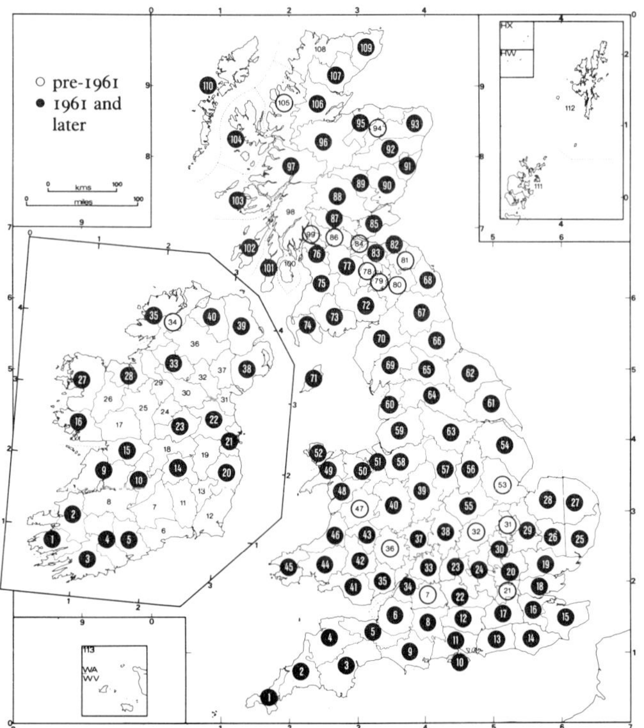

Myrmeleotettix maculatus

over sand, chalk or limestone; typically on the steep sides of old quarries and road or railway cuttings; on heathland, dry hillsides and the coast. It is occasionally found also on damp grassy heath over clay but rarely in areas where there is any degree of shading.

Distribution and Status (Map 33, page 182)

This grasshopper occurs in suitable habitat over most of the British Isles. There are large populations on the heathlands of Dorset, the New Forest and West Surrey; on all the major sea-cliffs and sand-dunes around the coast, and, at Dungeness, on shingle – not one of its usual habitats. It also occurs on all the chalk and limestone hill ranges and around the edges of the higher moorlands of the West Country and north Yorkshire. It is common on the Isle of Man, but there is no record for Lundy since 1960 and none for the Scilly Isles. It is widespread and common in many places around the Welsh coast, including Anglesey and the offshore island of Skomer.

M. maculatus is widespread over drier ground in southern Scotland and throughout eastern Scotland as far north as Keiss Links, by Sinclair's Bay, and on dunes by Dunnet Bay, both in Caithness, where it was found by R. Cumming in 1979 – the only post-1960 records for this county. The only recent records for the Western Highlands are from the Kintyre peninsula and Ardnamurchan Point, but it is present in both the Inner and Outer Hebrides with good colonies on the western side of Islay and other sites on Colonsay, Tiree, Mull, Iona, Rum, Barra, South Uist (where extensive colonies exist on the machairs) and Harris (where it is the only grasshopper recorded from the island). In Ireland, it is recorded locally throughout the country (Cotton, 1982) and was also found in 1984 on the cliffs of Inisheer, one of the Aran Islands.

M. maculatus fills a distinct ecological niche in that it can survive in short, sparse turf in very exposed situations from the shingle beach at Dungeness to the gale-swept machairs of the Atlantic coast of Scotland. It is surprising that it has never colonized the Scillies or the Channel Islands. It also seems very slow to colonize new habitats, such as urban wastelands and motorway embankments, although Whiteley (1981) records it from urban sites in South Yorkshire. Although it flies well, it nearly always returns to the area from which it was flushed, and is thus unlikely to spread far from existing sites. This behaviour is to its advantage in very exposed situations but makes it more vulnerable to such hazards as heath fires, moor-burn and recreational activities, particularly on coastal dunes and chalk downland.

Generally widespread throughout Europe from France through southern Italy and Greece (though mainly at high altitudes in southern Europe), the U.S.S.R. to Siberia.

Order DICTYOPTERA

The Dictyoptera differ from the saltatorial Orthoptera in not having very enlarged hindlegs, though the more active, long-legged species are capable of jumping a short distance, and the winged species may flutter their wings to assist the jump; fully-winged species are capable of active flight. As in most orthopteroid insects, the male usually has longer wings than the female. They have five-segmented tarsi, and do not show the nymphal wing-pad reversal which is typical of the Saltatoria; nymphal wing-pads are visible as continuous outgrowths of the meso- and metanota. Dictyoptera do not have the complex organs of sound production and reception seen in most Saltatoria, although there are other forms of sound production among the Blattodea, and recent studies have shown the presence of an ultrasonic hearing organ in the Mantodea, in the ventral midline of the body between the metathoracic coxae (Yager & Hoy, 1987). Members of both suborders produce eggs in batches within protective egg-pods, or oothecae, from which the vermiform larvae hatch before emerging into the true first-instar larvae.

Suborder Blattodea

The Blattodea are typically flattened or dorso-ventrally compressed insects (text fig. 48), often having a beetle-like appearance. The pronotum is usually flattened and shield-shaped, and, at rest, the head is often concealed beneath it. The forewings are hardened and modified into protective elytra or tegmina and, unless very small, always overlap in the mid-line dorsally, whereas beetle elytra always abut in the mid-line. The hindwings are membranous, fan-folded, some groups with longer hindwings having additional folds so that the alae are fully protected beneath the elytra (text figs 49a,b).

The eggs are produced within a purse-like egg-case or ootheca (text fig. 50, p. 122), which is clearly visible during development in most of the British species. The number of eggs within an ootheca may vary from about sixteen in some groups to more than sixty, lying in a double row. The external lateral grooves or lines on the oothecae mark the position of the eggs. When newly formed, the ootheca projects from the female in a vertical position, with the keel dorsally and, in the British Blattidae, remains so for the few days during which it is carried. In other groups the ootheca is rotated by 90° so that the keel is lateral; the rotation may be to the left or the right within the same species, as seen in *Ectobius* spp. (Brown, 1973b), though rotation is probably closely

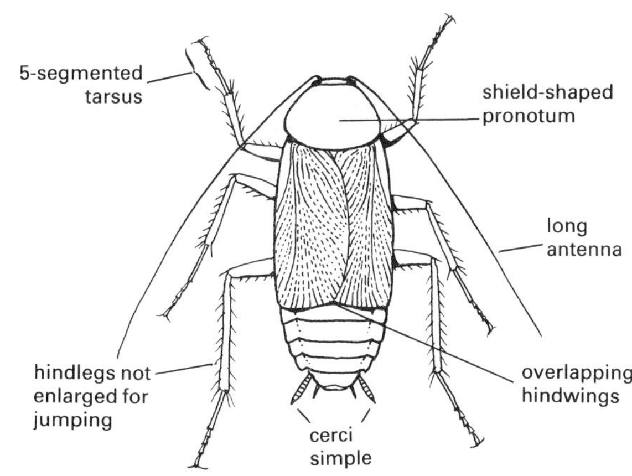

Text Figure 48 *Blatta orientalis* ♂, showing distinguishing characters of cockroaches (Blattodea)

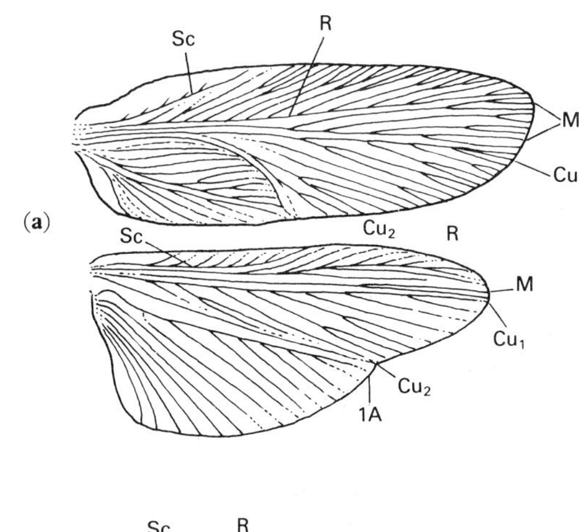

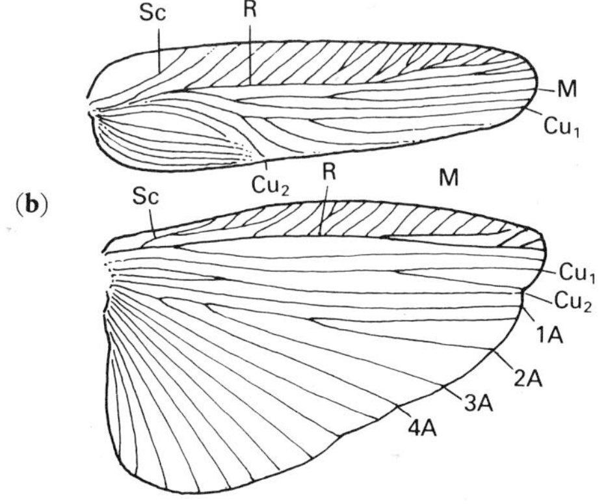

Text Figure 49 Wings of cockroach species.
(**a**) *Periplaneta americana* (Blattidae); (**b**) *Blattella germanica* (Blattellidae)

linked with the structure of the male genitalia and is of significance in taxonomic studies (Roth, 1967). The rotation to a lateral position permits more expansion of the eggs to occur than if they remained vertical, and in some groups the newly-formed ootheca is extruded and then retracted into the female's brood-pouch where the eggs absorb water and complete their development. This is termed ovoviviparity. This extrusion and retraction occurs rapidly and, as the eggs are protected by only a membranous ootheca, if the female is disturbed during extrusion, the eggs may be damaged and then dropped by her and will not develop any further. This may be observed in *Pycnoscelus surinamensis*. When the ootheca is carried for a longer period by the female, as in *Blattella germanica*, the membrane of the ootheca is thin where it remains in contact with the body tissues of the female, and through this the eggs may obtain water from her during their development. The ootheca may be carried until just before hatching when it is deposited by the female, often being buried or otherwise concealed. The keel of the fully developed ootheca forms the suture through which the young nymphs emerge.

There are more than 4000 described cockroach species, although of these only about 20 or so species, less than one per cent, are recognized pests. Unfortunately these may occur in such large numbers in domestic environments that the very word 'cockroach' is used as a term of disgust. The three native species in Britain, as with the majority of the 130 or so native European species, are small, delicate-looking creatures with only a slight resemblance to the pest species (text fig. 51).

All species on the British list are omnivorous.

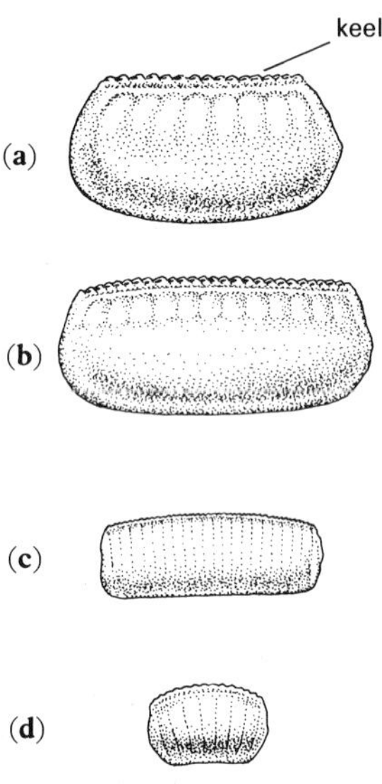

Text Figure 50 Oothecae of blattid and blattellid species, showing keel.
(**a**) *Blatta orientalis*; (**b**) *Periplaneta australasiae*; (**c**) *Blattella germanica*; (**d**) *Ectobius pallidus*

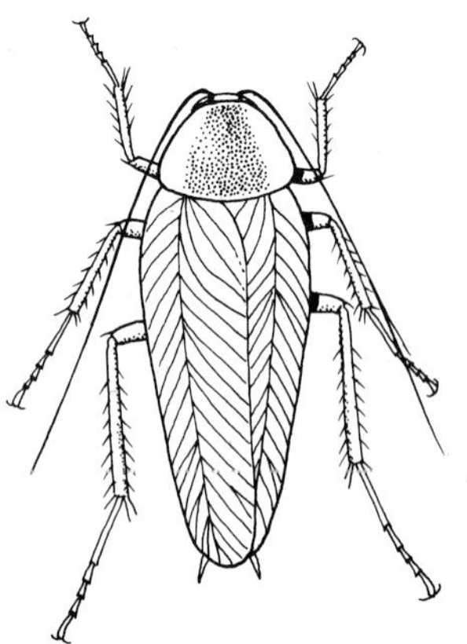

Text Figure 51 *Ectobius lapponicus* ♂ (Blattellidae), a native cockroach

Some characteristics of families of Blattodea:

POLYPHAGIDAE (p. 148)

The oothecae have pronounced keels and are not rotated after formation.

BLABERIDAE (p. 123)

The oothecae are rotated 90° and then retracted into the female's brood pouch where the eggs complete their development while absorbing water from her.

BLATTIDAE (p. 124)

The oothecae are held vertically with the keel uppermost, are not rotated, and are usually deposited within a few days of formation.

BLATTELLIDAE (p. 127)

All British Blattellidae rotate their oothecae 90° after formation. Some are deposited after a few days, though *Blattella* may carry the oothecae until hatching is due. The males have complex tergal glands.

Suborder Mantodea

The Mantodea are easily recognized (text fig. 52) by their raptorial forelegs which are strongly spined for catching their prey, and have enlarged highly mobile coxae, sometimes as long as the femora. The forelegs are also used in walking, but at rest are held folded under the head in the typical 'praying' position. Mantodea are totally carnivorous and capable of catching prey as large as themselves, holding the catch firmly with the powerful forelegs whilst eating it. Mantids in nature will eat other insects, including other mantids, and it is not unusual for a female in captivity to catch and eat the male which was her intended mate. It may be observed that the abdomen of a half-eaten male is still performing copulatory movements, and it has been suggested that this cannibalistic routine is part of the normal mating sequence, and likened to similar behaviour patterns in spiders. However it has recently been shown (Liske & Davis, 1987) that, in *Tenodera* (though not necessarily in all mantids), this is an artefact of captivity or of starved females, and that the normal mating behaviour does not involve such a sacrifice on the part of the male. The female mantis lays her eggs in batches in an ootheca, producing a foamy secretion around the eggs which hardens to a tough, though sponge-like, mass. The vermiform larvae hatch from this, then immediately emerge into first-instar nymphs, leaving the cast vermiform larval skins attached to the ootheca.

Of the 2000 or so described mantid species, only 24 have been recorded in Europe, and only one specimen is so far known to have reached Britain by natural means (p. 148).

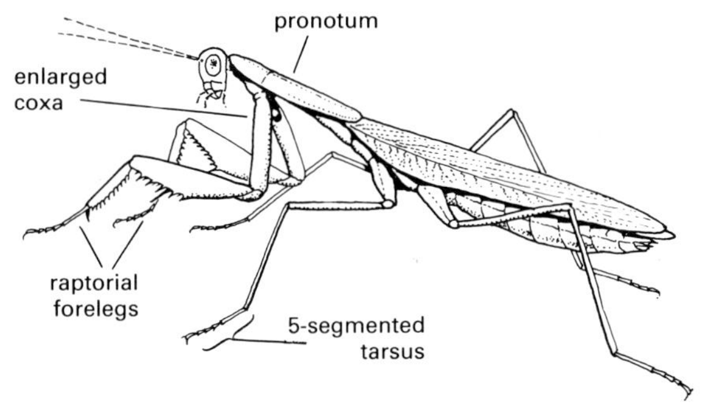

Text Figure 52 *Mantis religiosa* ♀, showing distinguishing characters of mantids (Mantodea)

Suborder Blattodea

BLABERIDAE

Pycnoscelus surinamensis (Linnaeus)
The Surinam Cockroach

Description (Pl. 8, fig. 11)

A medium-sized cockroach, with body reddish brown to very dark brown, and **pale band along fore-edge of pronotum. Wings are silvery grey** in life, though changing **to yellowish brown** in dried specimens. Reproduction in this species is by parthenogenesis – unfertilized eggs are produced which develop into females; males occur only very rarely. Female has smooth, rounded subgenital plate without valves. Nymphs reddish brown in colour and glossy, except for end of abdomen dorsally, last five segments of which rough-textured and not shiny.

Total length	♀ 20–25mm
Wing length	♀ 16–19mm
Ootheca	10.0 × 0.4mm

Life History and Behaviour

A female may start to reproduce only a week or so after becoming adult. She is ovoviviparous; she produces her eggs in a long ootheca which is not covered by the strong, protective outer shell seen in the Blattidae, and this ootheca is then retracted into her brood pouch where it develops internally, taking about two months. The 20–30 nymphs hatch directly from the mother's abdomen (see also p. 122) and will become adults in 4–7 months depending on temperature. This is a nocturnal, actively burrowing species; it is omnivorous but feeds largely on roots and plant shoots – which, in greenhouses, can prove unpopular!

Habitat

P. surinamensis has most frequently been recorded from horticultural nurseries, although there are a few records from office blocks and hospitals.

Distribution and Status

Although there are records from Hampshire, West Sussex, Surrey, Essex, Oxfordshire, Lancashire and South Yorkshire (including a 1975 record for Stannington), most English records are from the London area, particularly the Royal Botanic Gardens, Kew. In Scotland, it has been found in Lanarkshire and Edinburgh; and in Ireland, from the Glasnevin Botanic Gardens, Dublin (Cotton, 1982).

This alien was first recorded at the beginning of this century. One early record (Horrell, 1905) shows that it was established in a tanpit near Chelmsford, Essex, and feeding on plants in an adjoining greenhouse. It does

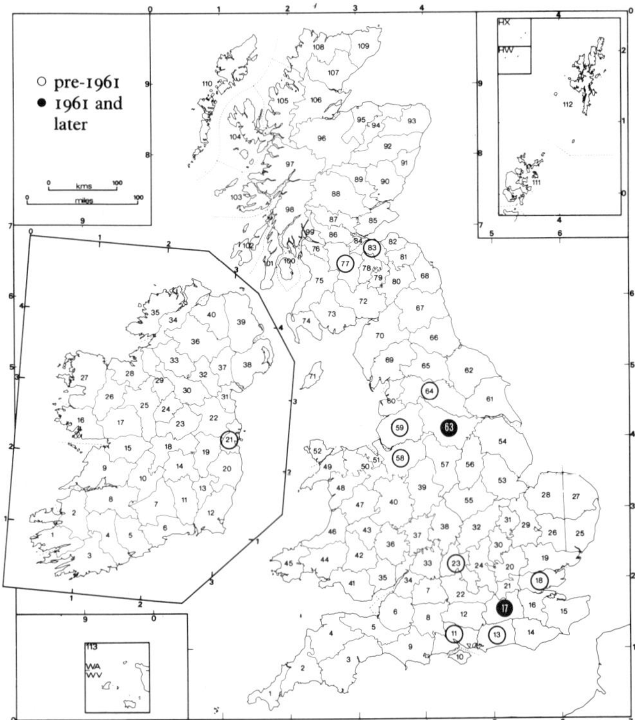

Pycnoscelus surinamensis

require a suitable medium in which to live and seems less adaptable than *Periplaneta americana* or *P. australasiae*, there being comparatively few certain breeding records. It is unlikely to survive for long outdoors.

This is a cosmotropical pest species, more likely to be found around dwellings than within them, and is probably Asian or Indo-Malaysian in origin (Rehn, 1945).

BLATTIDAE

Blatta orientalis Linnaeus

The Common or Oriental Cockroach

Description (Pl. 8, figs 1–4)

A **large, dark brown** cockroach; **males may be reddish brown, females very dark, almost black**, and sometimes referred to as 'blackbeetles' because of apparent similarity to large Coleoptera.

Males have both pairs of wings reduced in length, shorter than abdomen; in **females, wings reduced to small lateral lobes**. Males have symmetrical subgenital plate bearing pair of styles; females have no styles, and subgenital plate divided by ovipositor valves.

Total length	♂ 17–30mm, ♀ 20–30mm
Wing length	♂ 10–16mm, ♀ 3–6mm
Ootheca	8–11 × 0.5mm

Life History and Behaviour

Blatta orientalis requires warm, damp surroundings with an adequate food supply, where its life-cycle can be independent of the external environment. At room temperature, females produce five to ten, sometimes more, oothecae at intervals of 1–2 weeks. As the ootheca first emerges between the ovipositor valves it is white, turning pink and then brown as it hardens. When fully formed it is carried by the female (fig. 4) for a further day or so, and then deposited in a suitable place. Sometimes she cements it to the surface with a secretion from her mouth, perhaps with chewed-up cardboard fragments or camouflaged with other debris. The ootheca then becomes almost black, and very brittle. After 2–3 months the eggs hatch, all at the same time, by taking in air to open the keel or 'zip' of the purse-like ootheca (text fig. 50a, p. 122). There are normally sixteen eggs in this species, often fewer, occasionally more. The nymphs (fig. 3) may take up to a year to become adult, though can mature much faster at higher temperatures. Between six and twelve nymphal instars have been recorded, though eight to nine is probably the average. Adults may survive for several months.

The occasional cockroach seen in daylight may give little hint of the vast numbers which can exist in colonies, emerging at night to seek food. They are omnivorous scavengers, feeding on almost any available substance, and can be carriers of harmful bacteria as they often visit sewers. They may cause damage by chewing paper and other articles as well as food, and will contaminate surfaces with their droppings and leave a persistent and distinctively disagreeable smell. Their nocturnal behaviour requires high standards of hygiene where infestations are known to occur; it is essential to clean all food preparation surfaces on which they may have walked. They are

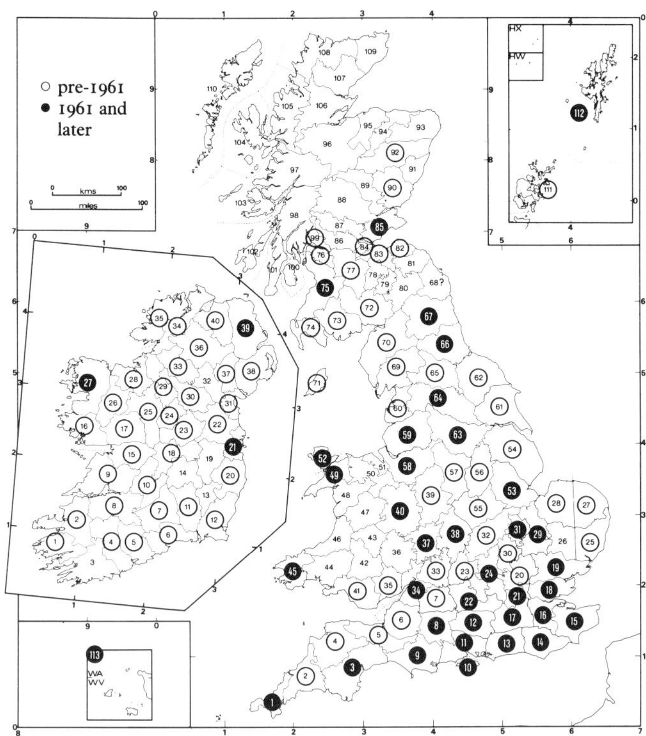

Blatta orientalis (see note on p. 199 re Irish records)

difficult to eradicate from large buildings such as hospitals, where the warmth, food and shelter available offer them an ideal habitat (Mason, 1985).

Although this species is not capable of flight it can climb up vertical surfaces, is very active and can move rapidly.

Habitat

B. orientalis is normally found in artificially heated premises such as warehouses, greenhouses, laundries, schools, hotels and restaurants, private houses and even coal mines. It may survive in the open away from heated buildings, provided that at least some protection is available, and preferably also some artificial warmth such as a fermenting rubbish tip.

Distribution and Status

There are records from almost all English counties as well as the Isle of Wight, the Scillies and the Isle of Man. Persisting outdoor colonies have been recorded on a chemical tip at Liverpool, a building tip in Kent and, most interestingly, a housing estate at Harlow, Essex, where specimens continued to be found outdoors for a period of fifteen years, surviving with cover but no extra warmth available (Beatson & Dripps, 1972). Whiteley (1981) recorded that *B. orientalis* was regularly brought into the Sheffield and Rotherham Museums for identification in the period 1976–80.

In Wales, it has been recorded from Monmouth, Glamorgan, Caernarvon and Anglesey: in Scotland, from nearly all counties from the Borders north to Stirling, Fife, Forfar and Kincardine; also from the Orkneys and Saxa Voe, Unst in the Shetlands in 1965, which is the only orthopteran record for the Shetland Islands (Ragge, 1973). It is widespread in Ireland where it has been reported as a common pest from thirty-five of the forty Irish vice-counties (Cornwell, 1968b; Cotton, 1980). Regularly recorded also from Guernsey and Jersey, Channel Islands.

B. orientalis has been established in Britain as a domestic pest since at least the sixteenth century (Moffet, 1634) (see p. 21), though it is not always recognized as such. There is some evidence that this alien is slowly adapting to the British climate.

This now cosmopolitan pest species probably originated in North Africa, entering Europe by way of trading vessels (Rehn, 1945). It can withstand summer heat and moderate winter cold, though not enjoying tropical or subtropical humidity as in South America, where *Periplaneta* species take over as the dominant cosmopolitan pests.

Wild-living *B. orientalis* have been found in the Crimean Peninsula, probably a relict population left from the invasion through Europe, and a related, very similar species with long-winged males, *B. furcata* (Karny), is found in Israel. A recent study showed that these two species will interbreed and produce fertile offspring of three forms, *B. orientalis*-type, *B. furcata*-type, and a form with intermediate wing-length, though such forms have not been found in nature (Bohn, 1985).

Periplaneta americana (Linnaeus)

The American or Ship Cockroach

Description (Pl. 8, figs 5–7)

A **large, reddish brown cockroach,** with **indistinct pale pattern on pronotum**, sometimes including submarginal ring and partial mid-dorsal line. **Adults of both sexes are fully winged** and can fly. Male has long, light brown supra-anal plate, and a pair of styles on subgenital plate; female has no styles, and ventral ovipositor valves. Nymphs are lighter brown on hatching, gradually darkening as they grow, with indistinct brownish markings on older nymphs (fig. 7).

Total length	♂ 35–43mm, ♀ 27–37mm
Wing length	♂ 28–36mm, ♀ 22–30mm
Ootheca	7–9 × 0.5mm

Life History and Behaviour

The life history of *P. americana* is very similar to that of *Blatta orientalis*. Oothecae are produced by the female and cemented in a suitable place. Nymphs hatch in 1–3

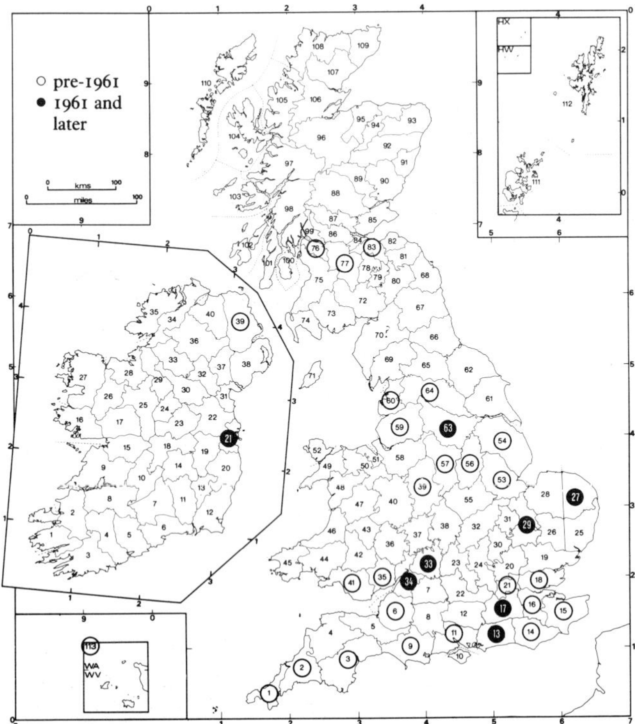

Periplaneta americana

months, depending on ambient temperature – this species requires at least room temperature for satisfactory development – and may take up to a year to become adult. About fourteen nymphs hatch from each ootheca, and a female may produce thirty to fifty, or more, oothecae, while surviving for many months as an adult. This species is particularly voracious, though it has been shown to be capable of surviving for long periods without food (Cornwell, 1968a).

Habitat

P. americana requires an appreciably higher mean temperature than *B. orientalis*. It has been recorded from warehouses, hotels, schools, zoological gardens, bakeries, greenhouses, coal-mines and occasionally private houses. Most recent records are from seaports or large glasshouse nurseries.

Distribution and Status

P. americana has a widely scattered distribution in England, mainly in the south and in the North Midlands, with records from Cornwall, Devon, Somerset, Hampshire, Sussex, Kent, Surrey, Greater London, Essex, Cambridgeshire, Staffordshire, Derbyshire, Leicestershire, and Lancashire. In Yorkshire, W. A. Ely discovered this species in 1976 inhabiting a sewer at Maltby (thought to be the only such case outside London), and specimens were regularly brought to Sheffield and Rotherham Museums for identification between 1976 and 1980 (Whiteley, 1981). In Wales, recorded from Glamorgan and Monmouth; in Scotland, from Renfrewshire, Lanarkshire and Edinburgh; in Ireland, from Antrim and Dublin (including a recent record (Cotton, 1982)); and in the Channel Islands, from Guernsey (Kevan, 1961).

This large alien was first recorded in Britain during the 1820s (Curtis, 1829–31). It is frequently imported with market produce and other goods. Although both sexes fly in warm conditions, it seems most unlikely to become established away from well-heated premises, and is unlikely ever to become as much of a pest here as it is in America.

This cosmopolitan pest species is commonly found throughout the warmer areas of the world and, in protected conditions, elsewhere, although its origins are in tropical Africa (Rehn, 1945), whence it originally spread to the Americas with the slave trade.

Periplaneta australasiae (Fabricius)

The Australian Cockroach

Description (Pl. 8, figs 8–10)

A large, reddish or dark brown cockroach. **Pronotum with distinctive yellow submarginal ring**, and **forewings having short yellow stripe basally on fore-edge**. Adults of both sexes, with fully-developed wings, can fly. Male has short dark brown supra-anal plate and pair of styles on subgenital plate; female no styles, and ventral ovipositor valves. First-instar nymphs very distinctive, being dark brown with two white bands (on mesonotum and second abdominal segment); older nymphs reddish brown with yellow markings on thoracic segments similar to patterns seen in adults, and with row of yellow spots on each side of dorsal abdominal segments (fig. 10).

Total length	♂ 27–34mm, ♀ 28–32mm
Wing length	♂ 21–28mm, ♀ 22–26mm
Ootheca	9–12 × 0.5mm

Life History and Behaviour

The life history of *P. australasiae* is very similar to that of *P. americana* and *Blatta orientalis*. The ootheca (text fig. 50b, p. 122), holding usually 20–26 eggs (sometimes up to 28), is buried or otherwise concealed by the female. Nymphal development is more rapid than in *P. americana*.

Habitat

Breeding colonies have been found particularly in horticultural glasshouse nurseries, as well as in warehouses and other heated buildings, where it is a pest.

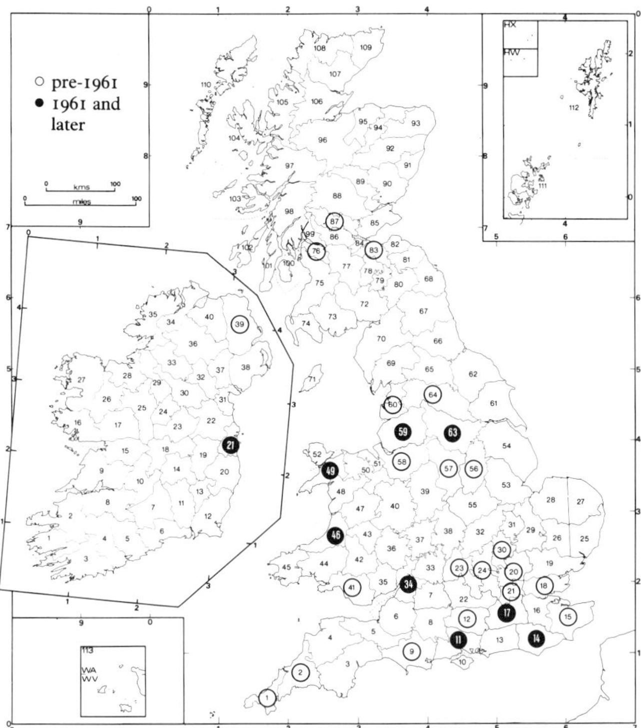

Periplaneta australasiae

Distribution and Status

There are records of this species from a number of English counties including existing colonies in Brighton, Sussex. It has been recorded from Glamorgan, Cardigan (Fowles, 1986b) and Caernarvon, Wales; and Renfrewshire, Edinburgh and Perthshire, Scotland. The earliest record in these islands is from Belfast (McLachlan, 1887), but most Irish records are from Dublin where it has continued to thrive in the Glasnevin Botanic Gardens (Cotton, 1980).

P. australasiae is more often imported with produce, including bananas, than are the other domiciliary pest species, and its frequent presence in horticultural environments may result from importation with planting material. It is perhaps less of a domestic pest in this country than *P. americana*.

This cosmopolitan pest species probably originated, like *P. americana*, in tropical Africa (Rehn, 1945), thence spreading first with slave ships and then with other forms of trade.

BLATTELLIDAE

Blattella germanica (Linnaeus)

The German Cockroach
(also known as the 'steamfly', 'shiner' or 'Croton bug')

Description (Pl. 9, figs 1–4)

A small, pale yellowish brown cockroach, with **pair of dark brown stripes on pronotum**. Both sexes **fully winged. Male has slender, pointed abdomen with dorsal glandular pits on seventh and eighth abdominal segments.** Female abdomen rounded and shorter than wings; but when ootheca carried, this projects beyond wings (fig. 4). Young nymphs dark brown with pale yellowish dorsal stripe on thorax; during development the two dark pronotal stripes seen in adult become increasingly distinct (fig. 3).

Total length	♂ 10–13mm, ♀ 12–15mm
Wing length	♂ 8–10mm, ♀ 9–12mm
Ootheca	7–8 × 3.0–3.5mm

Life History and Behaviour

The pale yellowish brown ootheca produced by the female (text fig. 50c, p. 122) is carried by her until it is almost ready for hatching. When first developed, the keel appears dorsally, and is then rotated and carried sideways. Because the wall of the ootheca is thin, and a large part of its surface is in intimate contact with the mother, she is able to provide the developing embryos with a constant environment (see also p. 122). She may carry the ootheca for 4–6 weeks and deposit it when the eggs are fully developed and ready to hatch; occasionally the nymphs may hatch whilst the ootheca is still being carried by the female. About 30–45 nymphs may emerge, taking 2–4 months to become adult. Adults may live for several months, and will produce three to seven or more oothecae. Both sexes fly readily in hot weather and so colonies may suddenly appear in new areas in good summers.

Habitat

B. germanica is often numerous in heated buildings, favouring a warm, moist environment such as hotels, restaurants, bakeries, and warehouses, and is less frequently found in private houses and greenhouses. Temporary colonies sometimes build up in rubbish tips, but this species seems less persistent there than *Blatta orientalis*.

Distribution and Status

Blattella germanica has been recorded from almost every vice-county in England, with many colonies thriving to the present time. In Wales, only one certain record, from Glamorgan. In Scotland, recorded from five vice-counties (Kevan, 1961). In Ireland, recorded from eighteen vice-counties (Cornwell, 1968b; Cotton, 1982). In the Channel Islands, recorded only from Guernsey (Kevan, *loc. cit.*).

This alien has been known in the British Isles since the eighteenth century. It is probably the most serious pest species here because of its capacity to build up considerable populations without being detected. It is adaptable, but, despite its presence here for two centuries, there is no evidence of colonies becoming established away from heated premises.

This cosmopolitan pest species was thought to have originated in North Africa (Rehn, 1945), but recent studies on *Blattella* and related genera have shown that its closest relatives are found in eastern Asia (Roth, 1985). It is now probably the most widespread domestic cockroach pest.

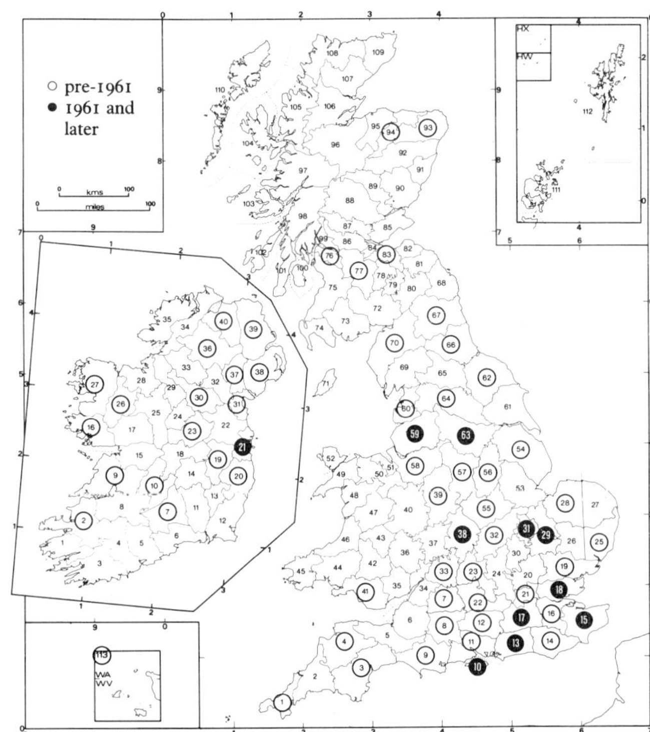

Blattella germanica (see note on p. 199 re Irish records)

Supella longipalpa (Fabricius)

[= *S. supellectilium* Serville]

The Brown-banded Cockroach

Description (Pl. 9, figs 5–7)

A **small, brown-patterned** cockroach, **pale yellow or reddish brown in colour with darker brown bands on forewings**; Female often darker than male. Pronotum brown centrally with clear lateral margins. Male, which is capable of flight, has both pairs of wings fully developed, and long slender abdomen with **dorsal glandular pit (containing hairy tubercle) on seventh segment**. Female brachypterous, with wings tapered and rarely reaching end of abdomen, which is broad and rounded. Nymphs a pale reddish brown with brown and yellow patterning (fig. 7), but never with pair of dark brown stripes as in *Blattella germanica*.

Total length	♂ 10–14mm, ♀ 10–13mm
Wing length	♂ 11–16mm, ♀ 7–8mm
Ootheca	4–5 × 2–3mm

Life History and Behaviour

The female produces a small pale reddish brown ootheca which she deposits after a day or so, sticking it down with a secretion from her mouth. There are up to eighteen eggs in each ootheca which rarely all hatch, taking about 2–3 months. The nymphs mature in about 3–6 months, and live as adults for 5–9 months, each female producing ten to thirty oothecae.

Habitat

This little cockroach has been recorded in centrally heated houses and office blocks.

Distribution and Status

Nearly all recent English records are from the London area, although there is one record from South Devon (Kevan, 1961), and in 1980 a singleton was found in Hyde

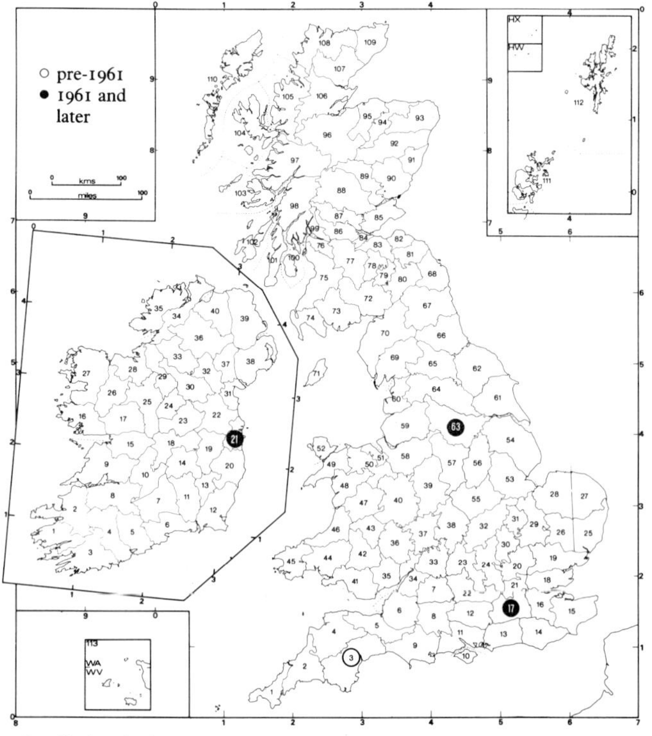

Supella longipalpa

Park Flats, Sheffield, where by 1985 a colony was present (Whiteley, 1981; 1985). There are no records from Wales or Scotland, but an established colony was recorded in 1971 in a house in Dublin (Goodhue, [1980]).

S. longipalpa has been recorded on various occasions in the last thirty years, and is the most recent among alien cockroach species to form breeding colonies in Britain and Ireland. It is too early to make an assessment of its status, but there is good evidence that it could become a well-established member of the British fauna in artificially heated premises.

Like its larger fellow-cosmopolitan pest cockroaches, this species also had its origins in tropical Africa (Rehn, 1945).

Ectobius lapponicus (Linnaeus)

The Dusky Cockroach

Description (Pl. 9, figs 8,9)

A **small, light brown** cockroach, usually with **dark brown pronotum in male**, lighter in female; **female has a mainly dark brown abdomen ventrally**. Males fully winged; females have slightly reduced wings, barely reaching end of abdomen. **Males have dorsal glandular pit on seventh abdominal tergite containing bilobed tubercle** (text fig. 31, p. 77). Nymphs brown, with no regular patterns or dark spots on dorsal surface (Brown, 1973d).

Total length	♂ 9–11mm, ♀ 7–10mm
Wing length	♂ 7.5–9.5mm, ♀ 5–6mm
Ootheca	3.2–4.1 × 2.0mm

Life History and Behaviour

E. lapponicus has a two-yearly life-cycle. Adults appear from about the end of May until early September, and reddish brown oothecae are produced from June onwards, and carried by the female for a day or so before being deposited in leaf-litter or in grass-tussocks. The oothecae then undergo a diapause until the following year, when the nymphs hatch in early June (Brown, 1969) and develop through to the second, third or fourth instars. At the fourth instar they undergo a further diapause, and overwinter at this stage. Nymphs which have not attained the fourth instar do not undergo diapause but overwinter in a quiescent state (Brown, 1973c). All nymphs select the interior of tussocks of such grasses as cock's-foot (*Dactylis glomerata*) and red fescue (*Festuca rubra*) and may be found there from October until March. From April, they leave the tussocks and continue development, with fourth-instar nymphs becoming adult from May and the younger nymphs becoming adult later in the year. There are five nymphal instars. Although oothecae are thus produced by maturing females throughout the summer, all of them hatch in the same brief period during the

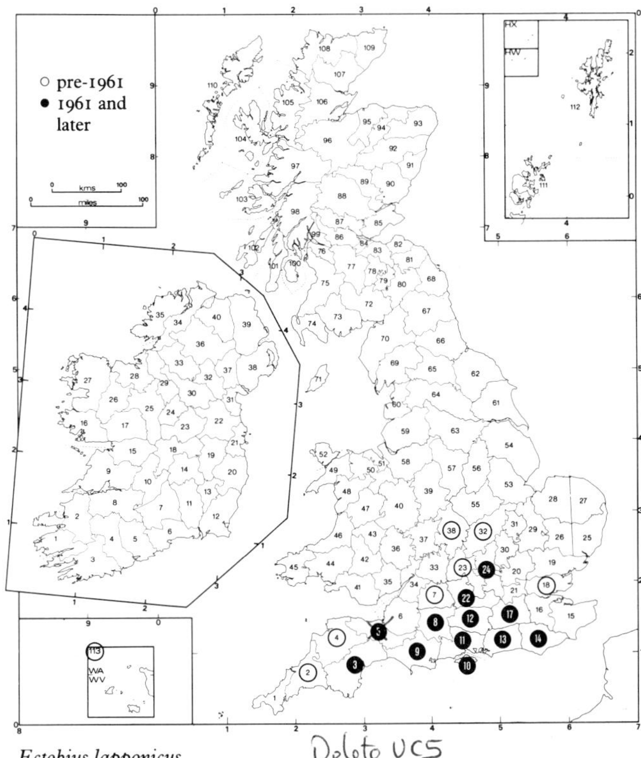

Ectobius lapponicus

following June, and although a small proportion (30 per cent) may hatch if kept at room temperature, a far higher proportion hatch when overwintered at lower temperatures (Brown, *loc.cit*).

This is an active species, particularly in warm weather, and the male, if 'put up', will fly quite readily, settling again on trees or herbage where it can be quite conspicuous in bright sunshine; the female usually remains on the ground.

Habitat

This cockroach is present in quite a wide range of habitats in warm, sheltered localities. It is locally numerous in scrub and coarse herbage along woodland rides and in clearings over sand, clay or chalk soils. It is also locally frequent on scrubby heathland but is rare in short heather that is regularly cut or burnt. Small isolated populations may also be found on scrub-invaded chalk downland and on roadside verges where there is rank herbage.

Distribution and Status (Map 35, page 183)

Although *E. lapponicus* is the most easily observed of the three native British cockroaches, it has the most restricted range and is confined to two main areas in central southern England, except for a few outlying colonies to the west and north. Since 1960, its most northerly known locality (and the only recent record from north of the Thames) is at

Stoke Common, near Slough, where it was found in 1982. South of the Thames, this species has been recorded from a broad belt of country across Berkshire, eastern Hampshire, western Surrey and West Sussex, almost to the Channel coast. It is present in chalk scrub at the Devil's Dyke, north of Brighton, and on Chailey Common, north of Lewes, East Sussex, which, as there are no records for Kent, is its most easterly known colony (Haes, 1972). The second main centre of distribution for this species is the New Forest, where it is widespread and quite common in many localities. It has also been recorded recently from the Isle of Wight and from scrubby heathland around Wareham, Dorset. The only current record from the South-West is again from scrubby heathland at Woodbury Common and the coast near Sidmouth, South Devon, although there are pre-1961 records from isolated localities in North Devon and East Cornwall. Doubtfully from Jersey, Channel Islands.

E. lapponicus is probably a late post-glacial arrival that could have reached Britain with *Chorthippus vagans*, and which has spread considerably within central southern England where there are large populations in favoured localities. Some of the older records around the periphery of its known range may be of strays. Its absence from Kent is intriguing, since, although there is apparently suitable habitat, it has never been recorded there.

This species occurs through Europe from northern Italy to Lapland, eastwards through Yugoslavia to the Urals.

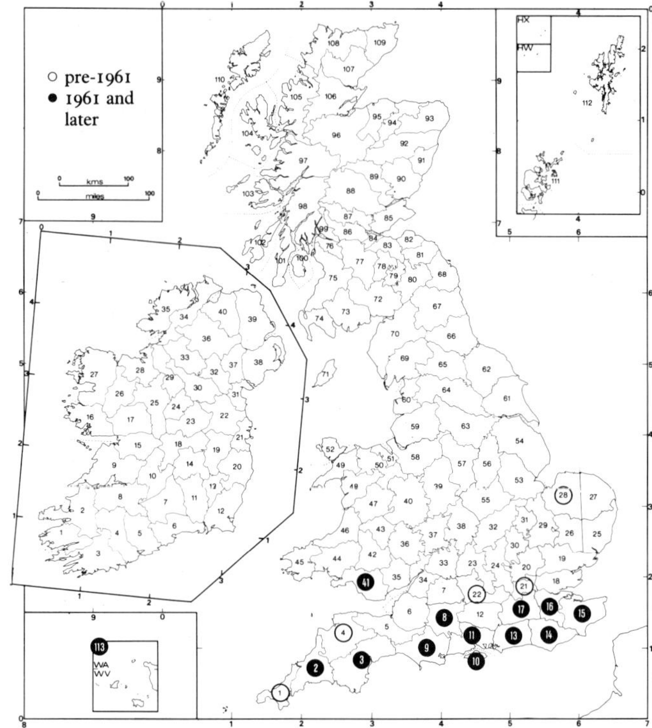

Ectobius pallidus

Ectobius pallidus (Olivier)

The Tawny Cockroach

Description (Pl. 9, figs 10,11)

A **small, golden-yellowish brown** cockroach, females alone having small amount of dark brown ventrally on abdomen. Both sexes fully winged and capable of flight. **Males have empty dorsal glandular pit on seventh abdominal tergite**. Nymphs golden brown, with dark spots on head, thorax and abdomen dorsally (Brown, 1973d).

Total length	♂ 8–9.5mm, ♀ 8–9mm,
Wing length	♂, ♀ 6–7mm
Ootheca	2.5–3.1 × 2.0mm

Life History and Behaviour

E. pallidus has a similar two-year life-cycle to that described for *E. lapponicus*, differing only in *pallidus* having six nymphal instars – one more than *lapponicus*. This means that although some *pallidus* nymphs may reach their fifth instar, they never reach the final instar before hibernation (Brown, 1973d). Overwintering nymphs in their third and fourth instars undergo full diapause; those in the second and fifth instars are quiescent, though the majority of nymphs overwintering are in their fourth instar. (Brown, 1980). Nymphs resume their development in April, and adults appear from late June until September. Dark brown oothecae (text fig. 50d, p.122) are produced during the summer, and carefully buried by the females (Brown, 1973b).

Both sexes may fly but otherwise its behaviour is similar to *E. lapponicus*. It is more nocturnal than either of the other native species and has been taken in light traps.

Habitat

E. pallidus occupies a wider range of habitats than *E. lapponicus* and *E. panzeri* (lesser cockroach). It is commonest in woodland rides and clearings on sand, chalk and clay soils, but is also widespread on chalk downland and is the only British cockroach that can be regarded as a typical downland insect. It is also widespread on southern heathlands and, unlike *E. lapponicus*, may be quite numerous in short or recently-burnt heather. It is also present on coastal dunes – even on the most seaward, where there is little vegetation; however, it does not appear to occur on stabilized shingle beaches where *E. panzeri* is sometimes quite common.

Distribution and Status (Map 36, page 183)

This species is widespread in England, south of the Thames, from West Cornwall to East Kent, including the

Isle of Wight. Specific post-1960 West Country sites are on National Trust land at Pencarrow Head, East Cornwall; Woodbury Common and sea-cliffs in East Devon, to the west of Lyme Regis. Farther east, it is numerous on the Dorset heathlands and in the New Forest. There are good colonies both on crumbling clay sea-cliffs and on chalk in the Isle of Wight, and on scrubby chalk downland in Sussex, where its most easterly recorded sites are on chalk at the Devil's Dyke, near Brighton, and in two isolated heathland sites in Ashdown Forest, East Sussex (Haes, 1972). Its most extensive range in England is along almost the entire length of the North Downs from the Hog's Back to Dover, where it has been found on the sea-cliffs. There are pre-1961 records from West Cornwall, North Devon, Middlesex, Berkshire and West Norfolk.

The sole Welsh population of *E. pallidus* is on the Gower Peninsula, where several good colonies have recently been found, mainly on sand-dunes. In the Channel Islands, it has also been recorded lately from several places on Jersey, Guernsey and Alderney.

In Britain, *E. pallidus* has a distinctly more maritime distribution than *E. lapponicus*, with some of its best colonies occurring on or near the coast. Its presence in the Channel Islands suggests that it was an earlier post-glacial arrival than *E. lapponicus*, but as it has been unable to spread far from the southern coasts of England and Wales it is clearly on the edge of its range here.

This species occurs throughout western, central and southern Europe.

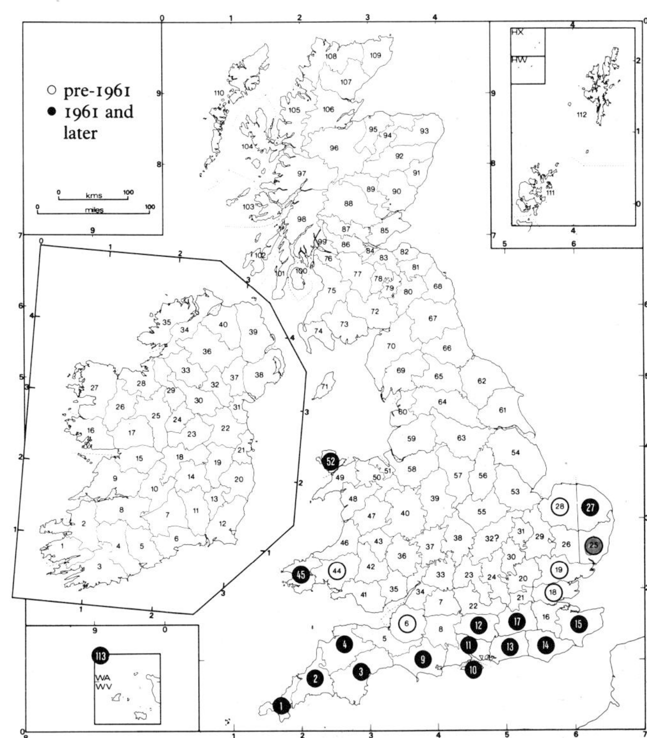

Ectobius panzeri

Ectobius panzeri Stephens

The Lesser Cockroach

Description (Pl. 9, figs. 12,13)

A **small, darkish brown** cockroach, male varying to very dark brown; with some speckled patterning on pronotum in both sexes and in **female** on dorsal surface of abdomen, visible beneath **short, truncate forewings; hindwings vestigial.** Male fully winged and capable of flight; **dorsal glandular pit on seventh abdominal tergite contains hairy tubercle.** Nymphs very dark in colour: head and body mainly black, but with distinct white markings on thoracic tergites (Brown, 1973d).

Total length	♂ 6–8mm, ♀ 5–7mm
Wing length	♂ 4.5–6mm, ♀ 1.6–2mm
Ootheca	2.5–3.1 × 2.00mm

Life History and Behaviour

E. panzeri has only a one-year life-cycle, in contrast to the other native *Ectobius* species; the dark brown oothecae remain dormant during the winter, hatching in late April or May. The nymphs then all mature during the summer, between July and August, surviving as adults until September and late October. Like the other *Ectobius* species it is more active in warm weather, but it has a skulking nature and retreats rapidly under cover when disturbed.

Habitat

E. panzeri occurs in a variety of mainly coastal habitats. There are scattered colonies on maritime cliffs of many rock formations: serpentine and granite in Cornwall; slate and sandstone in Devon; and chalk, limestone, clay and sandstone in Dorset, Hampshire and Kent. Sea-cliff colonies are often small and difficult to locate. Most are under wind-clipped scrub such as heather (*Calluna vulgaris*) or western gorse (*Ulex gallii*). Substantial colonies may occur under low vegetation on sand-dunes or on extensive areas of stabilized, vegetated shingle beach. Its few known inland sites are either under heather in warm, sheltered places on dry heathland, or on chalk downland.

Distribution and Status (Map 37, page 184)

This very small cockroach is widespread around the coast of southern England from the Bristol Channel to East Kent, with pre-1961 records for the coasts of Essex, Suffolk and Norfolk, as well as the offshore island of Steepholm (the only Somerset record). It has been recorded recently, however, from Lundy and, in the Scillies, from Bryher and Gugh. The largest cliff populations are on the Lizard Peninsula and on the crumbling clay cliffs around St. Catherine's Point, Isle of Wight. There are substantial sand-dune populations at Braunton Burrows, North Devon; the vicinity of Littlesea on the west side of Poole Harbour, Dorset; and at Sandwich, Kent. Probably the largest population in this country is on shingle at Denge Beach, Dungeness, where it occurs inland almost as far as Lydd.

Inland sites are of considerable interest: the species was found on chalk at Fontmell Down, Dorset in 1982; there are also several heathland records in East Dorset and the New Forest, and the discovery in 1983 of a good colony on dry heathland at Yateley Common, in the extreme north of Hampshire, complements a pre-1961 record from near Oxshott, Surrey. The pre-1961 inland site in the West Norfolk Breckland merits further investigation but the Northamptonshire record (Gent, 1966) is now considered doubtful and is not, therefore, included on the maps. However, this unobtrusive little insect might well exist in the wild in other inland sites elsewhere.

There are several sea-cliff colonies around the Pembroke coast of Wales, including on the National Trust Stackpole Estate and on both sides of St. Bride's Bay. The most northerly known British populations are on Anglesey, where it has long been known from dunes at Newborough Warren and was also found on South Stack, Holy Island, in 1970.

In the Channel Islands, there are recent records only from Jersey and Guernsey, but it was recorded by Burr (1899) as common in Alderney.

E. panzeri is the most maritime and the most widespread of our three native species of cockroach. Its presence in the Scilly Isles and in Guernsey points to an early post-glacial arrival, but its apparent absence from the Isle of Man and Ireland indicates a possible climatic barrier to its spread. However, it is a very unobtrusive species and, like the grasshopper, *Chorthippus albomarginatus*, which had escaped detection in the Midlands until recently, it is quite conceivable that *E. panzeri* also remains undetected in many localities beyond the limits of its known British range.

This species also occurs in western and central Europe.

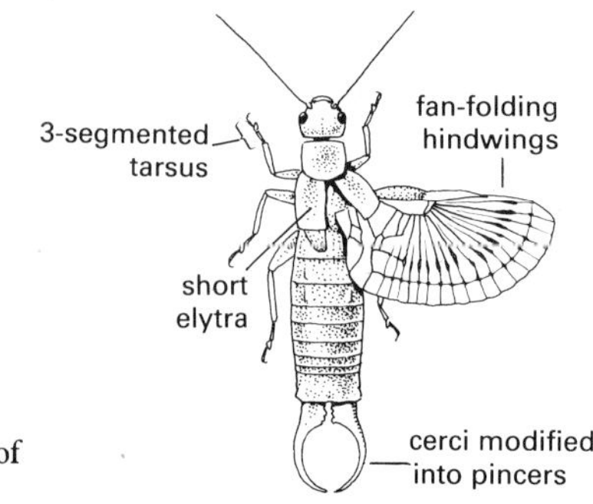

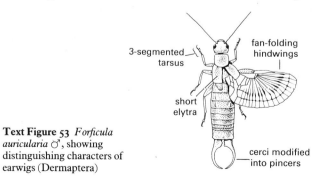

Text Figure 53 *Forficula auricularia* ♂, showing distinguishing characters of earwigs (Dermaptera)

Order DERMAPTERA

Earwigs are well-known and widely distributed insects, easily recognized by the large pincers or forceps at the end of the abdomen. Few people will not know the common earwig, *Forficula auricularia* (p. 137) which often makes a nuisance of itself by eating flower buds or young plants, or by 'invading' houses during an earwig population explosion. Normally their omnivorous scavenging behaviour could be regarded as beneficial, though probably few keen gardeners would agree, and since their introduction into North America they have proved to be a considerable nuisance there. The name 'earwig' is derived from the Old English 'ear wicga', meaning ear-insect or beetle, and exemplifies the liking of earwigs for dark cavities. Whilst doubts have been expressed as to the validity of this derivation of the name, some years ago a 'gentleman of the road' called into the Entomology Department of the British Museum (Natural History), expressly to testify to interested experts that earwigs do actually enter ears! It is understandable that when seeking a suitable dark cavity in which to rest during the day, nocturnal earwigs might find human ears offer a suitable resting place, and particularly so in former days when sleeping conditions for the population were more closely linked with nature. The similarity of earwig names in other languages, such as the German *öhrwurm* (ear-worm) and the French *perce-oreille* (ear-piercer), seem to bear this out.

Anyone handling an earwig will appreciate that the forceps are used defensively, the creature agilely curving its abdomen to 'pinch' with them, though the more showy forceps of the male may be less effective as weapons than those of the female. Male forceps may vary immensely in size, the larger or macrolabic forms having the apical, untoothed part much extended in comparison with the basal portion. Whilst various studies have named different 'morphs' (Ollason, 1972) it seems that there is a continuous variation in size and length, with healthy, well-nourished nymphs which undergo their final ecdysis in ideal conditions producing the largest forceps (Burr, 1939a). The forceps are also used offensively in seizing and killing their prey.

Although many species of earwig have only reduced wings or none at all, others have fully developed hindwings which are folded and concealed beneath the forewings. The forewings, often referred to as elytra or tegmina, are reduced and highly chitinized, resembling the short 'wing-cases' of staphylinid beetles with which they may be confused. The hindwings are highly modified, the main veins (subcosta, costa, radius and mediocubitus) being reduced to specialized areas (Henson, 1951), and the anal veins being greatly enlarged into a delicate fan-like structure (text fig. 53). When closed they are folded up like a fan, then folded over about half-way down the fan, finally being folded again and tucked under the forewings, with a chitinized portion, the squama, remaining the only part visible when folded. Once the delicate flying area has been safely tucked away, the forewings are held firmly in place to protect them when burrowing. On the underside of each elytron, near the inner margin, is a row of minute hook-like spines; these engage on each side with a corresponding double row of hook-like spines in the centre of the metanotum. This has been illustrated in *F. auricularia* (Burr, 1939b) and *Labia minor* (Eastop, 1953).

One of the great insect questions is 'can earwigs fly ?', to which many have replied 'no' – even though wings may be present. Certainly in the case of *F. auricularia*, very few people have witnessed flight, or at least have not recorded their observation. However, there had been enough reports for Burr (1939b) to be convinced that it can and does fly. It is widely recognized that *L. minor* flies readily, and in this species Fulton (1924) observed that the forceps are used to 'unzip' the two rows of hooks holding the elytra in place over the wings. The earwig curves over its forceps and flicks the tips under the ends of the elytra to open them. When landing after flying the wings are folded away very rapidly, no doubt contributing to the lack of recorded observations. It would seem that earwigs cannot be persuaded to fly unless they choose to do so; one laboratory study of *Labidura riparia* stated that 'all attempts to induce the animal to take to wings failed' (Hardas, 1960), whilst another observed that 'two females were seen flying slowly in the laboratory, around the electric lamp' (Tawfik *et al.*, 1972).

About 1000 species of Dermaptera are known, but few of them have been studied in any detail. The maternal care shown by *F. auricularia* (see p. 137) has been observed by several authors and was summarized by Lamb (1976), who also listed works on other species. Although this behaviour has been observed in only a few species it is assumed that similar maternal care is shown by all earwigs.

There are usually four nymphal instars in earwigs, adults being recognized by the fully-developed forceps, which are modified unsegmented cerci, and are visible in all nymphal stages. (In some tropical species the nymphal forceps are segmented, but no British species show this feature.) The older nymphs of winged species have flat wing-pads (Pl. 9, fig. 22).

Earwigs have prognathous heads, with no ocelli. The pronotum is a single, dorsal plate and the tarsi are three-segmented. Dorsally males have ten visible segments or tergites, the eleventh forming the pygidium (or epiproct, (Harz & Kaltenbach, 1976)) which in some species is visible between the forceps. In females, segments 8 and 9 are concealed so that dorsally only eight segments are visible.

There are only four native species of Dermaptera and three established aliens, which present little difficulty in identification. However, in many of the world Dermaptera, including the 45 European species, the structure of the internal genitalia of the male is often the only positive means of identification. The number of antennal segments is also an important taxonomic feature, or at least it would be if specimens could be relied upon to retain full-length antennae; unfortunately the antennal tips are frequently broken off in life, and almost invariably broken in dead specimens and so are an unreliable feature for purposes of identification.

All species found in Britain are thought to be omnivorous.

Characteristics of dermapteran families (Brindle, 1973, 1978):

ANISOLABIDIDAE (p. 134)
[= Carcinophoridae]

Typically large, dark-coloured earwigs without elytra or wings, ranging in size from very small to very large. Second tarsal segment simple. Forceps relatively short and simple, those of male not very much more elaborate than those of female, though sometimes more curved. This is a primitive group in which the structure of the male internal genitalia is diagnostic to species. The antennae have 16–17 segments.

LABIIDAE (p. 135)
[= Spongiphoridae]

Typically small species; second tarsal segment simple (text fig. 32, p. 77). Male pygidium visible dorsally between cerci. In Labiinae, 3rd antennal segment always shorter than 5th, eyes always small and elytra usually punctate or pubescent. In Spongiphorinae, 3rd antennal segment as long as or longer than 5th, eyes usually large, and elytra usually smooth. Antennae have 11–12 segments.

FORFICULIDAE (p. 136)

Second tarsal segment broad and flattened, having heart-shaped appearance (text fig. 33, p. 77). Internal genitalia of male more uniform in structure and of less value in specific identification. Antennae have 11–14 segments.

LABIDURIDAE (p. 139)

Second tarsal segment simple. Antennae have more than 20 segments, usually 27–30.

ANISOLABIDIDAE

Euborellia annulipes (Lucas)
The Ring-legged Earwig

Description (Pl. 9, figs 14,15)

A **shiny, blackish brown** earwig, with **yellow legs; femora ringed with blackish bands. Completely apterous** – both wings and elytra being absent. **Forceps short and broad** (fig. 15), **often shorter and slightly more curved in male, and with right branch more incurved than left**.

Body length ♂ ♀ 9–11mm
Forceps length ♂ 1.25–2.5mm, ♀ 2–2.5mm

Life History and Behaviour

As with other species in this order, maternal care of the eggs in a subterranean nest, and of the nymphs up to the second instar occurs (see p. 133). Storage of food for the nymphs to feed on in or near the nest has been observed in this species and the related *Anisolabis maritima* (Lamb, 1976).

Habitat

A littoral species found under stones in damp places throughout the Mediterranean region, but sometimes carried north in produce (Chinery, 1986). In Britain, *E. annulipes* has become established near ports and there are also inland records from refuse-tips.

Distribution and Status (Map 39, p. 185)

There are English records indoors from the vice-counties of South Devon, East Kent, Surrey, Middlesex, Stafford and Cheshire (Lucas, 1920) and from West Gloucestershire (Kevan, 1952; 1953) and outdoor records from rubbish tips at Barton, near Manchester, (Britten, 1933) and Mill Hill, Middlesex (Kevan, 1952). Recorded in Scotland from Lanark (Lucas, 1920) and from Leith, Midlothian, in 1950 (Biological Records Centre data).

This flightless adventive was imported in ship's ballast in the past and managed to persist for some time in suitable places. It is unlikely to be able to spread in the British Isles but, like *Euscorpius flavicaudis* De Geer, the little scorpion from southern and central Europe, might be able to persist in neglected corners of old docklands with an adequately warm micro-climate, such as those along the Thames.

This is a cosmopolitan species with a very widely known distribution.

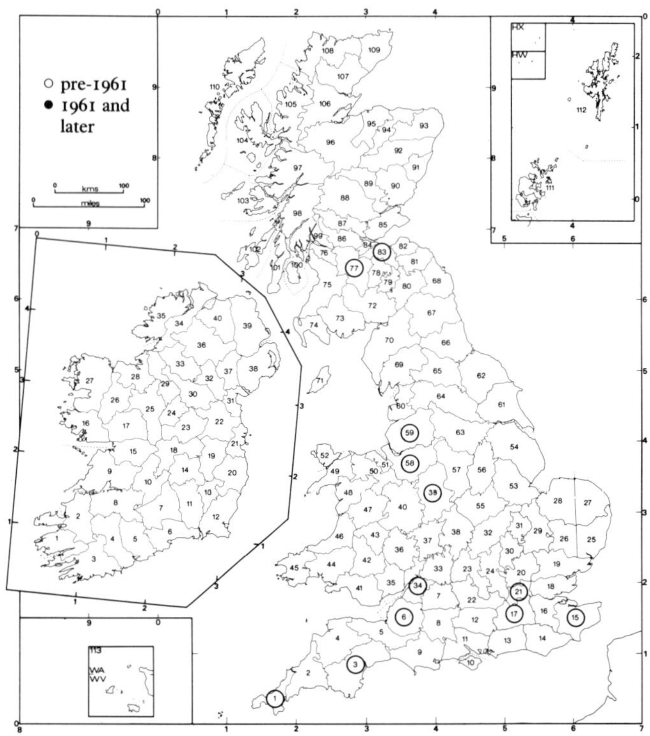

Euborellia annulipes

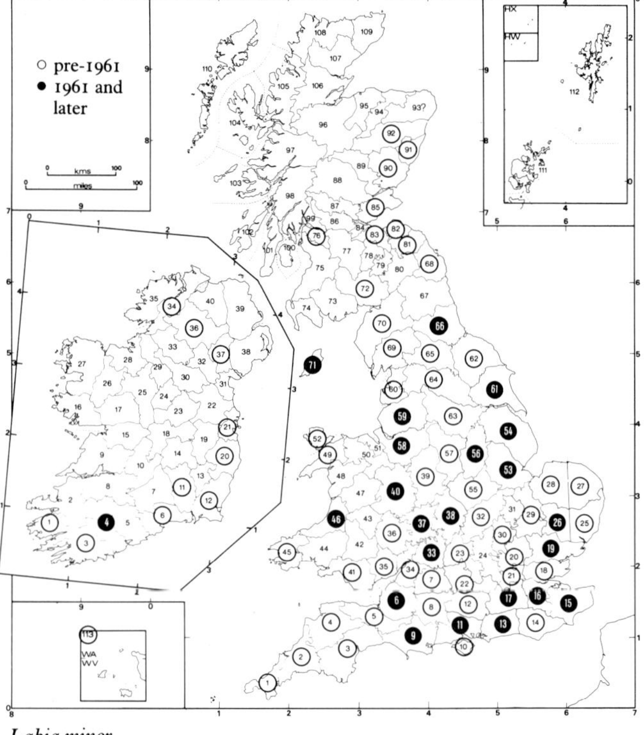

Labia minor

LABIIDAE

Labia minor (Linnaeus)
The Lesser Earwig

Description (Pl. 9, figs 16,17)

A **small, pubescent, dull yellowish brown** earwig with blackish head. Its **long hindwings** , when folded at rest, protrude from beneath elytra. **Forceps of both sexes slender** (fig. 17), gently curved in male. Species similar in appearance to, and can be confused with, small staphylinid beetle.

Body length	♂♀ 4–6mm
Forceps length	♂ 0.75–1.25mm, ♀ 0.5–1mm

Life History and Behaviour

The eggs of this species, which are opaque white, ovoid and 0.8 × 0.6mm in size, require a high level of relative humidity to hatch. In a recent study of *L. minor* in Denmark (Mourier, 1986) it has been shown that they favour the lowest and most mature part of their dung-heap habitat, where temperatures are about 18–25°C. Maternal care is also essential, and the female remains with the eggs, which hatch in about 7–12 days, and then with the young nymphs for a further week or two before they disperse. In the heat of the dung heap, development can continue throughout the year so that all stages of the life-cycle may occur together. The life span at 25°C is about eighty days.

In hot weather, the adults may fly considerable distances from their normal habitat and are sometimes found in buildings or vehicles. They are also attracted to light.

Habitat

Whilst particularly favouring dung-heaps, this species can also be found in compost and rubbish-tips which provide similar conditions of warmth, humidity and shelter in both urban and rural districts.

Distribution and Status (Map 40, page 185)

There are records from all but three English counties, though few from exact localities. The 10km square records show that it is still widespread but must considerably understate the true distribution. Although there are pre-1961 vice-county records from Glamorgan, Pembrokeshire, Caernarvonshire and Anglesey, there is only one 10km square record for Wales (Fowles, 1988). Again, in Scotland, there are only old records from Dumfriesshire, Berwickshire, Renfrewshire, East Lothian, Midlotian, Fifeshire, Angus, Kincardineshire and South Aberdeenshire (Kevan, 1961). Kevan also reported this species from ten Irish vice-counties (1961), and there was a further vice-county record in 1976 from farmland near Riverstick, Mid Cork (Good, 1979). In the Channel Islands, recorded from Guernsey (Kevan, 1961), where it was noted as abundant in gardens at the end of the last century (Burr, 1899), and from Jersey.

It is clear that *L. minor* has long been a widespread British insect, although its status is difficult to assess. Probably it was much commoner in the days of horse transport and has declined over the last fifty years. However, with the greater popularity of recreational horse-riding, its numbers may have increased as stable yards and their associated dung-heaps have again become more numerous, even in quite built-up areas. This earwig can easily be overlooked or misidentified.

This species occurs widely in Europe and, though probably western Palaearctic in origin, is now also found in North America, Africa (including Madagascar) and through the Oriental and Australasian regions (Brindle, 1977).

Marava arachidis (Yersin)
The Bone-house Earwig

Description (Pl. 9, figs 18, 19)

A dark or less dark **reddish brown** earwig. **Elytra short** and **neither sex with visible hindwings**. A fully-winged form is known in tropical regions but has not been found here. **Male has slightly curved forceps, with single tooth near apex**, and **five-sided pygidium**.

Body length	♂♀ 5–9mm
Forceps length	♂ 1.5–2.75mm, ♀ 0.75–1.25mm

Life History and Behaviour

Maternal care has been observed in this species, in which the eggs hatch almost immediately after being laid, the female ensuring the nymphs are free of their egg-shells (Herter, 1965; Lamb, 1976). There are four nymphal instars.

This little earwig was initially associated with bone-stores used in the now out-dated method of making glue, hence its vernacular name. The scientific name *arachidis*, however, is derived from the origin of the type specimen – found in 1859 among a consignment of peanuts (Fr. '*arachides*') in Marseilles; not, as understood by Harz (Harz & Kaltenbach, 1976) in a spider's (arachnid's) web!

Habitat

Although linked by its name with 'bone-houses', it has been found in a variety of warehouses where dried organic materials are stored.

Distribution and Status

In the earlier part of this century, this alien became established indoors in warehouses and factories in East Kent, Middlesex, Cheshire and Yorkshire (Lucas, 1920) and more recently in West Gloucestershire (Kevan,

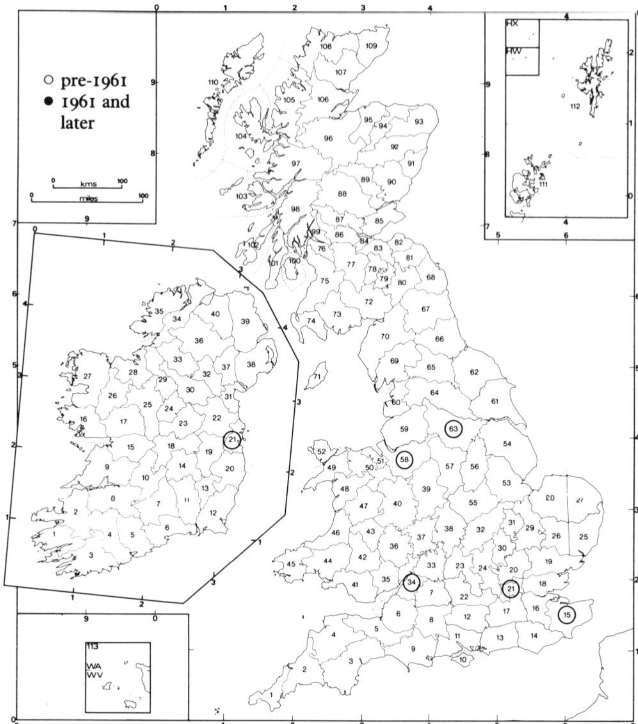

Marava arachidis

1952, 1953). In Ireland there is one record from Dublin of specimens imported with rice, all of which had been killed by fumigation (O'Mahony, 1950). There are no post-1960 records.

Though originally a native of the Oriental-Australasian regions this species now has a cosmopolitan distribution, being established in all warmer parts of the world (Brindle, 1977).

FORFICULIDAE

Apterygida media (Hagenbach)
[= *A. albipennis* (Charpentier)]
The Short-winged or Hop-garden Earwig

Description (Pl. 9, figs 20,21)

A **reddish brown** earwig, with **yellow legs** and **short, light brown elytra. Hind-wings reduced to tiny lobes and concealed by elytra.** Forceps of female straight (fig. 21); of **male long and gently curved with at least one tooth, sometimes two, on each branch**; both sexes with **prominent pygidium.** Female very similar in appearance to female *Forficula lesnei*, from which distinguishable by larger size and darker body colour.

Body length	♂♀ 6–10 mm
Forceps length	♂ 2.5–5mm, ♀ 1.5–2.5mm

Life History and Behaviour

Though not observed, this species is assumed to show the maternal care described for other species. Adults are seen in August-September and are nocturnal. In Europe it has been recorded throughout the year (Harz & Kaltenbach, 1976). It climbs vegetation and chews petals, commonly resting in flowers and hibernating under bark and moss.

Habitat

A. media was formerly a characteristic insect of Kentish hop-gardens before the widespread use of potent insecticides. It is now usually found in thickets, hedges and on woodland-edge scrub in warm localities.

Distribution and Status (Map 41, page 186)

This earwig is found only in the south-eastern part of Britain, where it is still widespread in East Kent, and also in East Anglia, where there are records from West and East Suffolk, most recently from Westhall, between Beccles and Halesworth in 1981. There are also old records from Norfolk and Cambridgeshire, and an unconfirmed report from Box Hill, Surrey, in June 1955 (Payne, 1958a).

A. media is probably a late post-glacial arrival across Dogger Land. It seems able to survive only in the drier parts of the extreme east of England where the climate is more Continental. However, within its very restricted British range, it is frequent and locally perhaps even numerous but, as with most other native species, it is easily overlooked and requires special search. Its British distribution does not appear to have changed over the last century.

This European species occurs from the Iberian Peninsula to Greece (including Crete), extending as far north as Denmark and Sweden.

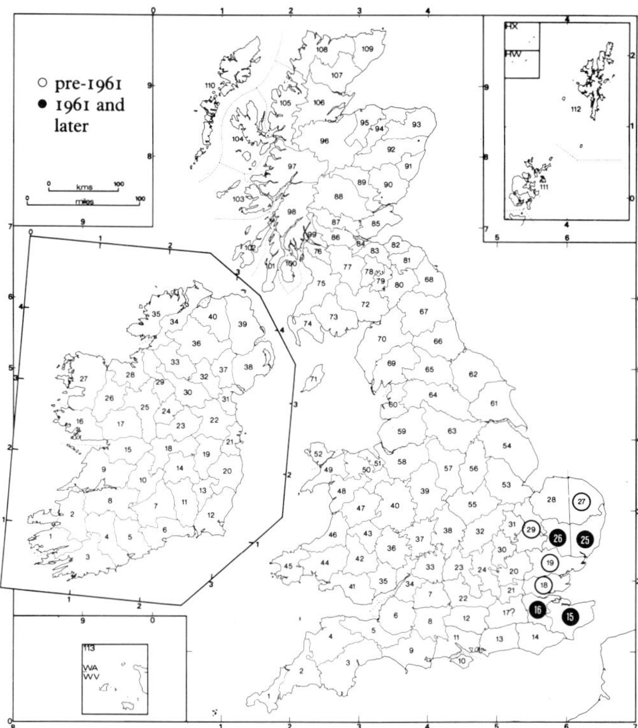

Apterygida media

Forficula auricularia Linnaeus
[= *F. forcipata* Stephens]
The Common Earwig

Description (Pl. 9, figs 22–25)

A **shiny, dark chestnut-brown** earwig, with yellowish legs, elytra and hindwing squamae, and **yellow-bordered pronotum. Hindwings large** (text fig. 53, p. 132), and folded up at rest, just projecting from underneath elytra, leaving most of abdomen visible (figs 22, 24). **Forceps large**, almost straight in female (fig. 25), but **strongly curved and widened basally, with inner knobs or teeth, in male**. Males may occur in the macrolabic form (described by Stephens (1835) as a distinct species, *forcipata*) which has much longer forceps (fig. 23). This form is particularly common on offshore islands where populations are often also larger in body size.

Body length	♂♀ 10–15mm
Forceps length	♂ 2.5–8mm, ♀ 2.5mm

Life History and Behaviour

The success of the life-cycle of *F. auricularia* is dependent upon maternal care of the eggs and young nymphs. In the autumn, mating occurs and the mated pairs retreat to small cavities or cells dug out in the soil. During the winter the male leaves – or is ejected by the female – and soon dies. The female then lays 30–50 pale creamish white eggs, 1.1 × 0.9mm and broadly elliptical, which she cares for by licking, collecting them together again if they become scattered. Eggs not kept clean and mould-free by licking or artificial cleaning will not hatch (Buxton & Madge, 1974). Sometimes nests may be found with as many as 80 eggs, where one female has taken over the eggs of another from an adjacent nest. In early spring the eggs hatch, the young staying in the nest with the mother for a time, dispersing after their first or second moult and becoming adult by about July. There are usually four nymphal instars (Brindle, 1977), though five have been recorded in Continental populations (Herter, 1965). Immediately after moulting, the earwig is pure white, giving rise to the belief that albino earwigs occur; however as the cuticle hardens and darkens, the normal hue soon appears. Females sometimes survive long enough to rear a second brood from eggs laid in May, adults appearing in the autumn. Although this species can fly, it is extremely rarely seen to do so and is mainly active at night.

Habitat

F. auricularia is very common in hedgerows, scrub and woodland rides, and also frequent on coarse, ungrazed herbage on scrubby heathland and mountains, and in marshland and waterside vegetation. It is infrequent in arable farmland, close-grazed turf and dry heathland. However, as adults and older nymphs need crevices in which to shelter, most gardens in both urban and rural areas provide suitable habitat. Coastally it occurs on sea-cliffs, vegetated dunes and shingle beaches, even in very exposed conditions, provided there is sufficient permanent cover, but does not normally occur in salt-marsh herbage.

Distribution and Status (Map 42, page 186)

In England and Wales, *F. auricularia* has been recorded from every vice-county, including many towns and cities; in Scotland, from most counties and many offshore islands including Islay, the Outer Hebrides, St. Kilda, Orkney and Shetland; and in Ireland, from most vice-counties as well as from the offshore islands of Inishmore, Clare and Tory Island, Co. Donegal. It has also been found on most of the Channel Islands, including the Guernsey offshore islands of Lihou and Chapelle Dom Hue (Kevan, 1961).

This earwig is clearly one of the most ubiquitous of larger British insects, but, because of its familiarity (and general unpopularity) it is also relatively one of the most poorly recorded of native species, as the dot-distribution map shows! A fair proportion of records are of the interesting macrolabic male form, which does receive some prominence in collections and the literature, unlike the more numerous typical form with normal-sized

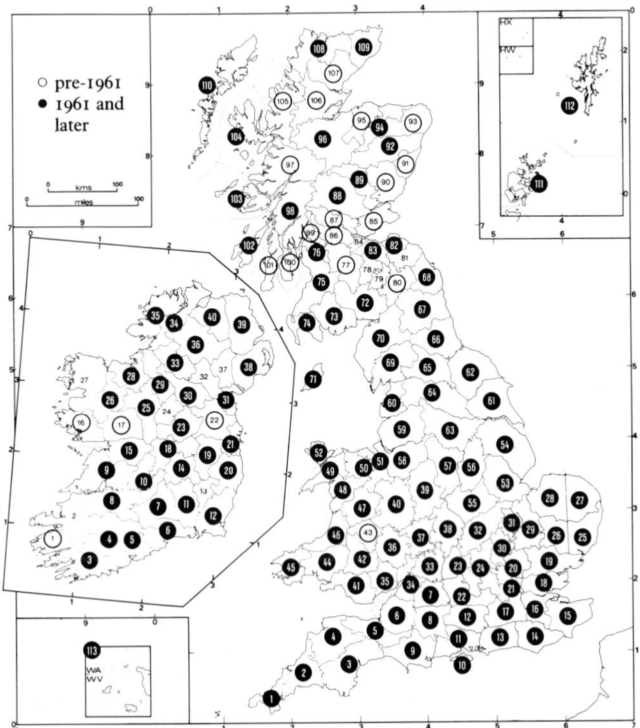

Forficula auricularia

forceps. Any long series of males will display a wide range of length of forceps.

It is almost certainly an early post-glacial arrival, but its natural range has doubtless been considerably enhanced by human activity. Since Neolithic times man has used boats for transport, and, because of its habit of seeking shelter in crevices, it readily enters packages, containers of produce and also the boats themselves and would thus have been transported to most of the remote islands around our shores. Its ability to remain active during the winter months and to reproduce during this season indicates its adaptation to the cool but relatively mild and oceanic climate of the British Isles.

This species is western Palaearctic in origin but now occurs thoughout the world as an adventive, and is well established in North America, Australia and New Zealand, and other areas, though it prefers cooler climates and in the tropics is established only at higher altitudes (Brindle, 1977).

Forficula lesnei Finot

Lesne's Earwig

Description (Pl. 9, figs 26,27)

A **smallish, light brown** earwig, with **short elytra; hindwings either absent or so small as to be concealed by elytra. Male forceps strongly curved with long widened basal portion**; those of female straight. Macrolabic forms have not been recorded for this species.

Body length	♂♀ 6–7mm
Forceps length	♂ 2.5–3.0mm, ♀ 2.0mm

Life History and Behaviour

Little is known of the life history of this species, although maternal care of the eggs and young nymphs is assumed to occur. The adults are nocturnal and unobtrusive and have usually been found in late summer, mainly by beating. I. S. Menzies found it in some numbers between the leaves and stems and about the flowering spikes of mullein (*Verbascum* spp.) (Payne, 1958a). Recorded from July to November in Europe (Harz & Kaltenbach, 1976).

Habitat

F. lesnei has most recently been found in oak woodland, chalk scrub (particularly near disused quarries), hedgerows and nettle-beds, as well as rough herbage on sea cliffs.

Distribution and Status (Map 43, page 187)

There are pre-1961 records for nearly all the Channel-coast counties as well as the Scillies and Lundy (Kevan, 1961). Since 1960, all the records have been from central-southern and south-eastern England, mainly as the result of detailed surveys. It has been found recently at Tollesbury, Essex; at a number of sites in Kent; in Surrey; in Berkshire; in Oxfordshire, including the old site at Wick Copse, Headington, mentioned by Lucas (1920); and along the Dorset coast.

Although Burr (1936) considered that *F. lesnei* had an Atlantic distribution with the south coast of Britain at the northern edge of its range, there have been no recent finds farther west than East Dorset; its present range in this country suggests a preference for a Continental rather than an Atlantic climate. However, as this earwig is not readily found except by deliberate search, it may still occur undetected in the Devonian peninsula and even on the Scillies. From what is known of its distribution, it is probably a fairly early post-glacial arrival at the extreme edge of its range. On these grounds, its presence may be anticipated in the south of Ireland and would be worth a search.

This species has a limited western European distribution through the Iberian Peninsula and France.

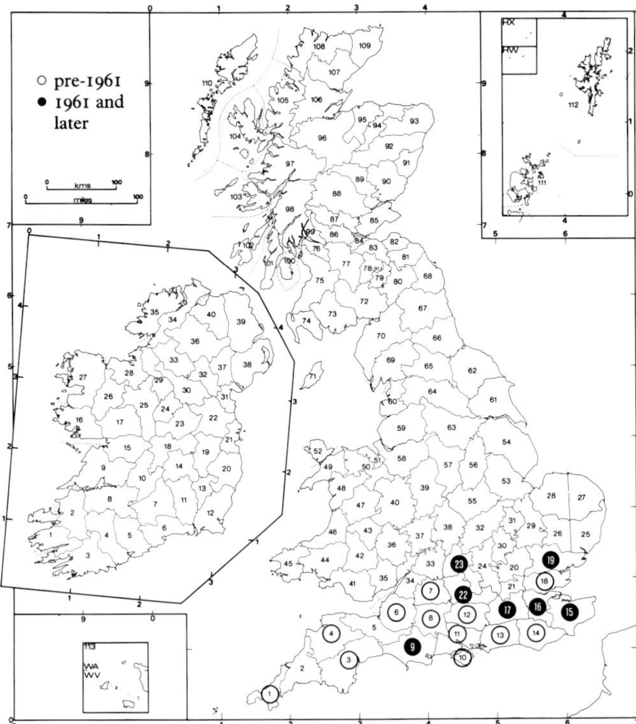

Forficula lesnei

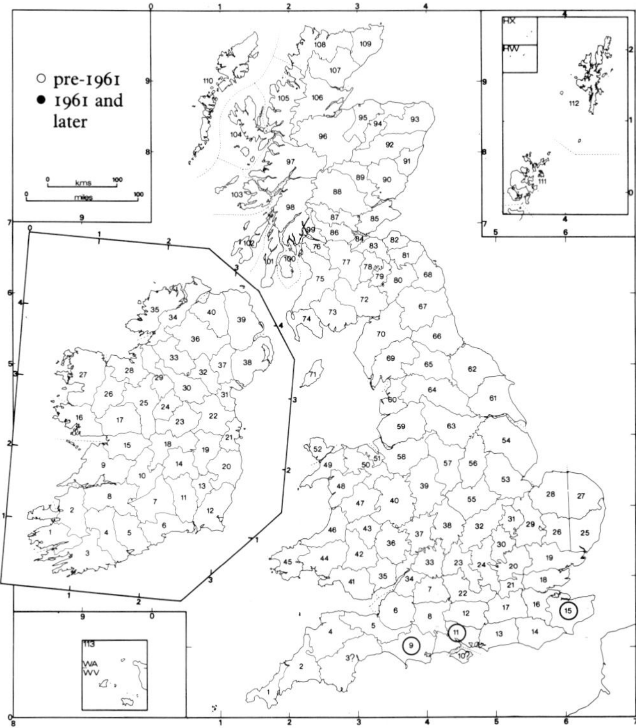

Labidura riparia

LABIDURIDAE

Labidura riparia (Pallas)

The Giant or Tawny Earwig

Description (Pl. 9, figs 28,29)

A **large, yellow** earwig, with **dark brown markings on elytra, pronotum and abdomen**. Both sexes **fully winged**, folded hindwings protruding from beneath elytra. **Forceps long and gently curved in male, with inner tooth**, and **almost straight in female** (fig. 29). **Male has two blunt spines on hind margin of tenth tergite**, projecting between forceps.

This species varies greatly in size and depth of colour in different parts of the world; and between 1773 and 1930 it was described, under synonymous names, about forty different times.

Body length ♂♀ 12–26mm
Forceps length ♂ 5–10mm, ♀ 3.5–5.0mm

Life History and Behaviour

The maternal care of eggs and young nymphs shown in this species has been studied by several workers (Lamb, 1976), but its life-cycle in Britain has not been described. *L. riparia* hides during the day under dry seaweed and jetsam and makes long tunnels in the sand. It is active in the evening and at night.

Habitat

L. riparia is a coastal species in Britain. It is most likely to be found on white sand (Burr, 1936), where its burrows may be close to the high-water mark. It has also been recorded as a casual introduction in ballast.

Distribution and Status (Map 44, page 187)

L. riparia was first found near Christchurch, Hampshire, in 1808 and was known at Pokesdown, a suburb of Bournemouth, possibly until the early 1930s (Burr, 1936). Its only other certain locality was at Folkestone, East Kent (Wood, 1872). There are doubtful records from Dorset and the Isle of Wight, but none since 1940. However, a specimen may have been seen in the early 1980s between Sidmouth and Beer on the South Devon coast. A sketch made was mislaid before identification could be confirmed. This, the largest of the European earwigs, may be a native species at the extreme limit of its range or a temporarily established alien (Kevan, 1953) but it has always been a rarity in Britain, existing only precariously in a few places on the South Coast where there were colonies. As it is difficult to locate, it could yet survive, undetected, in some subterranean site by the English Channel. It would be worth a search.

This cosmopolitan species is widely distributed in Europe, though north of the Alps it is very local (Harz & Kaltenbach, 1976).

Order PHASMIDA

The Phasmida found in Britain are all very characteristic stick-insects, slender and stick-like (text fig. 54). They are nocturnal insects, though may be found by day when resting on vegetation. The antennae are fairly long and slender, though not thread-like. They have no conspicuous shield or saddle-shaped pronotum; the prothoracic region is short and simple. Both meso- and metathoracic regions are much longer, thus extending the distance between the mid- and hindlegs; the hindlegs are only very slightly larger than the mid-legs and are not saltatorial. Indeed phasmid movement often seems slow and laborious by comparison with other orthopteroid insects. The tarsi are five-segmented. The Phasmida are particularly good at the regeneration of lost or damaged limbs or antennae, though the regenerated leg may be smaller than normal and have fewer tarsal segments. Occasionally a 'mistake' is made in regeneration and, instead of an antenna, a very small leg may regrow on the head. Adults may also be found with very stunted limbs which were lost too late in the nymphal life for complete regrowth. The abdomen is long and slender, bearing at the tip a pair of cerci; there are ten segments visible dorsally, including the first or 'median segment' which is between the hindlegs and appears to be part of the thorax. There are eight visible segments ventrally in the male, and seven in the female.

The head in phasmids is prognathous, that is the jaws are at the front and the head capsule appears to be a forward continuation of the body. The base of the fore femora have an inner depression which, when the legs are stretched forwards at rest, contour themselves around the head and aid the stick-like appearance.

The 'British' species, all belonging to the family Phasmatidae, do not have wings, though there are many tropical species cultured here which are winged; when present, the forewings are always reduced to fairly small lobes, the species that can fly using the larger hindwings only. Many of the tropical species are very spiny or have leaf-like lobes on the legs and/or abdomen. True leaf-insects, in which the abdomen of the female is wide and flat and the forewings very leaf-like, are also kept in culture. Some of the tropical or subtropical species have glands from which an offensive spray may be produced when the insect is disturbed.

The eggs of stick-insects are all seed-like in appearance (text fig. 55); those of species found in the British Isles all have a capitulum – a variable process above the operculum or lid of the egg which has proved valuable in the ootaxonomic study of relationships within the Phasmida (Clark Sellick, 1988). Eggs are usually simply dropped to the ground by the female, or more actively dispersed by flicking the egg from the tip of the abdomen; however, some tropical species lay their eggs in soil, moss or crevices in bark. The British species all develop by parthenogenesis, laying unfertilized eggs which hatch into females. Males may occur rarely in *Carausius morosus* (see p. 144).

There are from four to six nymphal instars in the British phasmids, though more in the tropical species, particularly in the much larger insects; often, as the female grows to a considerably larger size than the male, she has one (or more) extra instar.

There are over 2,000 described Phasmida species of which under 20 are native to Europe.

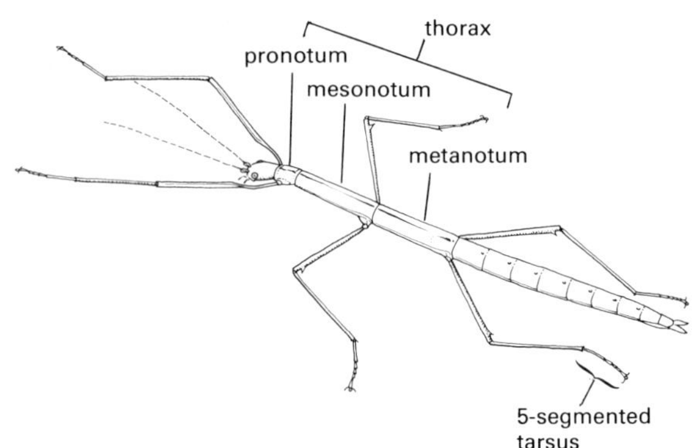

Text Figure 54 *Clitarchus hookeri* ♀, showing distinguishing characters of phasmids (Phasmatidae)

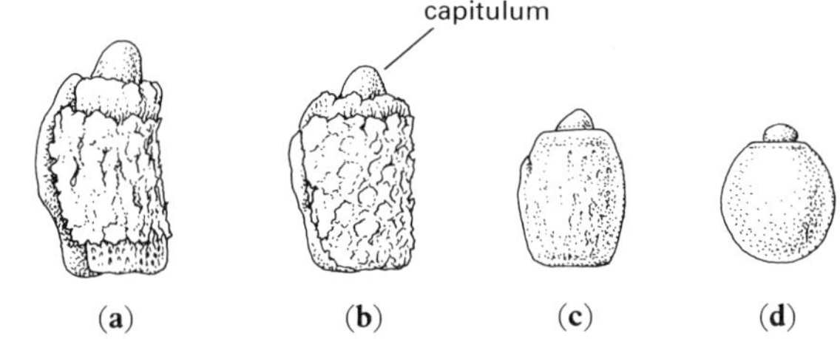

Text Figure 55 Eggs of 'British' phasmids showing capitulum (**a**) *Acanthoxyla geisovii*; (**b**) *A. inermis*; (**c**) *Clitarchus hookeri*; (**d**) *Carausius morosus*

PHASMATIDAE

Acanthoxyla geisovii (Kaup)
[previously identified as *A. prasina* (Westwood)]
The Prickly Stick-insect

TAXONOMIC NOTE: This species was originally identified in Britain by Kirby (1910) as *Macracantha geisovii* Kaup.

However Uvarov (1944) determined it as *Acanthoxyla prasina* (Westwood), a closely-related species with which he thought it might prove to be synonymous. In that case, it would retain the name *prasina* under the rule of priority (see p. 17), being the senior (older) name. However it has recently been confirmed as *A. geisovii* and considered a distinct species, after comparison with specimens in the National Museum of New Zealand (Brock, 1986).

Description (Pl. 10, fig. 1)

A medium-sized stick-insect, usually green but occasionally brown; **head and thorax always covered with many black spines or tubercles often also present on abdominal segments 1–5 or 6. Lateral foliaceous lobes present on abdominal segments 4** (but not always), **5 and 6.** In **adults inside base of fore femora is pink. Opercular spine usually long (2 mm), straight or slightly curved. Cerci are large, flattened, rounded lobes.** Males not known, here or in New Zealand; females reproduce by parthenogenesis.

Total length	♀ 79–103mm
Egg	4.5 × 3.0mm

Life History and Behaviour

The eggs are large, with a spiky bark-like texture, and a large broad peg-shaped operculum (text fig. 55a). Adults have been found from July onwards and survive for about three months, having one generation each year. *A. geisovii* will take a wide variety of food plants; in Devon and Cornwall the Japanese Cedar (*Cryptomeria japonica*), cypress (*Cupressus* spp. and *Chamaecyperis* spp.), common myrtle (*Myrtus communis*) and various Rosaceae are eaten. The Rosaceae include rose, raspberry and loganberry as well as bramble, a widely-accepted alternative food-plant of many tropical or subtropical stick-insect species. In the Scilly Isles it is also found on *Pittosporum* shrubs, several species of which have been introduced from New Zealand.

Habitat

In Britain, this species has been found only in public and private gardens in districts with very mild, moist climates where the food-plants mentioned above occur.

Distribution and Status (Map 46, p. 188)

This phasmid is restricted to the Scilly Isles, Cornwall and South Devon. It is believed to have occurred in and around the grounds of Tresco Abbey since its introduction with plants from New Zealand in 1907, but was not reported until 1943 (Uvarov, 1944). It is now known from Old Grimsby, about half a mile away, and is probably present between here and Tresco Abbey. In 1959 it was deliberately introduced to St. Mawes, near Falmouth, whence it has spread to several neighbouring gardens

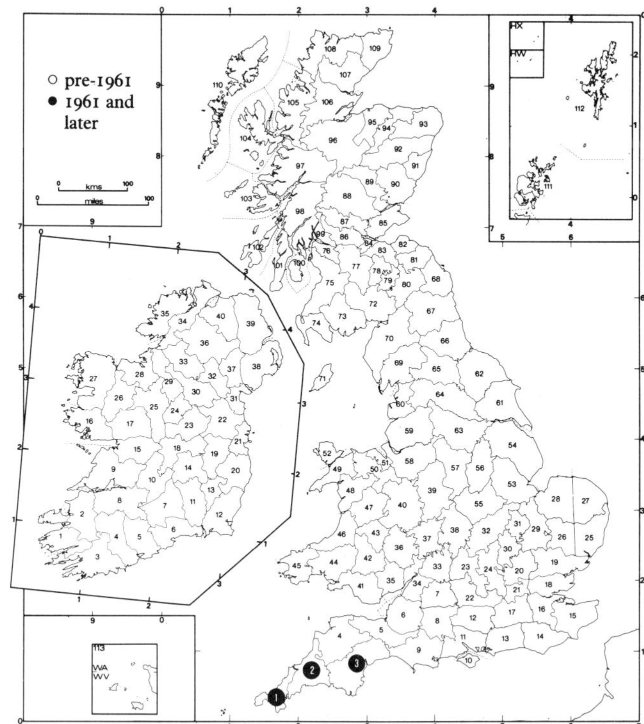

Acanthoxyla geisovii

(Turk, 1985) and now seems to be well established in the area. In 1969 it was found in a garden at Bar Road, Helford Passage, probably having been introduced on a tree fern (*Dicksonia antarctica*) imported from New Zealand (Turk, 1985).

In South Devon it has been recorded from the grounds of Paignton Zoo since 1908 (Kirby, 1910; Rivers, 1953). Despite much disturbance to its habitat, including the removal of a large Japanese cedar (*Cryptomeria japonica*) which was the main centre of the colony, it has apparently survived there and in other gardens in Paignton, and has been recorded in the town as recently as 1984. A long-known colony in the Palm House, Torquay, was exterminated with insecticides in the 1960s (Brock, 1985); however *A. geisovii* has since been recorded, in 1985, in a nearby garden. There is also a colony at Galmpton, between Paignton and Brixham, which has been known since the early 1970s.

This native of New Zealand was imported with plants and has survived in the South West and the Scilly Isles for over eighty years. Further colonies have spread from these original introductions as well as from later importations of New Zealand plants. Although a difficult species to rear in captivity, it has obviously adapted successfully to the mild wet climate of the far south-west of England and seems able to survive where established.

Acanthoxyla inermis Salmon
The Unarmed Stick-insect

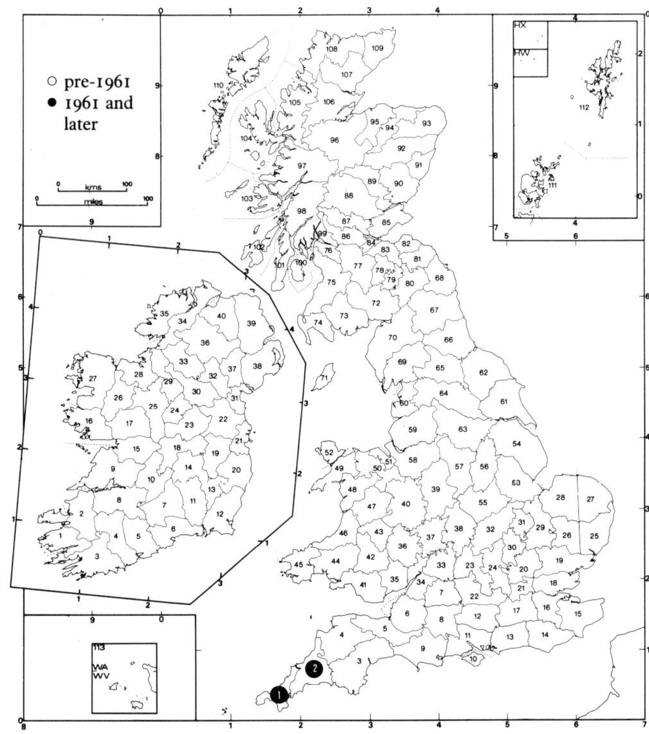

Acanthoxyla inermis

TAXONOMIC NOTE: This species has only recently been distinguished in Britain from *Clitarchus hookeri* (White), (Brock, 1986).

Description (Pl. 10, fig. 2)

A medium-sized stick-insect, green or brown, with **dorsal black line and central spot on prothorax only**. Sometimes with **a few scattered tubercles on head and/or thorax, always unicolorous; no foliaceous lobes on abdomen. In adults inside base of fore femora a bright pink. Opercular spine short and thick**; its presence readily distinguishes this species from *C. hookeri*, which never has an opercular spine. Only females known so far, reproducing by parthenogenesis.

Total length	♀ 94–115mm
Eggs	3.9 × 2.3mm

Life History and Behaviour

The eggs are very similar to those of *Acanthoxyla geisovii*, but smaller and slightly less spiky in texture (text fig. 55b). Nymphs and adults have been found in June and adults as late as December, though there is presumably only one generation each year.

Habitat

In Cornwall it has been found feeding on Banks' rose (*Rosa banksiae*), bramble, *Potentilla* spp. and also *Hypericum* spp. It is also now being successfully cultured, feeding on *Eucalyptus gunnii*.

Distribution and Status (Map 47, p. 189)

This recently-discovered New Zealand phasmid has so far been recorded with certainty in Britain only from West Cornwall. It was first recorded in a Falmouth garden in 1981, established on a rose bush. Specimens from this colony were collected and bred successfully and resulting nymphs were distributed around the area in the spring of 1982. A separate colony at Helford Passage has also been identified by Brock as *A. inermis* (1987, pers. comm.); this has probably arisen from a different plant importation. Another colony was discovered in late September 1987 in a Truro garden on the site of a former nursery, feeding on a shrubby *Potentilla*.

The Falmouth colony of *A. inermis* on *Rosa banksiae* has been traced to an importation of a number of these Chinese roses from New Zealand by a nurseryman at Merriott, Somerset, in the mid-1970s, who also found specimens in his greenhouse.

The early history of this species in Britain has been summarized by Brock (1986). In view of the relative ease with which it can be reared in captivity and the way it has been able to survive in West Cornwall, it is likely that discarded, escaped or deliberately 'planted' individuals will have formed colonies elsewhere in warm localities in the British Isles.

Clitarchus hookeri (White)

[= *C. laeviusculus* Stal]

The Smooth Stick-insect

Description (Pl. 10, fig. 3)

A medium-sized stick-insect, **usually green, with an interrupted black line dorsally on thorax**. In **adult females, inside base of fore femora a bright pinkish red. No opercular spine. Cerci are flattened and fairly long, pointed at tip**. Males have not been found in Britain although common in New Zealand; females here reproduce by parthenogenesis.

Total length	♂ 65–90mm
Eggs	3 × 2mm

Life History and Behaviour

The eggs are rough textured but not spiky; the operculum is a flattish conical shape (text fig. 54c). Nymphs have been collected in both June and August, and adults found from June to September. It is probable, however, that there is only one successful generation during the year; late-hatching nymphs being unlikely to reach maturity. It is known to feed on 'bottlebrushes' (*Callistemon* spp.), bramble (*Rubus* spp.), rose (*Rosa* spp.) and also ferns.

Habitat

Found in gardens and adjacent wasteland in a mild, moist climate feeding on above-mentioned plants and shrubs.

Distribution and Status (Map 48, page 189)

There are several British and Irish localities for this New Zealand alien. In England it was first recorded from the Abbey Gardens, Tresco, Isles of Scilly, in 1949 (Uvarov, 1950), where it has been found regularly since (Brock, 1986). On the mainland, it had been recorded from four localities near Falmouth, Cornwall (Turk, 1985), but it now seems possible that these were, in fact, *Acanthoxyla inermis* which had not, at that time, been distinguished in Britain from *C. hookeri*. The first introduction of *C. hookeri* into the British Isles may have been in the early years of this century with exotic plants imported into gardens on the island of Rossdohan, in the Bay of Kenmare, Co. Kerry, Ireland (Goodhue *et al.*, 1964). A species of smooth stick-insect has been found at two nearby sites in South Kerry recently. However, Brock (1986) warns that, with the recent discovery of *Acanthoxyla inermis* in Cornwall (previously misidentified as *C. hookeri*), all such 'smooth stick-insects should be carefully examined and, apart from those at Tresco, confirmation of identity is still needed.

C. hookeri was probably introduced from New Zealand at about the same time as *Acanthoxyla geisovii*, despite the fact that it was not recorded from Tresco until nearly 50 years later. It is able to survive in the mildest areas in small and easily-overlooked populations for many years.

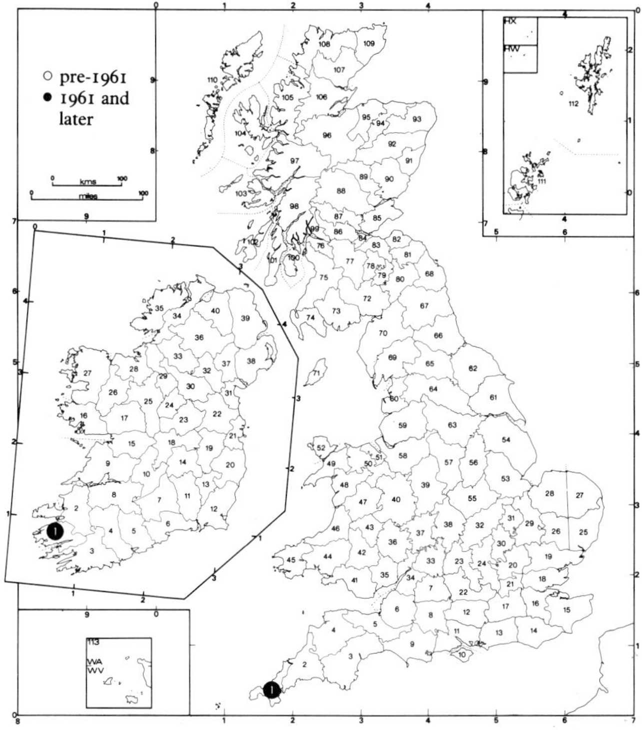

Clitarchus hookeri

Carausius morosus (Sinéty)

The Laboratory or Indian Stick-insect

TAXONOMIC NOTE: In 1900, the physiologist Sinéty needed a name for the laboratory culture on which he was working, and consulted the expert orthopterist (Carl) Brunner von Wattenwyl, who informed Sinéty that the culture belonged to a new species which he would be naming as *Dixippus morosus*. Sinéty then (in 1901) published his work and called the species *Dixippus morosus* Brunner. Unfortunately, Brunner eventually named the species as *Carausius morosus* in 1907. However, according to the internationally agreed rules of nomenclature (see page 17), Sinéty had actually published sufficient of a description in 1901 to establish its identity – and is thus the author of the species *Dixippus morosus* Sinéty. Since *morosus* was then transferred by Brunner to the genus *Carausius*, the correct combination for the name is therefore *Carausius morosus* (Sinéty).

Description (Pl. 10, figs. 4,5)

A **medium-sized** stick-insect, usually **dull green** or brownish, sometimes with darker mottling. In **adult females inside base of fore femora always a bright pinkish red**. Adult **males smaller and thinner than females, brown, without pink base on fore femora, but with red ventrally on meso- and metathorax**. In live males green lateral stripes visible on metathorax and dorsal pair of red patches (Clark, 1977).

Both sexes have only **very short cerci**.

Total length	♂ 49–61mm, ♀ 70–80mm
Eggs	3 × 2mm

Life History and Behaviour

The eggs are dull brown in colour and seedlike (text fig. 55d). The lid or operculum, which the nymph pushes off when emerging from the egg, bears a shiny yellowish knob. At room temperature eggs hatch in about 4–6 months; at higher temperatures the development period may be greatly reduced. In dry conditions the newly-emerged nymph may carry the egg-shell attached to a hind foot or the tip of the abdomen, or even be unable to hatch properly. There are usually six nymphal instars, taking 4–7 months to develop depending on temperature. During nymphal development their amazing ability to regenerate limbs may be seen; if a leg is lost by a young nymph an almost perfect replacement may be grown, sometimes being slightly smaller than the normal size, and with fewer tarsal segments. A leg lost by an older nymph will not be fully regenerated as there is insufficient growth period available.

The usual food-plant is common hedging privet (*Ligustrum ovalifolium*), but a variety of other plants will be eaten – ivy (*Hedera helix*) being a useful evergreen alternative, and lilac (*Syringa vulgaris*) a summer food. Bramble (*Rubus* spp.) will also be eaten if offered to the young nymphs. Food preference is random on hatching; only after about 20 days is a significant preference shown for the food on which it has been reared (Cassidy, 1978). Those fed on bramble from hatching show a preference for similar plants, *e.g.* rose (*Rosa* spp.) rather than privet – though not thriving as well as if fed on privet.

Adults are almost all females; males occur only rarely in cultures – perhaps only one in a thousand specimens – though occasionally unusually high numbers of males may develop. They are not necessary for the survival of the species, as the females reproduce by parthenogenesis: eggs being laid without fertilization and developing into normal females. Females will start laying eggs after a few weeks, simply dropping the eggs to the ground at night whilst feeding, each female producing several hundred eggs, all capable of hatching into another highly productive female. This facility makes them very useful as laboratory insects, but less popular (at least among human parents) as household pets!

Habitat

Eggs laid, or placed, out-of-doors during the summer will hatch and the young survive on privet or other suitable food plants until wiped out by the first frosts of autumn.

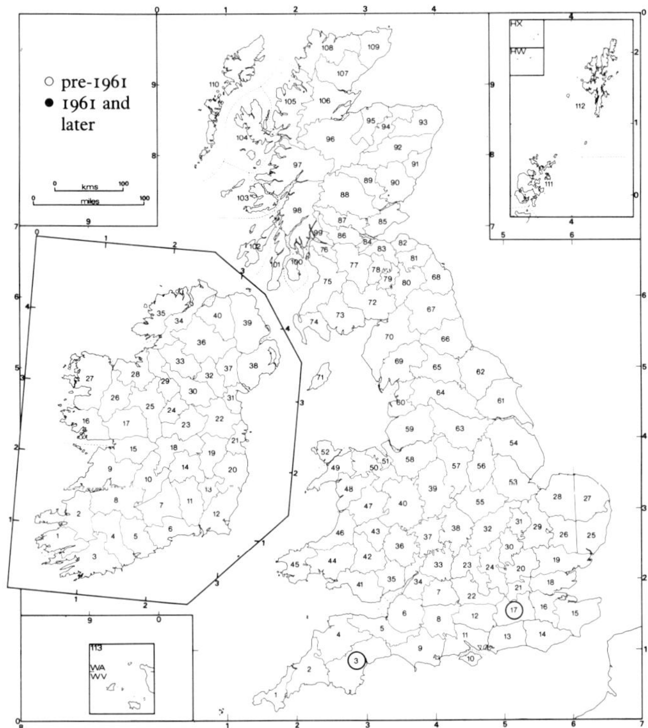

Carausius morosus

Distribution and Status

There are no permanent outdoor colonies of *C. morosus* in Britain or Ireland. All 'outdoor' finds result from cultured stock. One colony at Torquay in South Devon (Rivers, 1953) and another at the Royal Botanic Gardens, Kew, (Kevan, 1954) did persist under glass for many years but both died out.

This species was originally brought to Europe from southern India in about 1900 (Ragge, 1973) and immediately proved popular with biologists. This can be seen in the many hundreds of publications on physiological and other aspects of the species (*e.g.* Carlberg, 1983, 1985, 1986). However the once ubiquitous garden privet hedge is now in steady decline, and many other tropical or subtropical phasmid species are now available in culture in Europe, almost all of them being more attractive than the rather dull laboratory stick-insect. Some are winged and brightly coloured, or interestingly spined (Brock, 1985); most are bisexual and almost all are easier to feed as they will happily eat bramble and many other food plants (including a wide variety of house plants – again bad news for parents!).

CASUAL INTRODUCTIONS AND MIGRANT SPECIES

For centuries, insects and other animals have been entering Britain but only those that establish breeding colonies here are regarded as having become British species. However, the line between established aliens and casual introductions is somewhat obscured at times by the fact that some introductions are of already-established alien pest species. In such cases it may be difficult to decide whether a new record is of an extension of an established species' range or an introduction. With the increase of commerce and intercontinental travel, the number of possible introductions of foreign species has become almost unlimited, as also is the possibility of their establishment here. Single imported specimens may be found at docks or airports after escaping from their involuntary confinement with imported goods. The discovery of such a specimen should not be regarded as anything but a casual introduction. Early historical records are also confusing, as misidentifications may indicate the apparent presence of a Continental species. For example, an early record of the bush-cricket, *Ephippiger ephippiger*, was, in fact, a misnamed *Leptophyes punctatissima*.

Many foreign species of orthopteroid insects have been introduced here with fruit, vegetables and other imported goods, and a few other species have managed to fly here, assisted by favourable wind conditions. The major source of foreign introductions in recent years has been cargoes of bananas, from West Africa and the West Indies. During the 1950s and 1960s two species, known only from imported material and recognized as new to science by Ragge, were described by Gurney (1965): *Henschoutedenia tectidoma* (short-winged cinereous cockroach) from West Africa and *Pelmatosilpha larifuga* (vagabond cockroach) from the West Indies (see below). Several tropical species were given common names by Ragge (1965) because they are imported here so frequently. However, although the West Indian species are still fairly regular importations, African material is no longer regularly introduced. Specimens imported with bananas are not to be regarded as pests of bananas. Because banana bunches or 'hands' contain a large inner space providing suitable refuge, many nocturnal insects and other animals (spiders, lizards) seek shelter there during the daytime, and are then rather abruptly separated from their environment when the bananas are picked, packed and exported. Many specimens are later discovered in greengrocers' shops among other fruits and vegetables, causing no little surprise and even consternation.

ORTHOPTERA

RHAPHIDOPHORIDAE

Occasional specimens of *Tachycines asynamorus* (p. 78) are imported with plants, which provide a potential source of further establishments of the species in heated greenhouses. Specimens of one other camel-cricket, *Dolichopoda bormansi* Brunner, have been imported with *T. asynamorus* amongst plants, though when first recognized as a different species it was described as the synonymous *Chopardina importata* (Uvarov, 1921), but this species has not become established.

TETTIGONIIDAE

The majority of bush-cricket introductions are of large, brown species, imported with bananas. Ragge (1965) listed three species, including the West African *Cosmoderus maculatus* (Kirby) (prickly bush-cricket), which has not been recorded since the early 1960s. The other species he listed were *Jamaicana subguttata* (Walker) (mottle-winged bush-cricket) and *Mastophyllum scabricolle* (Serville) (brown-winged bush-cricket). Both of these, with *Jamaicana flava* Caudell and several species of the genus *Nesonotus*, have been imported occasionally, and can cause considerable excitement at their appearance. *Jamaicana* spp. are from 30–50mm in length, *Nesonotus* spp. from 40–70mm, and *Mastophyllum* up to 90mm. All are sturdy specimens with powerful legs, the females having long, broad ovipositors, and though all have a rather dull brown appearance, live *Nesonotus* spp. have beautiful turquoise-blue eyes. On one occasion a putative breeding colony of *N. tricornis* (Thunberg) was reported, after a load of rotting bananas had been deposited on a tip at Gerrards Cross in 1971. However the possibility of any tropical insect surviving for very long out-of-doors in our climate, even in summer, is remote in the extreme.

The establishment of a tropical species here is possible only in a protected environment: the tropical bush-cricket *Phlugiolopsis henryi* Zeuner was described from specimens found breeding in the Tropical Fern House in the Royal Botanic Gardens, Kew (Zeuner, 1940b), but its country of origin was unknown.

With the increased importation of tropical houseplants, single specimens of several unusual species have been recorded. In 1974 a large consignment of bromeliads and cacti, imported by air from the West Indies and South America, contained several live tree-frogs and lizards, and a number of bush-crickets of the genus *Arrhenotettix*, which present a bizarre appearance as they have several extra-long spines on their hind femora.

Some species may arrive in Britain without human agency. The records of *Phaneroptera falcata* from Cornwall and possibly Dorset are of single strays, probably wind-assisted immigrants (see also p. 23). It is also possible that the populations of *Conocephalus discolor* (p. 89) in southern Britain originate from such wind-borne strays which managed to establish viable colonies here.

GRYLLIDAE

The cosmotropical pest species *Gryllodes sigillatus* (Walker) (tropical house-cricket), is an occasional importation, and has become established in the Zoological Society of London's Gardens, Regent's Park and the Royal Botanic Gardens, Kew. Several species of crickets are occasionally imported with bananas and other goods. *Gryllus bimaculatus* De Geer (southern field-cricket), a fully-winged close relative of our rare *G. campestris* (p. 95), is perhaps the most frequent importation and is also widely cultured as a laboratory insect, though, having a southern European/North African/Asian distribution, it is unlikely to become established here out-of-doors.

ACRIDIDAE

Single specimens of foreign grasshoppers are occasionally imported with foodstuffs and plants. *Calliptamus italicus* (L.) (Italian locust), a southern European species, was included as a 'casual visitor' by Hincks (1949), probably on the basis of a single specimen found in Dorset in 1933 which may have reached England unaided, but is not known to have done so since.

The majority of 'locust' introductions with fruit, vegetables and other goods from the Mediterranean region are of *Anacridium aegyptium* (L.), the Egyptian grasshopper (Pl. 5, fig. 4). This is a large, brown species, 50–80mm in length, with dark patches on its hindwings.

Migrant specimens of *Locusta migratoria* (L.), (migratory locust) (Pl. 5, figs 2, 3), occasionally reach Britain and Ireland from mainland Europe, but so far never in sufficient numbers to cause problems. The locust plagues of Africa and Asia are well known, but there have been plague outbreaks in Europe over the centuries. *L. migratoria* has a very wide distribution, occurring in most of the temperate and tropical parts of the eastern hemisphere. It is divided into geographical subspecies which are distinguishable both biologically and morphologically; two of the European subspecies have been found in Britain. The principal northern subspecies is *L. migratoria migratoria* (L.), which, like most northern European grasshoppers, has an obligate egg diapause and thus only one generation each year. By contrast the African subspecies, *L. m. migratorioides* (Reiche & Fairmaire), has no diapause and from two to five generations a year are possible. The majority of the migrants to Britain are of the northern subspecies, *L. m. migratoria*, usually arriving here during August and September from mainland outbreaks which have arisen in the Danube delta area by the Black Sea. The distribution and migrations of *Locusta* in Europe were examined in detail by Waloff (1940). Specimens are apparently known to have reached here in 1347 and 1693, though the most impressive early records are for 1748 and the 1840s. Swarms occurred in Europe from 1745–54, with many reaching the British Isles in 1748, being brought over by east winds which predominated during the very hot summer of that year. Numbers were recorded in September from many English counties, and from Scotland and Ireland; by October some had even reached the Orkneys. During the major outbreaks of 1842–50, locusts reached as far as Yorkshire in September, 1842, with many more arriving in 1846. The majority again arrived in September, spreading up the east coast to Scotland, and around southern England to Devon and Cornwall. From examination of four specimens caught in 1846, Waloff (*loc.cit.*) established that they were of both the swarming, gregarious phase and the transient form which is intermediate between gregarious and solitary phases, proving they originated from swarm outbreaks. Further invasions occurred in 1857 and 1858, though single specimens of locusts have been found on various occasions both before and since, as detailed by Waloff.

The main outbreaks in Europe in this century, from which numerous specimens reached the British Isles in 1946, 1947 and 1948, were of *L. m. gallica* (Remaudière), a western European subspecies, allied to *L. m. cinerascens* (Fabricius). Both these subspecies are smaller than *L. m. migratoria*, with shorter elytra, and Harz (1975) suggested that *L. m. gallica* is probably merely a smaller, ecological form of *L. m. cinerascens*, which had become isolated in the Landes and Gironde regions of France. The outbreak in this area, where previously only solitary forms had been found, was a result of four very dry seasons with fires and subsequent growth of purple moor-grass (*Molinia caerulea*), thus providing both oviposition sites and good food-plants. The immigrants which reached the southern counties of England in 1946 were all of the gregarious phase; in 1947, five out of twenty-two recorded specimens were of the transient phase (Uvarov, 1949). This indicates that breeding outside the swarm area had occurred. Two specimens of *L. m. migratoria* also arrived in 1947. The only recorded instance of locusts breeding in Britain naturally occurred during this invasion when a fifth-instar nymph of *L. m. gallica*, solitary phase, was found in Jersey in late August 1948 (Uvarov, *loc.cit.*), which would have developed from eggs laid the previous season. That it was still nymphal, and would therefore not have matured early enough in the season to breed, shows that we need have little fear of locusts becoming pests in the British Isles.

Mature adults of the gregarious or swarming phase are

yellowish brown in colour, with the pronotum flat dorsally (fig. 3). Solitary adults are more brightly coloured, often green, and their hind tibiae are usually red towards the tip; the pronotum is distinctly humped dorsally (fig.2). They are 60–80mm in length and, with their green or brown colouring, have the appearance of over-sized grasshoppers. They differ from *Anacridium* and *Schistocerca* in the absence of a prosternal peg or spine between the bases of the forelegs.

Schistocerca gregaria (Forskål) (desert locust) (Pl. 5, fig 1), is occasionally recorded both as an introduction with imported goods and as an immigrant assisted by strong southerly winds from north-western Africa. Its landfall is usually western Britain and Ireland; in 1954 several were recorded in southern Ireland and others were found in the Scilly Isles (Baynes, 1955; Cotton, 1982); and in 1979 a specimen arrived in Co. Cork at the same time as red Saharan dust was being deposited in southern areas of the British Isles (Bond & Blackith, 1987). The country of origin of a specimen in the British Museum (Natural History), which was collected in Plymouth in October, 1869, cannot be determined. *S. gregaria* is 60–85mm in length and has a less recognizably grasshopper-like appearance, being a pink colour when newly adult, turning yellow when fully mature, but never having the dark brown body-colour of *Anacridium*. The hindwings are clear.

Locust specimens which may be genuine migrants should be reported to the Overseas Development Natural Resources Institute (which includes the former Anti-Locust Research Centre), Central Avenue, Chatham Maritime, Chatham, Kent ME4 4TB, or to the Department of Entomology, British Museum (Natural History), Cromwell Road, London SW7 5BD.

It should be noted that locusts are frequently reared by schools and colleges and escapes may occur. Even deliberate releases are known, so it cannot be assumed that a locust at large is necessarily a genuine immigrant.

DICTYOPTERA

Suborder BLATTODEA

Cosmopolitan pest species, particularly *Periplaneta americana* (p. 125) and *P. australasiae* (p. 126), and also their near relative, *P. brunnea* Burmeister, a pest in the U.S.A., are occasionally imported. The last-named species closely resembles *P. australasiae* but has no yellow band on the pronotum and forewings; a yellow anchor-like pronotal pattern is usually visible.

Neostylopyga rhombifolia (Stoll) (harlequin cockroach), is a cosmotropical pest species which is occasionally brought into Britain. Both sexes are brachypterous as adults, having the appearance of yellow-patterned *Blatta orientalis* females (p. 124). The largest cosmotropical pest species to be imported on occasion is *Rhyparobia maderae* (Fab.) (Madeira cockroach), formerly known as *Leucophaea maderae* (Kevan, 1980a). This is a fully-winged, greyish brown species, 40–50mm in length. Curtis (1829) listed it as a 'doubtful native', and it was illustrated by Moffet (1634) – though among the cicadas! A smaller related species, *Nauphoeta cinerea* (Olivier) (cinereous cockroach), 25–30mm long, is also brought in from time to time with fruit and other goods.

The majority of the cockroach importations are not pest species but are truly casual introductions, usually with bananas. *Henschoutedenia flexivitta* (Walker) (large cinereous cockroach), 25–40mm in length, and *H. tectidoma* (mentioned above), 19–27mm in length, are larger relatives of *Nauphoeta cinerea* which used to be imported with bananas from West Africa. All the recent introductions to Britain with bananas are now Neotropical in origin, mainly from the West Indies.

Several species of the genus *Pelmatosilpha*, all of them brachypterous, are regular introductions with bananas, the largest being *P. larifuga* (mentioned above) which may be up to 40mm in body-length. The wings cover about two-thirds of the abdomen, and there is a broad yellow band on the sides of the pronotum and forewings. The main body-colour in all *Pelmatosilpha* species is a reddish brown. Some of the smaller species have a yellow band on the pronotum and occasionally on the forewings; others are unicolorous. All have short wings, some rounded at the tips and others truncate. A very distinctive character of several species in this group is the production of an aromatic secretion with an almond-like smell, presumed to be a predator-repellent (Roth *et al.*, 1956), which is most unlike the malodorous secretions normally associated with cockroaches.

Several species of the delicate pale-green cockroach genus *Panchlora* are occasionally imported, among the largest being *P. nivea* (L.) (Cuban cockroach) which is 20–30mm long.

Two of the more common introductions during the 1950s and 1960s were *Nyctibora laevigata* (Beauvois) (smooth cockroach) and *Nauclidas nigra* Brunner (round-backed cockroach) but these are now only rarely imported.

Other occasional importations with bananas and other goods from the West Indies and South America have been members of the Blaberidae, notably several *Blaberus* species ranging in size from 45–60mm, and *Archimandrita marmorata* (Stoll), one of the largest cockroaches known, with a body-length of 70mm and a wing-span of 140mm. *Blaberus giganteus* was among the species recorded by White (1855), with the annotation that it had been 'introduced by shipping'.

Several small Blattellidae genera are also imported, including *Neoblattella* and *Cariblatta* species, distant non-domestic relatives of *Blattella germanica* (p. 127).

In addition to the remarkable assortment of cockroach species brought in with bananas, specimens from the Mediterranean region, which would not normally be regarded as pests, such as the almost spherical, wingless, burrowing female of *Polyphaga aegyptiaca* (L.) (Polyphagidae), occasionally find their way here with imported fruit and vegetables.

Although to many people such a plethora of introduced cockroaches could be regarded as horrific, a recently formed group of enthusiasts, the Blattodea Culture Group, regards them all as potential culture species – pets not pests! Additionally, cultures are kept of many tropical species specially imported for this purpose. For example, many schools and laboratories rear the impressive *Gromphadorhina portentosa* (Schaum) (Madagascan hissing cockroach), a large, heavy-bodied, totally wingless species, whose adults' average dimensions are 65 × 25mm. This species, which has been in culture here for many years, is endemic to Madagascar.

Details of the Blattodea Culture Group may be obtained from Adrian D. Durkin, 8 Foley Road, Pedmore, Stourbridge DY9 0RT.

DICTYOPTERA

Suborder MANTODEA

Only once so far, in 1959, has *Mantis religiosa* (L.) (praying mantis) (Pl. 5, fig. 5) been recorded here as a possible migrant (Ragge, 1965), although it breeds as close to us as Brittany and the environs of Paris. However, many holiday-makers returning from Europe bring back this species (as well as other orthopteroids) as adults, nymphs or oothecae. *M. religiosa* is green or brown, 50–75mm in length, and easily recognizable by the black or black and white 'eye-spots' at the inner base of the fore coxae.

Many tropical species are kept as pets though, as mantids are totally carnivorous, rearing them can be a difficult procedure. Heath (1980) gives invaluable and amusing advice on this subject in a booklet based on his own experiences.

DERMAPTERA

As with the cockroaches, introductions may occur of species already known here as established aliens. One cosmopolitan species sometimes introduced is *Anisolabis maritima* (Bonelli) (maritime earwig) which is similar to *Euborellia annulipes* (p. 134) but larger, with legs entirely yellow. *A. maritima* was listed by Hincks (1949) as an established alien, based on records of importations with ballast and barrel-staves in the last century. *Labidura riparia* (p. 139) is another large cosmopolitan species which is occasionally imported. Its status as a native species has been questioned.

Several African species have been recorded here, notably under the bark of imported timber between 1945 and the late 1950s. The lack of more recent introductions is lamented by Brindle (1977).

PHASMIDA

The New Zealand species which have become established here are discussed in detail under each species, as is *Carausius morosus* (p. 143). Casual importations of Phasmida are otherwise unknown, but a large number of tropical species are now in culture in Europe, and are actively sought after by enthusiasts. Many of the cultured species are large and impressively spiny, and have been described by Clark (1974) and Brock (1985a). At least one specimen, originating from Papua New Guinea, escaped (or was released ?) in Surbiton, Surrey, making 'headline' news in 1984. Hopefully most enthusiasts take more care of their often delicate and difficult-to-rear charges, particularly as guidance is always available from the Phasmid Study Group. This was formed in 1982 to promote the care and study of stick-insects and information may be obtained from Paul D. Brock, 'Papillon', 40 Thorndike Road, Slough SL2 1SR.

PART III: HABITATS

1. Types of Habitat of British Orthopteroids

In his contribution on Distribution and History in the introductory section, Ragge has provided a background to the distributions of our native orthopterans. The habitats which are favoured by individual species are given briefly in the descriptive section. The following summary is designed to provide a more detailed account of the orthopteroid species principally associated with various types of habitat, with indications of their status within each. Species which are deemed to be stable within a given habitat are shown without a symbol; the status of others is marked as follows:

× species flourishing
★ species managing to persist
○ species almost always confined to this habitat

Although this data is of a superficial and over-simplified nature it should, nevertheless, provide a straightforward guide for the non-specialist who wants a general assessment of the habitat requirements and status of our native orthopteroids. A fuller account of the ecological factors that link populations of native species to specific habitats may be found in the published results of various local surveys listed in the Historical Account of the Study of Orthoptera (p. 21). These demonstrate the extent to which detailed and painstaking work is necessary to substantiate even the most simple conclusions.

The majority of our British orthopteroids clearly require a subtle admixture of habitats, the apparent exceptions being the wetland species, *Metrioptera brachyptera*, *Gryllotalpa gryllotalpa*, *Stethophyma grossum* and *Tetrix subulata*. It is also clear that climate is a more decisive factor than vegetation in the British Isles, where all native species, except *Forficula auricularia*, exist somewhat precariously at the edge of their natural range and are critically influenced by delicately balanced forces. These can be identified only by careful investigation. However, observation in the field indicates that grasslands of various kinds are the most important habitats for the majority of species native to these islands.

GRASSLAND

1. *Roadside Verges and Wasteland*

The herbage along verges and around parks, factories and other similar sites is usually dominated by a small range of coarse grasses, notably false oat-grass (*Arrhenatherum elatius*). Several orthopterans are able to build up large populations in this uncultivated habitat. All are species which are tolerant to some extent of pollution from exhaust fumes, as is the case in particular with *Chorthippus brunneus* (Port & Thompson, 1980). Good examples of this now extensive habitat are too numerous to list comprehensively, but the following trunk-route verges are notable for the size of their populations of Orthoptera:

A38	between Plympton	and	Chudleigh, Devon
A361	between Avebury	and	Roundway Hill, Wiltshire
A353/352	between Osmington	and	Wareham, Dorset
A338	between Hurn	and	Ashley Heath, Dorset
A3	between Horndean	and	Petersfield, Hampshire
A272	between Sheet	and	Stedham, Hampshire/W. Sussex
A27	between Fishbourne	and	Fontwell, West Sussex
A256	between Sandwich	and	Cliffs End, Kent
A24	between Bobbing	and	Queenborough, Kent
A18	between Orsett	and	Herongate, Essex
A12	between Darsham	and	Pakefield, Suffolk
A11	between Mildenhall	and	Thetford, Suffolk/Norfolk
A48	between Cheltenham	and	Cleeve Hill, Gloucestershire
A38	between Slimbridge	and	Hardwicke, Gloucestershire
A487	between Tal-y-Bont	and	Machynlleth, Cardigan
A497	between Pwllheli	and	Criccieth, Caernarvon
A715/716	between Drummore	and	Glenluce, Wigtownshire
A9	between Brora	and	Helmsdale, Sutherland

Typical species of this habitat (within their range):

Tettigoniidae: *Tettigonia viridissima*, *Pholidoptera griseoaptera*×, *Metrioptera roeselii*×, *Conocephalus discolor*×, *Leptophyes punctatissima*

Acrididae: *Omocestus viridulus*, *Chorthippus brunneus*×, *C. vagans*, *C. parallelus*×, *C. albomarginatus*

Forficulidae: *Forficula auricularia*

2. *Coastal Grasslands*

(a) Salt-marsh and estuarine margins (Plate A, fig. 3)

There is an unmistakeable, often narrow, serpentine belt of coarse vegetation immediately landward of the normal limits of spring tides and often backed by extensive marshy pastures. It is dominated along its margin by sea couch (*Elymus pycnanthus*), a distinctive population of rushes (*Juncus* spp.) and sea aster (*Aster tripolium*). In southern and south-eastern England and South Wales this zone often supports very large numbers of Orthoptera of the few species well adapted to the habitat. The extensive marshy pastures on both sides of the Thames Estuary and northwards up the Essex coast provide outstandingly good examples of this type of Orthoptera-rich locality. Others are:

ENGLAND – *Cornwall*: St. Germans, Lynher Estuary; Camel Estuary. *Dorset*: Abbotsbury; Brand's Bay, Poole Harbour. *Hampshire*: Stanpit Marsh, Christchurch. *West Sussex*: Langstone and Chichester Harbours; Pagham Harbour. *Kent*: Pegwell Bay; Elmley Island. *Essex*: Roach Estuary; Colne Estuary. *Norfolk*: Cley and Wells Marshes. *Yorkshire*: Spurn Head.

WALES – *Glamorgan*: Landimore Marsh, Gower. *Cardigan*: Dovey Estuary.

Typical species of this habitat (within their range):
Tettigoniidae: *Metrioptera roeselii*, *Conocephalus discolor*★, *C. dorsalis*×
Tetrigidae: *Tetrix ceperoi*
Acrididae: *Chorthippus brunneus*★, *C. parallelus*, *C. albomarginatus*×

(b) Sand-dunes (Plate A, figs 1, 2)

In the unstable fore-dunes dominated by marram grass (*Ammophila arenaria*), orthopteroids are usually scarce and incidental, but on the stabilized parts, which include dry areas with an almost downland flora and marshy dune slacks and scrub, there may be very substantial populations. Furthermore, coastal dunes are often the only sites for an abundant Orthoptera fauna in more northern parts of the British Isles, even where there may be only two or three species present. To the south, the fauna may be comparatively rich in species as well as in numbers. Particularly good coastal dunes for orthopteroids include:

ENGLAND – *Cornwall*: Penhale Sands. *Devon*: Dawlish Warren; Braunton Burrows. *Dorset*: Littlesea. *Isle of Wight*: The Duver, St. Helens. *Kent*: Sandwich Bay. *Lancashire*: Ainsdale Dunes. *Yorkshire*: Spurn Head. *Northumberland*: Bamburgh and Ross Dunes.

WALES – *Glamorgan*: Margam and Kenfig Burrows; Oxwich Bay. *Anglesey*: Newborough Warren.

SCOTLAND – *Wigtown*: Torrs Warren. *Angus*: Montrose Dunes. *Elgin*: Burghead Bay and Culbin Sands. *Sutherland*: Littleferry.

IRELAND – *Co. Kerry*: Inch Point and Strand.

CHANNEL ISLANDS – *Jersey*: St. Ouen's; L'Ouaisné and Quennevais.

Typical species of this habitat (within their range):
Tettigoniidae: *Tettigonia viridissima*×, *Pholidoptera griseoaptera*, *Platycleis albopunctata*×○, *Metrioptera roeselii*, *Conocephalus discolor*×, *C. dorsalis*, *Leptophyes punctatissima*
Gryllidae: *Gryllus campestris* (Jersey only)
Tetrigidae: *Tetrix ceperoi*×, *T. subulata*, *T. undulata*×
Acrididae: *Oedipoda caerulescens*× (Jersey only), *Stenobothrus lineatus*★, *Omocestus viridulus*★, *Chorthippus brunneus*×, *C. vagans*× (Jersey only), *C. parallelus*×, *C. albomarginatus*×, *Euchorthippus pulvinatus elegantulus*×(Jersey only), *Myrmeleotettix maculatus*×
Blattellidae: *Ectobius pallidus*, *E. panzeri*×
Forficulidae: *Forficula auricularia*

(c) Vegetated shingle beach (Plate A, fig. 4)

Although there are many areas of shingle beach around the British coast, few are extensive enough to support a substantial orthopteroid fauna. Two notable exceptions are Chesil Beach, Dorset and Denge Beach, Kent. Both have oases of scrub and grass, as well as wet areas but, in essential features, the habitat is similar to that of sand-dunes. Extensive areas of shingle beach are also found at several places around Bridgwater Bay, Somerset; Orford Ness, Suffolk; and Blakeney, Norfolk.

Typical species of this habitat (within their range):
Tettigoniidae: *Tettigonia viridissima*, *Pholidoptera griseoaptera*★, *Platycleis albopunctata*×○, *Conocephalus dorsalis*, *Leptophyes punctatissima*★
Gryllidae: *Pseudomogoplistes squamiger* ○ (Dorset only)

Tetrigidae: *Tetrix ceperoi*, *T. subulata*★, *T. undulata*
Acrididae: *Chorthippus brunneus*×, *C. parallelus*, *C. albomarginatus*×, *Myrmeleotettix maculatus*×
Blattellidae: *Ectobius panzeri*×
Forficulidae: *Forficula auricularia*

(d) Sea-cliffs (Plate A, fig. 5)

Much of the coastline of Britain and Ireland is of sea-cliffs. In places, as at Eastbourne, East Sussex, and Dover, Kent, the cliffs are of chalk downland, combining two major habitats for native Orthoptera. Nevertheless, a distinction can be made for the Channel coast in that *Platycleis albopunctata* is strictly maritime in this country and, where it occurs (as at Dover), chalk downland may be assumed to be a sea-cliff habitat. Similarly Brean Down, Somerset, and the seaward edge of the Purbecks, Dorset, St. Boniface Down, Isle of Wight, the South Downs at The Seven Sisters and Beachy Head, Sussex, and the North Downs at Folkestone and Dover, Kent, are all sea-cliffs for the purpose of assessing the orthopteroids present. Elsewhere there is no real ambiguity.

Sea-cliffs may be of many different types and most provide a complex of small, distinct habitats: cliffs of hard rocks with extensive areas of sheer rock-face topped with thin turf are far less satisfactory for Orthoptera than those of softer rocks such as are a feature of the Channel coast from East Devon to East Kent. Here the landslips are often continuous and large, and thickly vegetated undercliffs have developed. The following is a selection of sea-cliff sites known to have good populations of orthopteroids:

(i) Cliffs of soft rocks, with frequent undercliffs and wet seepages include:

ENGLAND – *Devon*: Branscombe and Beer Head – chalk; The Rousdon landslips – chalk, sandstone, clay. *Dorset*: Black Ven – blue lias, sandstone, clay; West Bay – sandstone, clay; Durdle Door and Lulworth Cove – sandstone, shale, clay; Worbarrow Bay – chalk; Ballard Down – chalk. *Isle of Wight*: Totland Bay and Freshwater Bay – sandstone, chalk; Chale Bay and Rocken End – clay, chalk; St. Catherines Point – clay, chalk; St Boniface Down and Luccombe Chine – clay, chalk; Whitecliff Bay – sandstone, clay. *Hampshire*: Hengistbury Head – sandstone, clay. *East Sussex*: Seaford Head – chalk, clay; Belle Tout – chalk, clay. *Kent*: Folkestone Warren – chalk, clay; South Foreland – chalk.

Typical species of this habitat (within their range):

Tettigoniidae: *Meconema thalassinum*★, *Tettigonia viridissima*×, *Pholidoptera griseoaptera*×, *Platycleis albopunctata*×○, *Conocephalus discolor*, *Leptophyes punctatissima*
Gryllidae: *Nemobius sylvestris* (Isle of Wight only)
Tetrigidae: *Tetrix ceperoi*×, *T. subulata*★, *T. undulata*
Acrididae: *Stenobothrus lineatus*, *Omocestus rufipes*★, *O. viridulus*×, *C. brunneus*×, *C. parallelus*×, *Gomphocerippus rufus*, *Myrmeleotettix maculatus*
Blattellidae: *Ectobius pallidus*×, *E. panzeri*
Forficulidae: *Forficula auricularia*, *F. lesnei*

(ii) Cliffs of harder rocks include:

ENGLAND – *Cornwall*: The Lizard – Serpentine and other rocks; Penhale Point – shale; Trevose Head – shale and sandstone. *Devon*: Wembury Bay and Stoke Point – shale, slate, quartz; Bolt Head and Tail – schist; Berry Head – limestone. *Dorset*: Portland Bill –

limestone; Chapman's Pool to Durlston Head – limestone.

WALES – *Glamorgan*: Pwlldu Head – limestone and other rocks; Oxwich Point and Overton Cliff – limestone. *Pembroke*: Stackpole and St. Govan's Heads – limestone; Dale and Marloes – limestone.

ISLE OF MAN: Langness Peninsula – slate and limestone.

CHANNEL ISLANDS: *Guernsey* – granite; *Jersey* – granite.

Typical species of this habitat (within their range):

Tettigoniidae: *Tettigonia viridissima*×, *Pholidoptera griseoaptera*×, *Platycleis albopunctata*×, *Conocephalus discolor*, *Leptophyes punctatissima*

Tetrigidae: *Tetrix ceperoi*×, *T. undulata*

Acrididae: *Oedipoda caerulescens* (Guernsey and Jersey only), *Stenobothrus stigmaticus*○ (I.o.M. only), *Omocestus rufipes*, *O. viridulus*×, *Chorthippus brunneus*×, *C. vagans* (Jersey only), *C. parallelus*×, *Myrmeleotettix maculatus*×

Blattellidae: *Ectobius panzeri*×

Forficulidae: *Forficula auricularia*, *F. lesnei*

3. *Chalk and Limestone Downland* (Plates A, fig. 6; B, figs 1–3)

This is a major habitat for British orthopteroids. There is some indication that the coarser herbage that has developed on the North and South Downs during the last thirty years may have resulted in the enrichment of the orthopterous fauna. Species requiring at least some coarser herbage and scrub, such as bush-crickets: *Tettigonia viridissima*, *Decticus verrucivorus*, *Metrioptera roeselii* and *Conocephalus discolor*; and grasshoppers: *Omocestus viridulus*, *Chorthippus parallelus* and *Gomphocerippus rufus*, have clearly benefitted. On the other hand, once the growth of dense scrub and the strongest growing grasses increases, none of these insects are likely to benefit further and most of their downland populations may already have passed their peak.

Particularly good sites for orthopteroids of chalk and limestone grassland are:

ENGLAND – *Devon*: Beer Head – chalk. *Somerset*: Portishead Down – limestone. *Wiltshire*: Cherhill – chalk. *Dorset*: Black Down – chalk; Durlston Head – limestone; Ballard Down – chalk. *Isle of Wight*: St. Boniface Down – chalk. *Hampshire*: Portsdown – chalk; Old Winchester Hill – chalk; St. Catherine's Hill – chalk; Stockbridge Down – chalk; Broughton Down – chalk. *West Sussex*: Fairmile Bottom – chalk; Arundel Park – chalk; Shoreham Bank – chalk; *East Sussex*: Devil's Dyke – chalk; Castle Hill NNR and Kingston-near-Lewes – chalk; Deep Coombe and Lullington Heath NNR – chalk; Malling Down, Lewes – chalk. *Kent*: Lydden and Stonewall – chalk; Wye and Crundale NNR – chalk; Bluebell Hill – chalk. *Surrey*: Hackhurst and White Downs – chalk; Betchworth quarries – chalk; Box Hill – chalk; Riddlesdown – chalk. *Oxfordshire*: Path Hill – chalk. *Suffolk*: Wangford Warren NR – Breckland. *Gloucestershire*: Stinchcombe – limestone; Randwick Common – limestone; Cleeve Common – limestone.

Typical species of this habitat (within their range): (+ indicates a species which has benefitted from coarsening of downland turf):

Tettigoniidae: *Tettigonia viridissima*×+, *Decticus verrucivorus*×+, *Pholidoptera griseoaptera*+, *Metrioptera roeselii*+, *Conocephalus discolor*×+, *Leptophyes punctatissima*+

Tetrigidae: *Tetrix undulata*×

Acrididae: *Stenobothrus lineatus*×, *Omocestus rufipes*★+, *O. viridulus*×+, *Chorthippus brun-*

neus×, *C. parallelus*×+, *C. albomarginatus**, *Gomphocerippus rufus*×+, *Myrmeleotettix maculatus*×
Blattellidae: *Ectobius lapponicus**+, *E. pallidus*+, *E. panzeri**
Forficulidae: *Apterygida media*+, *Forficula auricularia*+, *F. lesnei*+

4. *Hay Meadows*

[NOTE: Hedgerow species are covered under WOODLANDS]

This was a major habitat for many interesting plants and insects up to the 1940s and 1950s. Some fragments of old, unimproved, 'permanent' grass fields still survive in many parts of the country, often in nature reserves, but because of the fragmented nature of this habitat these regularly mown areas are of limited significance for Orthoptera and no examples of national importance are cited.

Typical species of this habitat (within their range):
Tetrigidae: *Tetrix subulata**, *T. undulata*
Acrididae: *Omocestus viridulus*, *Chorthippus brunneus*, *C. parallelus*×, *C. albomarginatus**
Forficulidae: *Forficula auricularia*

5. *Siliceous Pastures*

There are certain commons and ranges of hills over non-calcareous soils in Britain which have been grazed over preceding centuries and are now covered with a turf of grasses such as fescue (*Festuca* spp.) and bent (*Agrostis* spp.). This superficially resembles the turf of chalk downland in many ways, but with the difference that 'forests' of bracken (*Pteridium aquilinum*) rapidly invade siliceous grassland once grazing ceases. Although this grassland has much in common with grassier portions of dry heathland, the underlying soils have much higher bacterial activity. Therefore peat does not form below the turf even though areas of true heath may lie adjacent to the pasture land. Siliceous pastures are not normally rich in orthopterans but several kinds of grasshoppers may build up large populations on them, notably *Omocestus viridulus* which is probably in its optimum habitat here. *Chorthippus albomarginatus* has been found recently on this kind of terrain in Warwickshire and may prove to be widespread in this habitat.

Surviving examples of siliceous pasture with good populations of Orthoptera include:

ENGLAND – *Devon*: Great Torrington Common. *Hampshire*: Balmer Lawn, New Forest; Selborne Common. *Surrey*: Ashtead Common; Wimbledon Common; Richmond Park. *Berkshire*: Windsor Great Park. *Hertfordshire*: Harpenden Common. *Worcestershire*: The Malvern Hills. *Warwickshire*: Edge Hill; Rough Hill.

Typical species of this habitat (within their range):
Tettigoniidae: *Pholidoptera griseoaptera*, *Leptophyes punctatissima*
Tetrigidae: *Tetrix undulata*
Acrididae: *Omocestus viridulus*×, *Chorthippus brunneus*×, *C. parallelus*×, *C. albomarginatus*, *Myrmeleotettix maculatus*
Blattellidae: *Ectobius lapponicus*
Forficulidae: *Forficula auricularia*

MOUNTAINS AND MOORLANDS (Plate B, fig. 6)

Of all the major habitats for wildlife in Britain, mountains and moorlands are of least importance for orthopterans. The only areas really suitable for the few species present are the grazed grassy margins of streams or tracksides which in most districts provide a comparable habitat to that of siliceous pastures. Even in the mountains of base-rich rocks such as the Breadalbanes in central Scotland or the limestone Pennines of northern England, the base status appears to exhibit no obvious effect on the grasshoppers present, compared with those on adjacent pasture over lime-deficient rocks. Except around their lower margins, even the most southerly moorlands such as Bodmin Moor, Dartmoor and Exmoor are almost as poor in orthopterans as the moors of Wales, northern England or much of Scotland, although, twenty years and more ago, parts of Exmoor were good but extensive 'reclamation' has ruined most of the suitable habitat. Irish moorlands seem similarly poor. *Omocestus viridulus* is certainly the only native species which seems to flourish on moorland, often with smaller numbers of *Chorthippus parallelus* in places. In drier sites, other species occur, but they are usually distinctly local and their populations small. The only moorland areas in Britain which now seem to support substantial populations of Orthoptera are the North York Moors and the Lake District.

Typical species of this habitat (within their range):

Tettigoniidae: *Pholidoptera griseoaptera**, *Metrioptera brachyptera**

Tetrigidae: *Tetrix undulata*

Acrididae: *Omocestus viridulus*×, *Chorthippus brunneus*, *C. parallelus*×, *Myrmeleotettix maculatus*

Forficulidae: *Forficula auricularia*

HEATHLANDS (Plate B, figs 4, 5)

Southern heathlands are of supreme importance for native orthopterans, as they support the widest range of species, often in close proximity to each other. Heathland provides two distinct types of habitat – dry heathland and wet heathland, which, for orthopterists, then need to be further subdivided respectively into dry and grass heath; and wet heath and quaking bogs. In relation to Orthoptera, this last subdivision needs to be considered primarily as part of Heathland rather than Wetland (*q.v.*). Similarly, heathy woodland is probably best included under dry heath, since almost the same range of species occur, with *Meconema thalassinum* the only major addition.

A selection of the most important surviving southern heathlands for orthopteroids are:

ENGLAND – *Cornwall*: The Lizard. *Devon*: Knighton Heath; East Budleigh and Woodbury Commons; Aylesbeare Common; Harpford Wood and Common. *Dorset*: Middlebere Heath and Hartland Moor; Studland Heath and Littlesea; Briants Puddle Heath; Holton Heath; *Hampshire*: Burton Common; Sopley Common; Wilverley Bog; Setley Common; Crockford Bridge; Cranes Moor, Vales Moor and Castle Hill; Rockford Common; Denny Bog, Shatter Ford Bottom and Woodfidley; Matley Passage and Bog; Browndown; Emer Bog; Kingsley Common; Woolmer Forest. *West Sussex*: Ambersham Common; Iping Common. *East Sussex*: Chailey Common; Nutley and Duddleswell. *Kent*: Hothfield Common. *Surrey*:

Frensham and Hankley Commons; Thursley Common; Bisley and Westend Commons; Chobham Common. *Berkshire*: Windsor Great Park. *Suffolk*: Sutton Common and Rendlesham Forest; Westleton Heath. *Norfolk*: Horsford Heath and Newton Common. *Shropshire*: Whixal Moss. *Yorkshire*: Hatfield Moors; Thorne Waste; Strensall Common. WALES – *Glamorgan*: Pengwern and Fairwood Commons. *Cardigan*: Borth Bog. *Denbigh*: Fenn's Moss.

Typical species of this habitat (within their range):

1. Species of dry heathland and heathy woodland

Tettigoniidae: *Meconema thalassinum*, *Tettigonia viridissima*×, *Decticus verrucivorus*, *Pholidoptera griseoaptera*, *Metrioptera brachyptera*×○, *Conocephalus discolor*×, *Leptophyes punctatissima*

Gryllidae: *Gryllus campestris*, *Nemobius sylvestris*×

Tetrigidae: *Tetrix undulata*

Acrididae: *Stenobothrus lineatus*×, *Omocestus rufipes*×, *O. viridulus*×, *Chorthippus brunneus*, *C. parallelus*×, *C. vagans*×○, *Myrmeleotettix maculatus*×

Blattellidae: *Ectobius lapponicus*×, *E. pallidus*×, *E. panzeri*

Forficulidae: *Forficula auricularia*

2. Species of wet heathland and quaking bogs

Tettigoniidae: *Metrioptera brachyptera*×○, *Conocephalus discolor*×, *C. dorsalis*

Gryllotalpidae: *Gryllotalpa gryllotalpa*

Tetrigidae: *Tetrix ceperoi*★, *T. subulata*★○, *T. undulata*

Acrididae: *Stethophyma grossum*×○, *Chorthippus parallelus*×, *C. albomarginatus*★

FRESHWATER WETLANDS

Until perhaps the middle of the last century there were still vast areas of marsh and fenland and well-managed, winter-flooded water-meadows in river valleys, which probably supported an impressive range of orthopterans. Certainly *Tettigonia viridissima*, *Gryllotalpa gryllotalpa* and *Stethophyma grossum* were widespread and locally common in the extensive wetlands of the time. However by the middle of this century much of the fenland and marshes had been reclaimed. *Gryllotalpa gryllotalpa* was already rare and *Stethophyma grossum* has not been recorded from East Anglia since 1939, and has survived in the Somerset Levels only on one or possibly two sites, now protected as nature reserves. Today there are really no wetland sites, apart from the coastal marshes and the wet heathland covered in earlier sections of this chapter (*q.v.*), which can be considered of great importance for their Orthoptera. Species typical of marshland still flourish in many parts of Britain and Ireland but usually only as relatively small populations in small areas where meadows and marshes have survived – again often in nature reserves.

Typical species of this habitat (within their range):

Tettigoniidae: *Tettigonia viridissima*, *Pholidoptera griseoaptera*, *Conocephalus dorsalis*×

Gryllotalpidae: *Gryllotalpa gryllotalpa*×

Tetrigidae: *Tetrix subulata*×○, *T. undulata*

Acrididae: *Chorthippus parallelus*×, *C. albomarginatus*×

WOODLANDS (and HEDGEROWS)

In remaining fragments of ancient broad-leaved woodland the only orthopteran likely to be present is *Meconema thalassinum*, but in plantations and coppiced woodland a good selection of species is usually present, often in large numbers. The ideal woodland site is a fairly broad, grassy ride regularly mown only in the centre, so that each side has a good growth of coarse herbage and scrub. Also, areas where clear-felling or coppicing has taken place between two and five years previously can become quite Orthoptera-rich before the canopy closes in again. Populations of orthopterans can also flourish surprisingly well in conifer plantations, in those parts of the country where the climate is suitable, so long as there are ample rides subjected to minimal cutting. Sometimes species restricted to chalk downland or heathland become isolated by the growth of new plantations, but persist so long as their immediate environs remain open. *Metrioptera brachyptera* survives in several woodland sites in this way, as does *Chorthippus vagans* in East Dorset, and *Stenobothrus lineatus* in several chalkland sites, such as Queen Elizabeth Forest on the Hampshire-Sussex border. As, however, these insects mainly belong to other, specific habitats, they are not included in the following list, which comprises those that can best be considered as woodland-glade or woodland-edge species, well adapted to ungrazed herbage in the early stage of scrub development. In primaeval Britain, this was probably their main habitat, and they would undoubtedly have benefitted from the clearance of woodland by man, resulting in the growth of coarse herbage around the fields and the development of hedgerows, providing them with a more stable and far more extensive range of new habitats. However in the last thirty years some of the less adaptable of these species have suffered from the catastrophic destruction of older hedgerows and banks which had supported most of them for many centuries.

For our native orthopteroids, ancient hedgerows may be regarded as virtually the same habitat as woodland rides and clearings and the species list applies to both. Although there are still too many such species-rich hedgerows to list individually, the majority are now restricted to comparatively few districts, with the very best to be found in the counties of Devon, Dorset and Herefordshire.

A selection of good woodland sites worth visiting include:

ENGLAND – *Devon*: Yarner Wood NNR and Holne Wood; Great Haldon. *Somerset*: Quantock Hills. *Dorset*: Bere Wood. *Isle of Wight*: Parkhurst Forest. *Hampshire*: Avon Forest Park; Linwood and Roe Inclosure; Bolderwood; Stubby Copse and Denny Wood Inclosures; Cranbourne Chase; Botley Wood; West Walk; Queen Elizabeth Forest; Harewood Forest. *West Sussex*: Rewell Wood. *East Sussex*: Friston Forest; Abbotswood; St. Leonards Forest. *Kent*: Challock Forest; Covert Woods; Church Wood; Blean Woods. *Surrey*: Hurtwood; Leith Hill; Wisley and Ockham Commons; Ranmore Common. *Essex*: Epping Forest. *Berkshire*: Windsor Great Park. *Oxfordshire/Buckinghamshire*: Bernwood. *Suffolk*: Rendlesham Forest. *Norfolk*: Thetford Warren; Beachamwell Warren; Swannington Bottom and Horsford Heath Plantations; Wolferton. *Bedfordshire*: Woburn. *Gloucestershire*: Forest of Dean; Cranham Woods;. *Herefordshire*: Haugh Woods, Mordiford NR. *Worcestershire/Shropshire*: Wyre Forest. *Staffordshire*: Cannock Chase. *Lancashire*: Silverdale. *Westmoreland*: Grizedale. *Yorkshire*: Scalby, Langdale and Harwood Dale Forests.

Typical species of this habitat (within their range):

Tettigoniidae: *Meconema thalassinum*×, *Tettigonia viridissima*×, *Pholidoptera griseoaptera*×, *Conocephalus discolor*×, *Leptophyes punctatissima*×

Gryllidae: *Nemobius sylvestris*×

Tetrigidae: *Tetrix undulata*×

Acrididae: *Omocestus rufipes*×, *O. viridulus* ×, *Chorthippus brunneus*×, *C. parallelus*×, *C. albomarginatus*, *Gomphocerippus rufus*×, *Myrmeleotettix maculatus*★

Blattellidae: *Ectobius lapponicus*×, *E. pallidus*×

Forficulidae: *Apterygida media*×, *Forficula auricularia*×, *F. lesnei*×

GARDENS AND PARKS

Most rural parks and larger gardens, mainly in southern districts, support some species of Orthoptera while even small gardens usually contain at least *Forficula auricularia*. In the south-west of England and Ireland three species of New Zealand phasmids have also become well established in such localities over very small areas.

Typical species of this habitat (within their range):

Tettigoniidae: *Meconema thalassinum*×, *Tettigonia viridissima*, *Pholidoptera griseoaptera*×, *Metrioptera roeselii*, *Conocephalus discolor*, *Leptophyes punctatissima*×

Gryllidae: *Nemobius sylvestris*

Acrididae: *Omocestus viridulus*, *Chorthippus brunneus*×, *C. parallelus*×, *C. albomarginatus*

Blattellidae: *Ectobius lapponicus*★

Labiidae: *Labia minor*

Forficulidae: *Forficula auricularia*×

Phasmatidae: *Acanthoxyla geisovii*, *A. inermis*, *Clitarchus hookeri*

URBAN

A substantial number of breeding populations of mainly alien orthopteroids have become well established in towns and cities. Despite vigorous control measures, particularly against cockroaches, some species have proved able to survive for over a century or more in houses, factories, hospitals, rubbish tips, commercial greenhouses and even mines. With the reduction in the indiscriminate use of insecticides in occupied premises, practised in the 1950s and 1960s, insects established in an urban environment are probably better able to survive now than they were during the previous thirty years. Some orthopteroids also flourish in city parks and gardens.

Typical species of this habitat (within their range):

Rhaphidophoridae: *Tachycines asynamorus*

Tettigoniidae: *Meconema thalassinum*, *Pholidoptera griseoaptera*, *Metrioptera roeselii*, *Leptophyes punctatissima*

Gryllidae: *Acheta domesticus*×

Acrididae: *Chorthippus brunneus*×, *C. parallelus*, *C. albomarginatus*

Blattidae: *Blatta orientalis*×, *Periplaneta americana*, *P. australasiae*

Blaberidae: *Pycnoscelus surinamensis*

Blattellidae: *Blattella germanica*×, *Supella longipalpa*

Forficulidae: *Forficula auricularia*×

2. Orthoptera as Habitat Indicators

Much urgent surveying is needed to ensure that prime natural history habitats are saved from further and often imminent destruction. To enable necessary conservation measures to be assessed and effected, answers are often needed quickly.

Fortunately there is a number of plants and insects, instantly recognizable to a non-specialist observer in the field, which are known to exist only in particular habitats. Many downland orchids and butterflies are in this category. The presence of one or both butterflies of the genus *Lysandra*, *L. coridon* (chalk-hill blue) or *L. bellargus* (Adonis blue), indicate the existence of ancient downland turf, while colonies of *Plebejus argus* (silver-studded blue) indicate surviving heathland. In the same way several species of British Orthoptera can be used for the quick evaluation of important habitats, for although they are not so readily visible in the field, they have the advantage of producing distinctive, audible stridulation which confirms their presence even when not seen.In this way the following important habitats may be recognized by the presence of the Orthoptera species listed in the Table below:

HABITAT	ORTHOPTERA INDICATOR
Short downland turf	*Stenobothrus lineatus, Myrmeleotettix maculatus*
Dry heathland	*S. lineatus, M. maculatus, Metrioptera brachyptera*
Wet heathland	*Stethophyma grossum, M. brachyptera*
Ancient broad-leaved woodland	*Omocestus rufipes; Tetrix undulata*
Ancient unimproved grassland	*Omocestus viridulus*
Streams, marshes and ponds unaffected by pollution	*Chorthippus albomarginatus,Tetrix subulata, T. ceperoi*

Other species might be added, such as *Meconema thalassinum* for ancient woodland, but those listed above can be detected easily in the field and tend to occupy their sites for long periods. Thus where they are found to be flourishing it may be assumed that the relevant habitat has survived reasonably intact and will support many other, perhaps less conspicuous, species of plants and animals which can be located when there is time for a more detailed survey.

3. Conservation of Orthopteroids and their Habitats

All that has been written recently about the conservation of insects, particularly Lepidoptera, is true for orthopterans. Since Orthoptera do not preserve well, they do not have the same appeal for collectors as butterflies, moths or beetles. The key to the continued survival of the more local or rare species lies almost entirely in the painstaking conservation of the particular habitat which supports them. Several species have now been afforded statutory protection under the Wildlife and Countryside Act (1981) (see p. 47), but there is little point in selecting such rarities as *Decticus verrucivorus*, *Gryllus campestris*, *Stethophyma grossum*, or *Chorthippus vagans* for protection as individual species, if there are no similar statutory safeguards for the protection of the fragile downland turf or lowland heaths upon which they are dependent for their survival in this country. Nearly all the more interesting species of native Orthoptera are sedentary, sometimes with a single small colony in a disused chalk quarry or patch of marshland. Such sites may have survived the ploughing of surrounding downland or the afforestation of the adjacent marshland. However, they remain highly vulnerable to disturbance by horse-riders, motocross enthusiasts or even just careless walkers. As a result the precious habitat is often severely damaged by the destruction of the sward, and by accidental – or even deliberate – fire, resulting in the loss of the resident flora and insect fauna.

Orthoptera habitats most in need of protection are given below.

Vulnerable habitats	Dependent orthopteroids
Quaking bogs: from draining or afforestation	*Metrioptera brachyptera*, *Stethophyma grossum*
Open heathland: from trampling, fires and afforestation	*M. brachyptera*, *Chorthippus vagans*
Downland and limestone turf, especially in old quarries: from scrambling, trampling or tipping	*Stenobothrus lineatus*, *Myrmeleotettix maculatus*
Extensive downland coombs: from treatment with fertilizers, excessive grazing or afforestation	*Decticus verrucivorus*, *Conocephalus discolor*, *S. lineatus*, *M. maculatus*
Coastal sand-dunes: from trampling or afforestation and camp sites	*Tettigonia viridissima*, *Platycleis albopunctata*, *C. discolor*, *C. dorsalis*, *Tetrix subulata*, *T. ceperoi*, *Ectobius panzeri*
Fens and marshland: from draining or tipping	*Tettigonia viridissima*, *Metrioptera brachyptera*, *C. dorsalis*, *Gryllotalpa gryllotalpa*, *Stethophyma grossum*, *Tetrix subulata*
Woodland and plantation rides: from close mowing, herbicides, excessive horse-riding or scrambling, and in the New Forest (Tubbs, 1986) excessive pony-grazing	*Pholidoptera griseoaptera*, *Leptophyes punctatissima*, *Nemobius sylvestris*, *Omocestus rufipes*, *T. undulata*, *Ectobius lapponicus*, *E. pallidus*
Ancient hedgerows: from herbicides, mechanical cutting in summer or total eradication	*Meconema thalassinum*, *Tettigonia viridissima*, *P. griseoaptera*, *L. punctatissima*, *E. lapponicus*, *E. pallidus*, *Apterygida media*, *Forficula lesnei*

Figure 1. Braunton Burrows, North Devon – Sand-dune grassland. Ideal habitat for the grey bush-cricket (*Platycleis albopunctata*)

Figure 2. Montrose, Angus – Sand-dune grassland. An outstanding orthopteran site in Highland Scotland

Figure 3. Chichester Harbour, West Sussex – Salt-marsh. Ideal habitat for the lesser marsh grasshopper (*Chorthippus albomarginatus*)

Figure 4. Denge Marsh, East Kent – Vegetated shingle beach. The lesser cockroach (*Ectobius panzeri*) is locally common in this species-rich area

Figure 5. St. Catherine's Point, Isle of Wight – Coastal undercliff. Supports colonies of Cepero's ground-hopper (*Tetrix ceperoi*)

Figure 6. Kingston-near-Lewes, East Sussex – Chalk downland. Typical of one of the richest habitats for orthopterans

Figure 1. Arundel Park, West Sussex – Wooded downland. Woodland (*Omocestus rufipes*) and rufous (*Gomphocerippus rufus*) grasshoppers abundant here

Figure 2. Wangford Warren, West Suffolk – Breckland. Supports large populations of grasshoppers

Figure 3. Cotswolds from Painswick, West Gloucestershire – Limestone grassland. Many species of Orthoptera thrive in this habitat

Figure 4. Ambersham Common, West Sussex – Dry heathland. The mottled grasshopper (*Myrmeleotettix maculatus*) favours this type of habitat

Figure 5. Denny Bog, New Forest, Hampshire – Wet heathland. A typical site for the bog bush-cricket (*Metrioptera brachyptera*)

Figure 6. Near Moffat, Dumfriesshire – Sheep-grazed grassland. Typical upland site for common green grasshopper (*Omocestus viridulus*)

PART IV: ATLAS OF BRITISH AND IRISH ORTHOPTERA

1. The Orthoptera Recording Scheme

The involvement of the Biological Records Centre (BRC) with the distribution of Orthoptera began in 1968 when, under the general 'Insect Mapping Scheme', the late John Heath initiated a programme for recording Odonata and the 'orthopteroid Orders' by ten kilometre squares, rather than the old Vice-county system then in operation. As part of the BRC's policy of devolving responsibility for national recording schemes and passing it to voluntary organizers, the Orthoptera Recording Scheme became a separate entity in 1977, in which year the co-author, E. C. M. Haes, took on the rôle of organizer.

Recording is based on the use of standard record cards supplied by the BRC. Three types of card are used:

1. The species list cards (RA4B), used mainly to list the species recorded at sites or in grid squares.

2. Individual record cards (GEN8 or, formerly, 'pink cards'), for recording more detailed information about important finds of individual species.

3. Single species cards (GEN7 or GEN13), for listing a series of records for a single species, for example when extracting records from a collection.

The record cards are used by the BRC to compile computer files of information on Orthoptera including locality name, grid reference, county, recorder, date of occurrence and habitat. The computer files are then used to compile distribution maps and to sort information under a variety of headings for use in nature conservation, research and rural planning.

Records on the maps for the Orthoptera Recording Scheme are plotted with a distinctive dot, representing the period in which the latest record for a given square has been obtained. In this book, the following symbols are used:

○	records of 1960 or earlier
●	records of 1961 or later
■	post-1980 records for certain Red Data Book species
×	post-1960 introductions
?	record is probable but unconfirmed

Ten-kilometre square distribution maps for country-wide coverage may be likened to views through the 'low-power' lens of a microscope. They provide an overall view of the distribution of a particular species. The 'high-power' views are provided by an ever-increasing number of regional and county-based recording schemes, using the popular tetrad (two-kilometre square) or, more precise, the one-kilometre square as a mapping unit. However, many of these more localized schemes do not record on a site basis so that the greater efforts of recorders result in only slightly more detailed maps.

The recording and mapping of British orthopteroids over the last twenty years has been a relatively simple task. There are comparatively few British species, the majority of which may be identified in the field; and most of the gathering of data for the Recording Scheme has been done by those with an enthusiasm for and a good knowledge of these insects. As a result, very few of the records sent in for the post-1960 period have been found to be inaccurate or otherwise unreliable. However, some of the data for the earlier period, and especially for records before 1940, have caused problems. For that period there are no contemporary record cards and much of the information has had to be extracted from papers or museum specimens that are frequently not easy to locate. Often, the only Orthoptera list for an entire county was that in the Victoria County History, which was compiled, in some cases, by a person who had little knowledge of what was then regarded as a comparatively unimportant group of British insects. With the Orthoptera, there is considerable evidence that, in the nineteenth and early part of the present century, misidentification was not infrequent, especially of the local but widespread grasshopper species, *Stenobothrus lineatus*, *Omocestus rufipes* and *Chorthippus albomarginatus*. Cited localities for species have frequently been insufficiently precise for them to be mapped on a ten-kilometre square basis even for the most widespread species such as *Forficula auricularia*. That is why, in this volume, vice-county maps showing pre-1961 and post-1960 records for each species are also shown, since they not only provide a direct comparison, in a way that the dot-distribution records do not, with Ragge (1965), but are also a means of including records of distribution throughout the country which have insufficient data for them to be plotted on a 10km square basis but which are nevertheless reliable.

It is not possible today to reconstruct a reliable distribution map for the British orthopteroids of over seventy years ago and earlier – the period when so much of the country must have been well suited to them. However, as most of our native species are invaluable as readily identifiable and reliable 'indicator species' of good insect habitat, a comprehensive survey of their present distribution will prove to be of great value in the conservation of what remains of our natural history and will provide a basis for future surveys.

2. The Maps

The following ten-kilometre square dot-distribution maps include all records received by the organizer of the Orthoptera Recording Scheme for Great Britain, Ireland and the Channel Islands up to mid-1988. When compared with the vice-county maps which are printed alongside the descriptions of each species in the systematic section, it will be apparent that some records on the vice-county maps do not appear on the dot-distribution maps. This is because these records lack sufficient data for a comparable 10km square dot to be shown. For example, *Meconema thalassinum* (p. 80) has been recorded pre-1961 from a locality in Cumberland (VC70) but the record is insufficiently precise to be represented on the 10km square distribution map (Map 3). Comparison of the two kinds of maps shows how much remains to be done to achieve accurate detailed recording for each species. However, comparison with the vice-county maps in Ragge (1965) demonstrates the advance in recording over the past two decades.

It is hoped that users of this book will send any records they obtain to the Biological Records Centre, Institute of Terrestrial Ecology, Monks Wood Experimental Station, Abbots Ripton, Huntingdon, Cambs. PE17 2LS, together with appropriate data.

Table of 10km square dot-distribution maps (pp. 166–189):

1. Orthoptera – all records received
2. Orthoptera – post-1960 records (5–9 spp.; 10+ spp.)
3. *Meconema thalassinum*
4. *Tettigonia viridissima*
5. *Decticus verrucivorus*
6. *Pholidoptera griseoaptera*
7. *Platycleis albopunctata*
8. *Metrioptera brachyptera*
9. *Metrioptera roeselii*
10. *Conocephalus discolor*
11. *Conocephalus dorsalis*
12. *Leptophyes punctatissima*
13. *Acheta domesticus*
14. *Gryllus campestris*
15. *Nemobius sylvestris*
16. *Pseudomogoplistes squamiger*
17. *Gryllotalpa gryllotalpa*
18. *Tetrix ceperoi*
19. *Tetrix subulata*
20. *Tetrix undulata*
21. *Oedipoda caerulescens*
22. *Stethophyma grossum*
23. *Stenobothrus lineatus*
24. *Stenobothrus stigmaticus*
25. *Omocestus rufipes*
26. *Omocestus viridulus*
27. *Chorthippus brunneus*
28. *Chorthippus vagans*
29. *Chorthippus parallelus*
30. *Chorthippus albomarginatus*
31. *Euchorthippus pulvinatus elegantulus*
32. *Gomphocerippus rufus*
33. *Myrmeleotettix maculatus*
34. Dictyoptera (native species) – all records received
35. *Ectobius lapponicus*
36. *Ectobius pallidus*
37. *Ectobius panzeri*
38. Dermaptera – all records received
39. *Euborellia annulipes*
40. *Labia minor*
41. *Apterygida media*
42. *Forficula auricularia*
43. *Forficula lesnei*
44. *Labidura riparia*
45. Phasmida – all records received
46. *Acanthoxyla geisovii*
47. *Acanthoxyla inermis*
48. *Clitarchus hookeri*

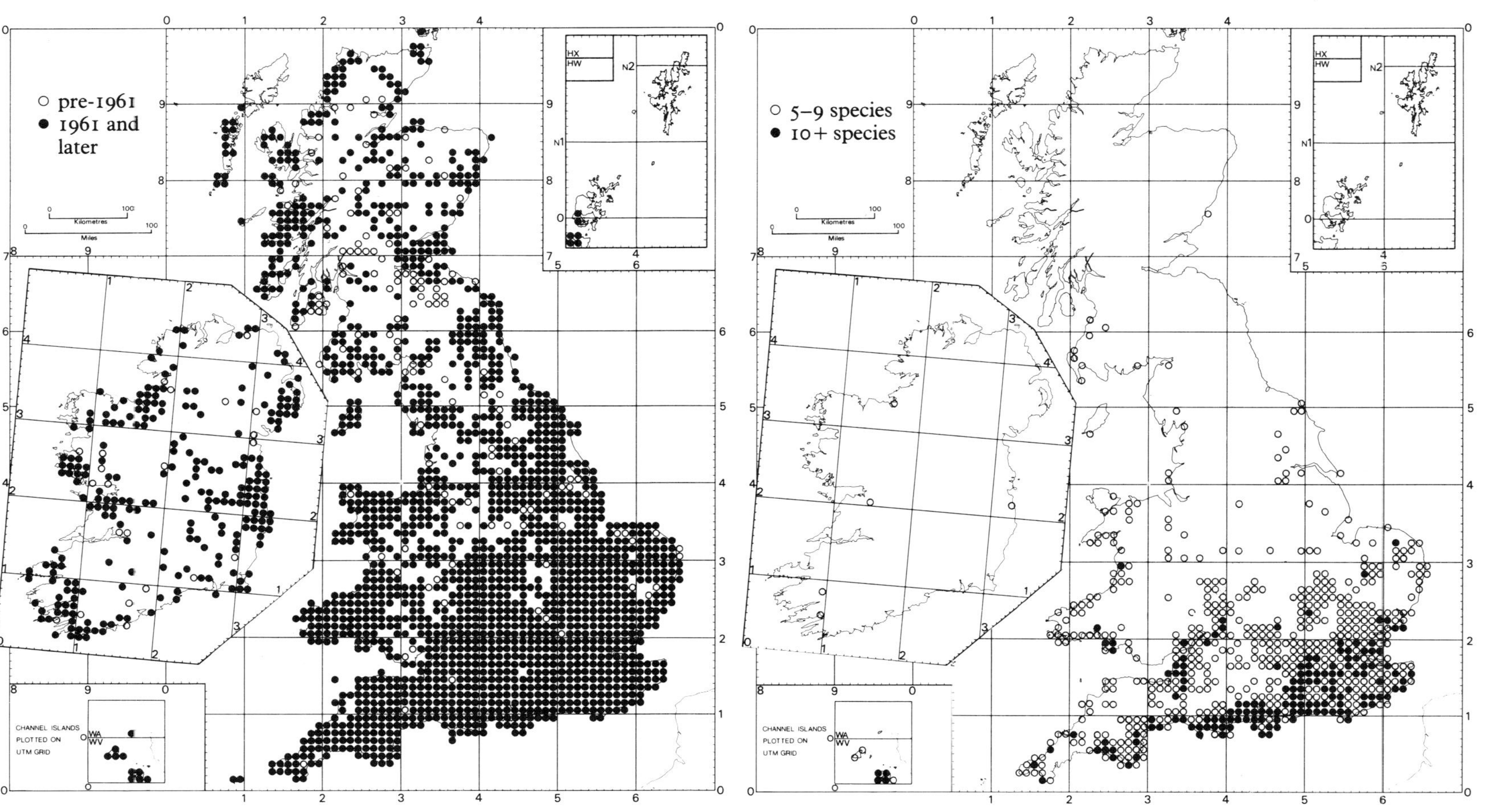

1. Orthoptera – all records received

2. Orthoptera – analysis of post-1960 records only

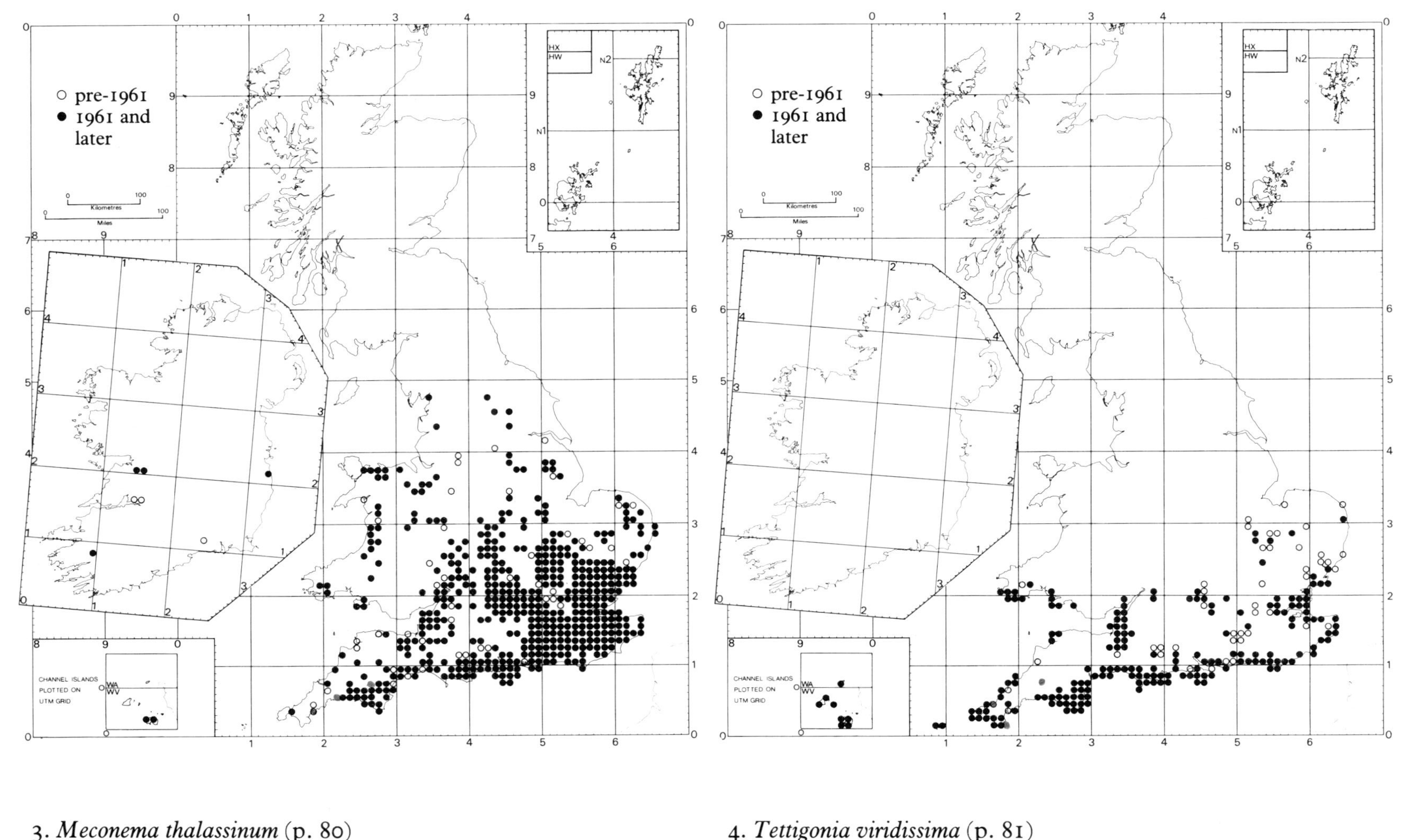

3. *Meconema thalassinum* (p. 80)

4. *Tettigonia viridissima* (p. 81)

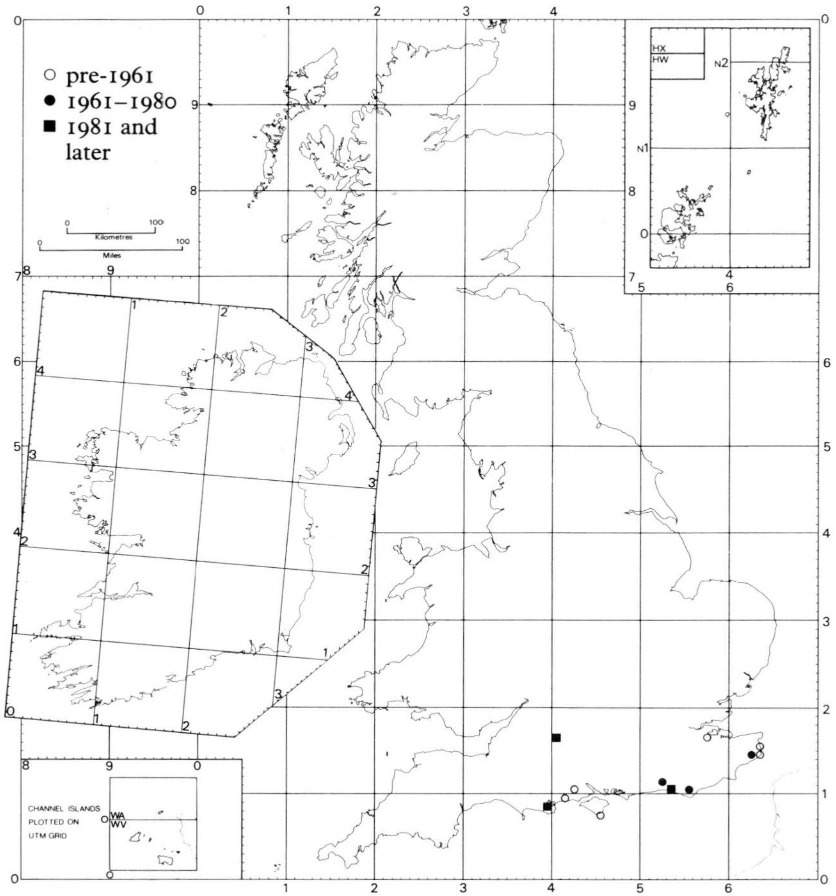

○ pre-1961
● 1961–1980
■ 1981 and later

Kilometres 0 100
Miles 0 100

CHANNEL ISLANDS PLOTTED ON UTM GRID

5. *Decticus verrucivorus* (p. 82)

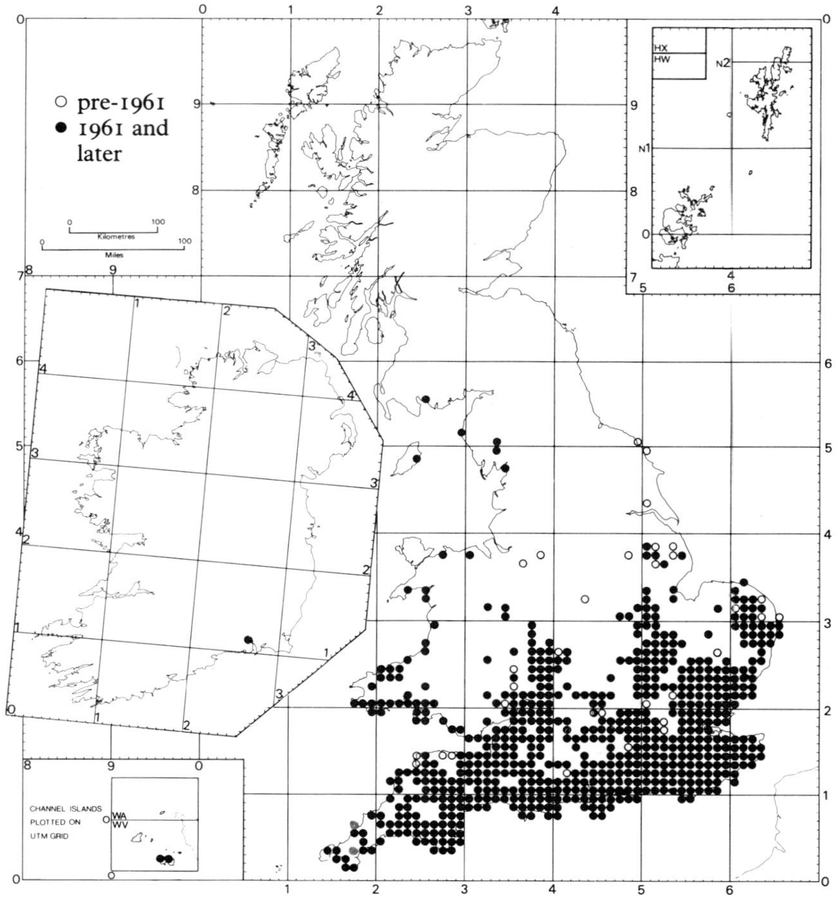

○ pre-1961
● 1961 and later

Kilometres 0 100
Miles 0 100

CHANNEL ISLANDS PLOTTED ON UTM GRID

6. *Pholidoptera griseoaptera* (p. 84)

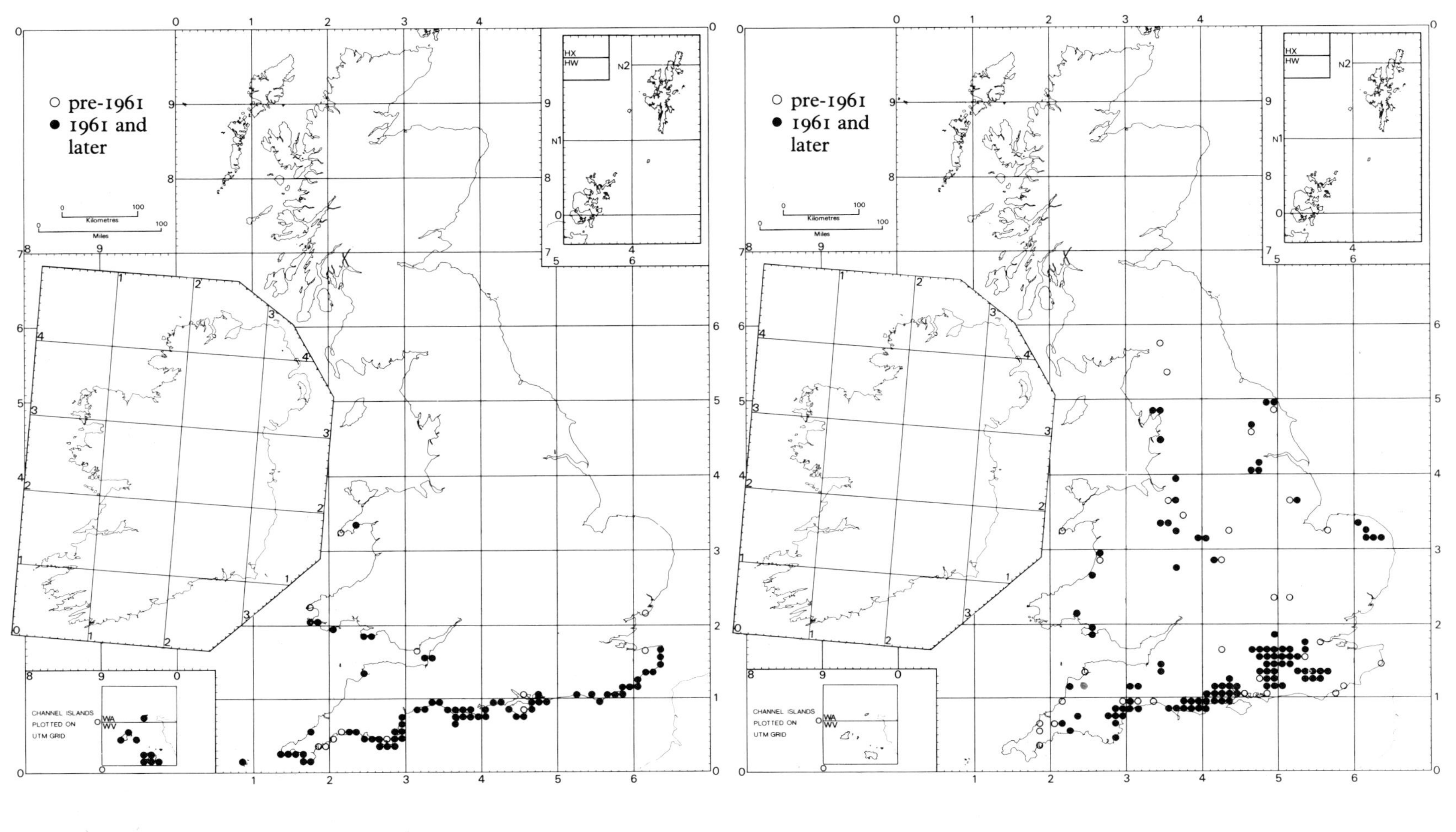

7. *Platycleis albopunctata* (p. 85)

8. *Metrioptera brachyptera* (p. 86)

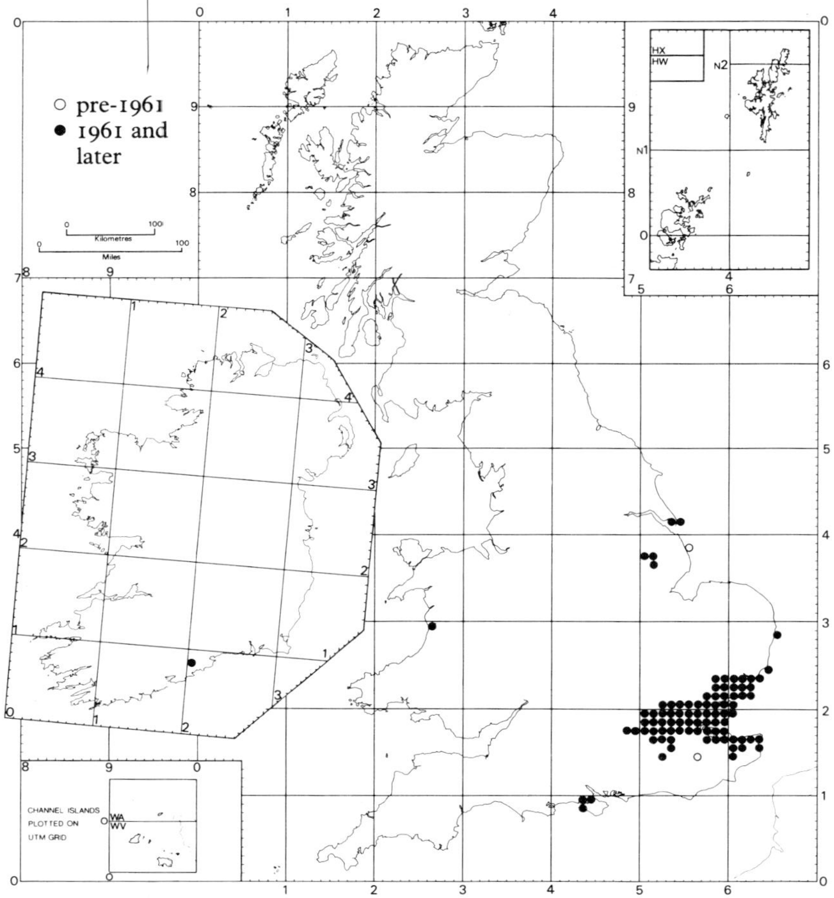

○ pre-1961
● 1961 and later

Kilometres 0 100
Miles 0 100

CHANNEL ISLANDS PLOTTED ON UTM GRID

9. *Metrioptera roeselii* (p. 87)

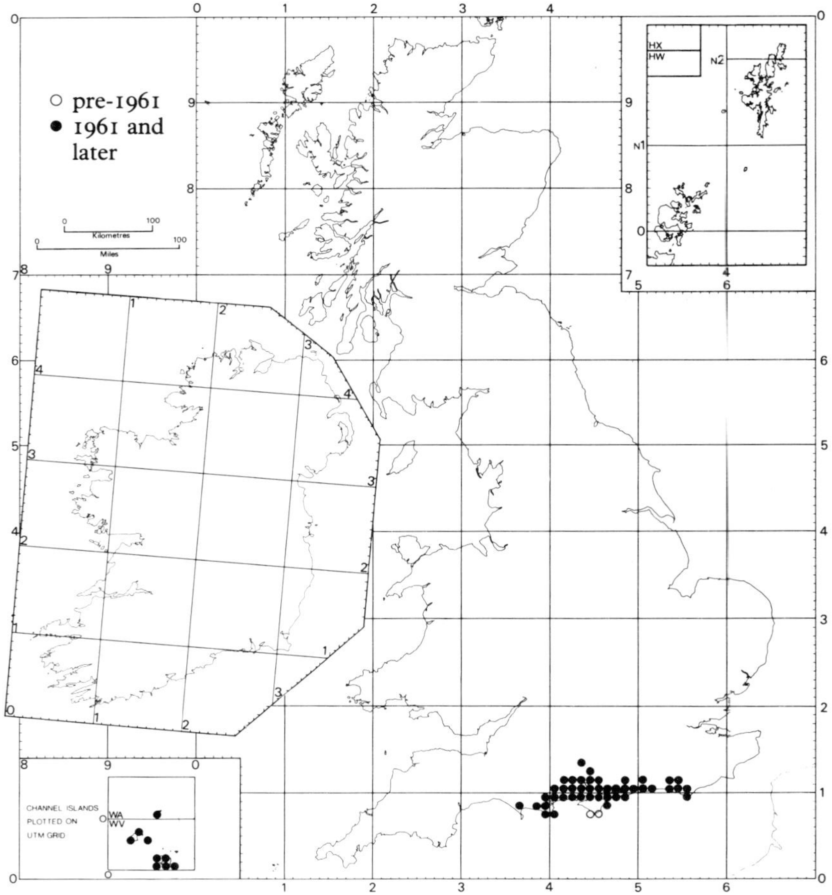

○ pre-1961
● 1961 and later

Kilometres 0 100
Miles 0 100

CHANNEL ISLANDS PLOTTED ON UTM GRID

10. *Conocephalus discolor* (p. 89)

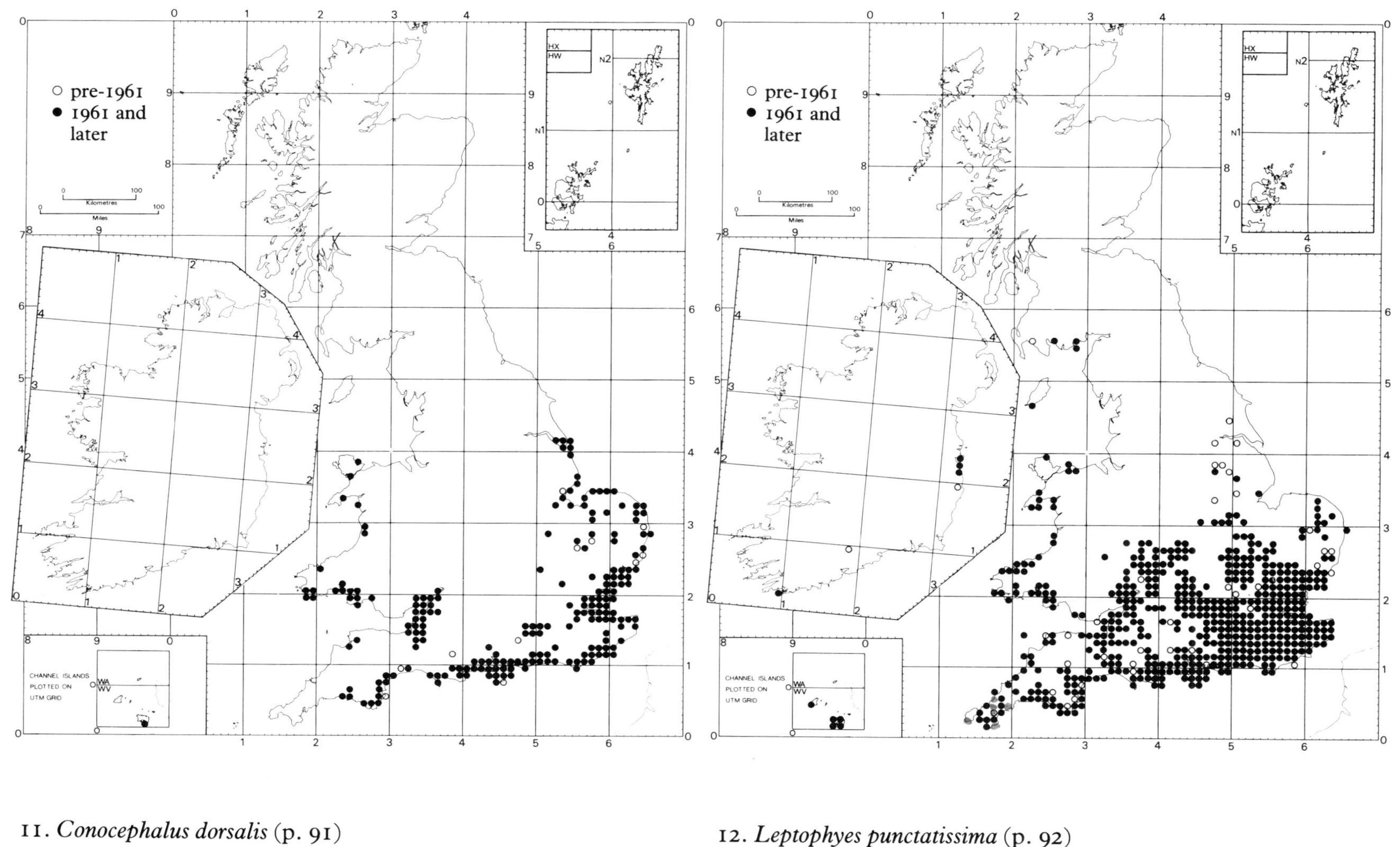

11. *Conocephalus dorsalis* (p. 91)

12. *Leptophyes punctatissima* (p. 92)

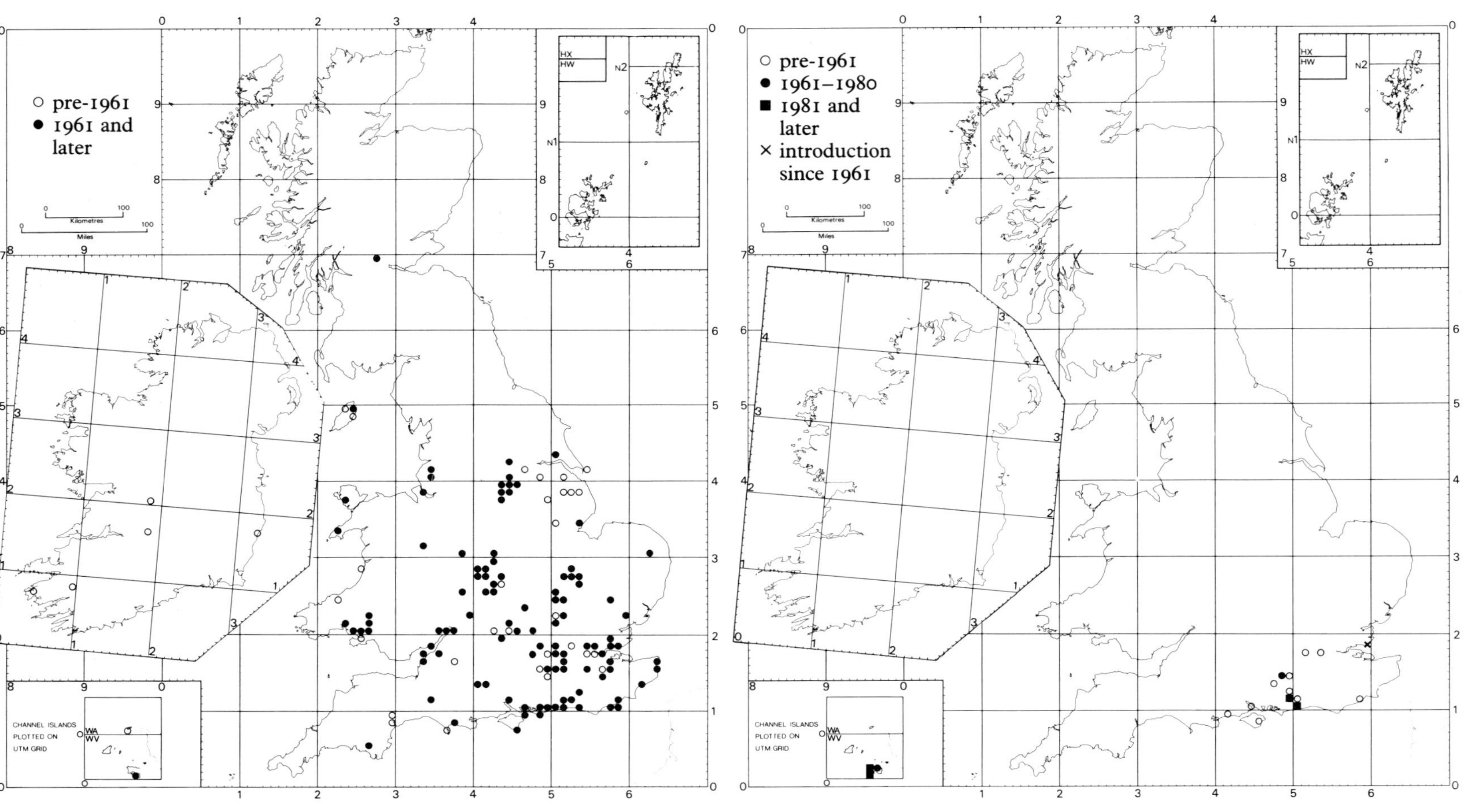

13. *Acheta domesticus* (p. 94)

14. *Gryllus campestris* (p. 95)

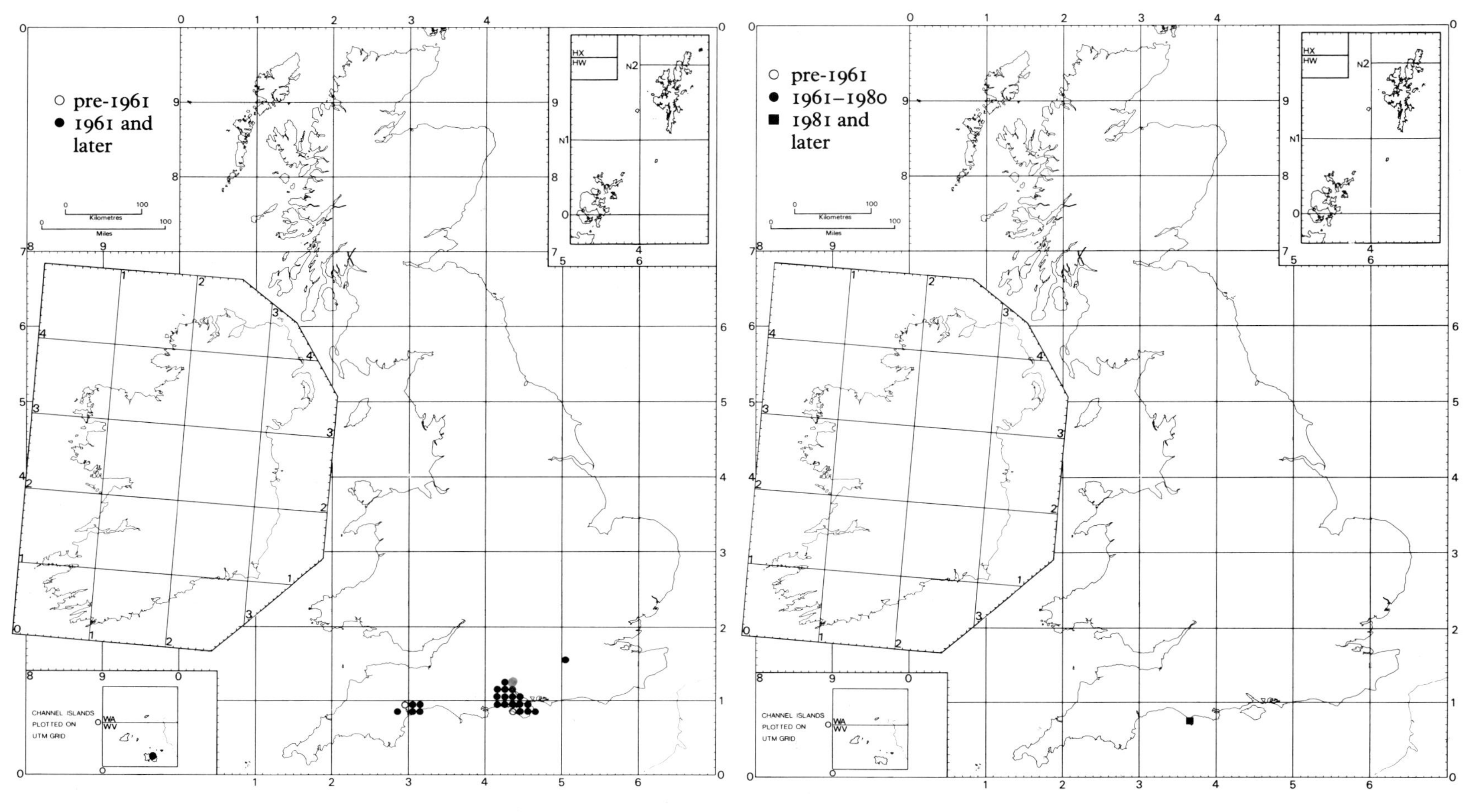

15. *Nemobius sylvestris* (p. 96)

16. *Pseudomogoplistes squamiger* (p. 97)

17. *Gryllotalpa gryllotalpa* (p. 98)

18. *Tetrix ceperoi* (p. 100)

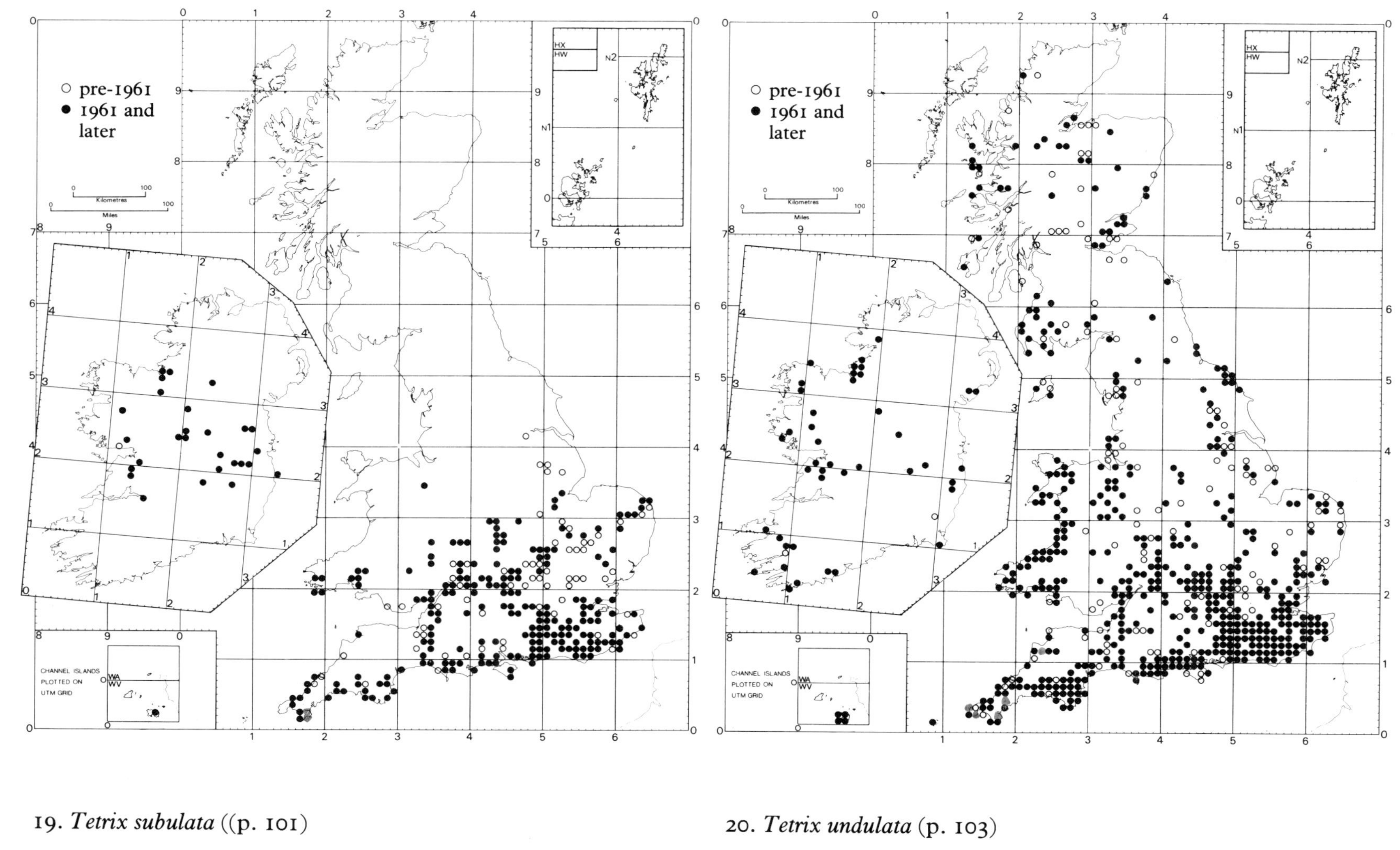

19. *Tetrix subulata* ((p. 101)

20. *Tetrix undulata* (p. 103)

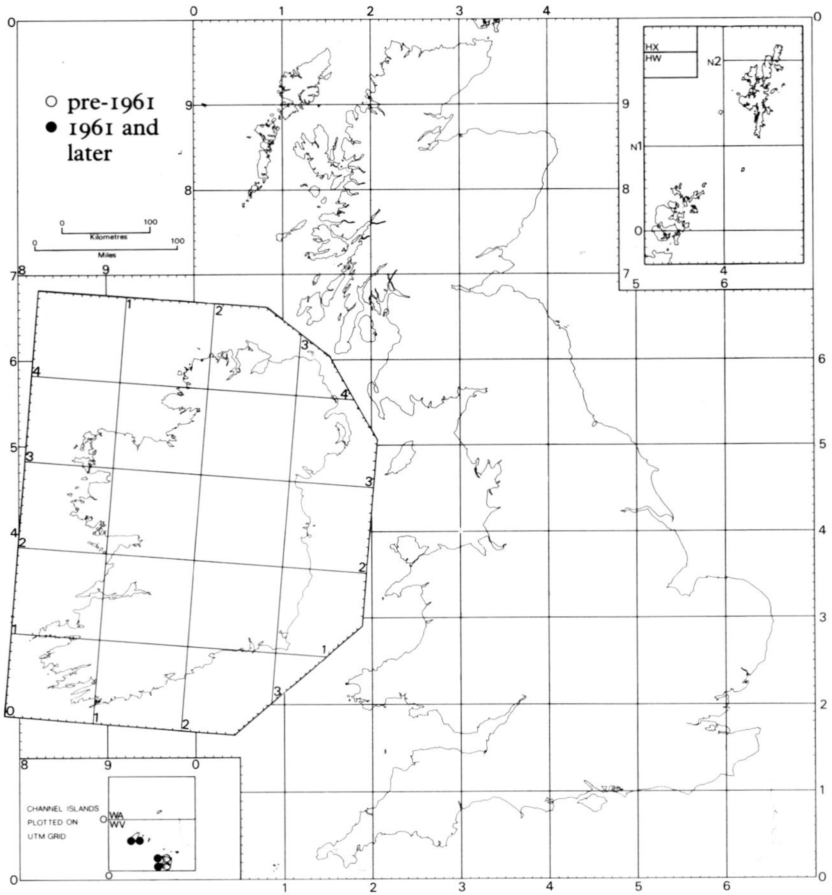

○ pre-1961
● 1961 and later

CHANNEL ISLANDS PLOTTED ON UTM GRID

21. *Oedipoda caerulescens* (p. 105)

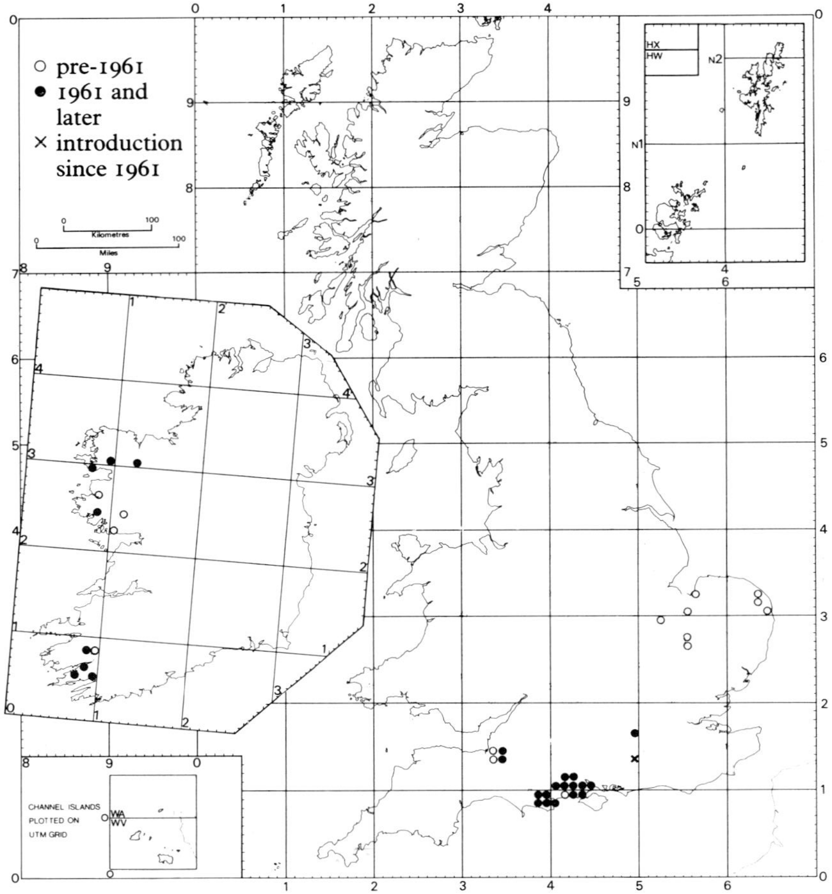

○ pre-1961
● 1961 and later
× introduction since 1961

CHANNEL ISLANDS PLOTTED ON UTM GRID

22. *Stethophyma grossum* (p. 106)

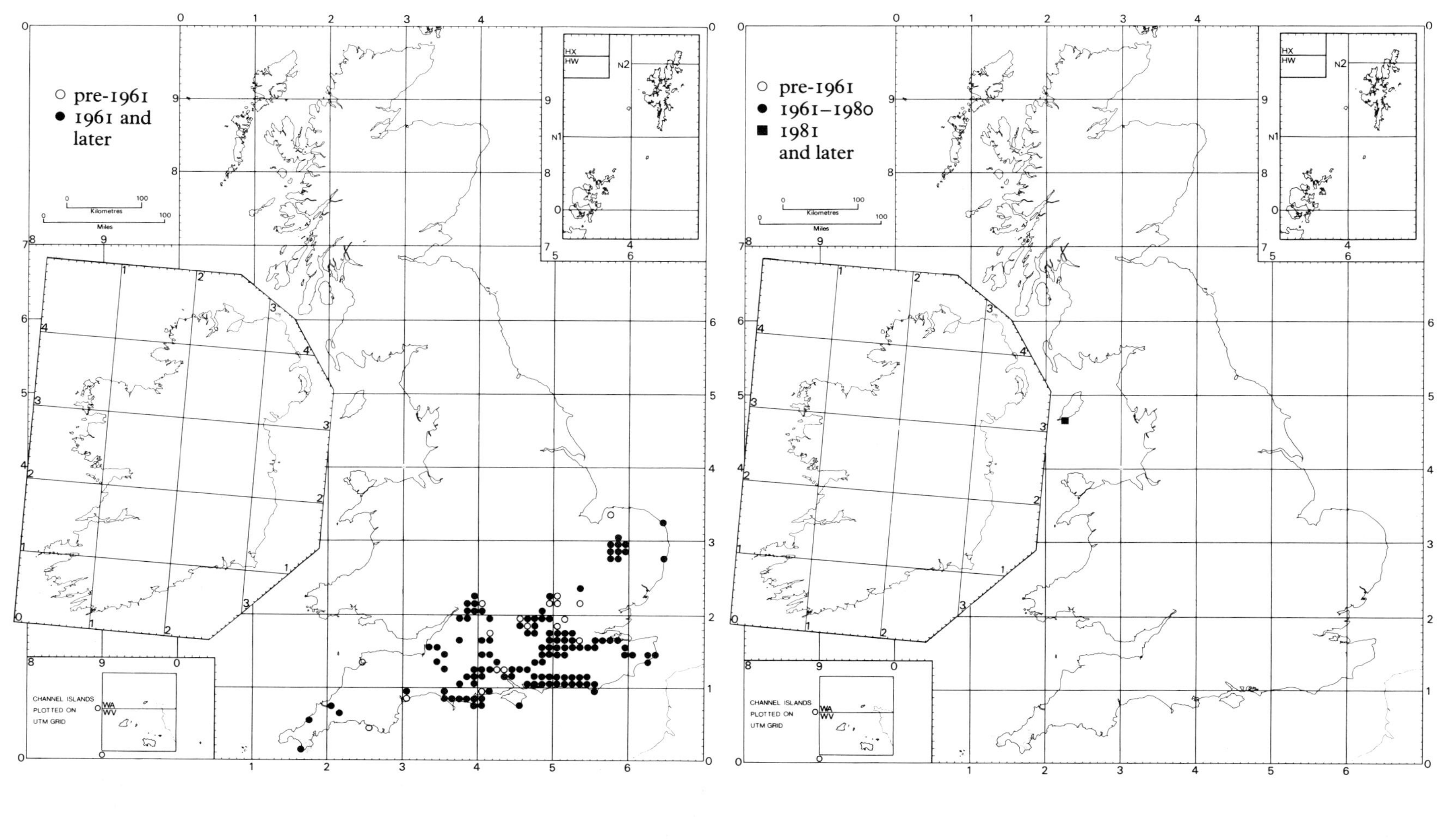

23. *Stenobothrus lineatus* (p. 107)

24. *Stenobothrus stigmaticus* (p. 108)

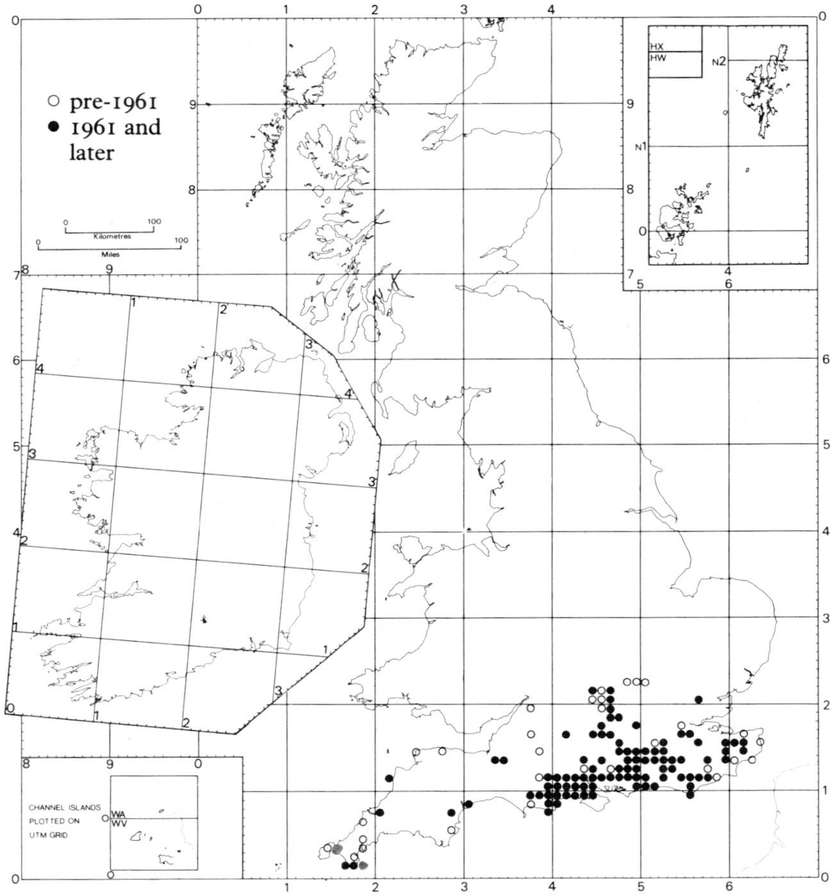

25. *Omocestus rufipes* (p. 109)

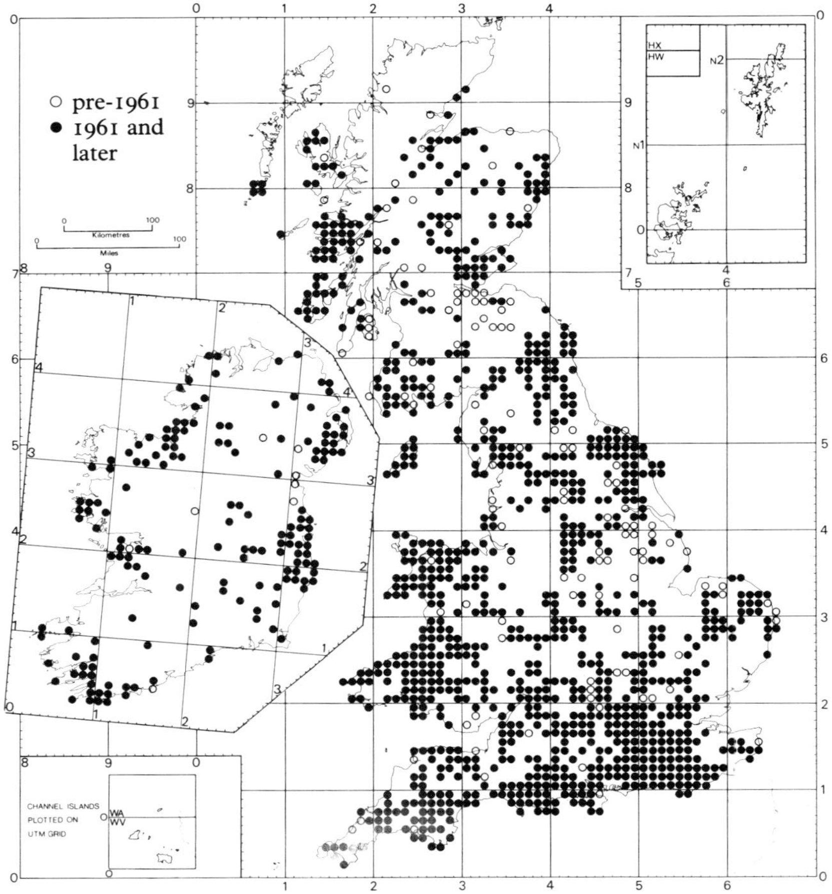

26. *Omocestus viridulus* (p. 110)

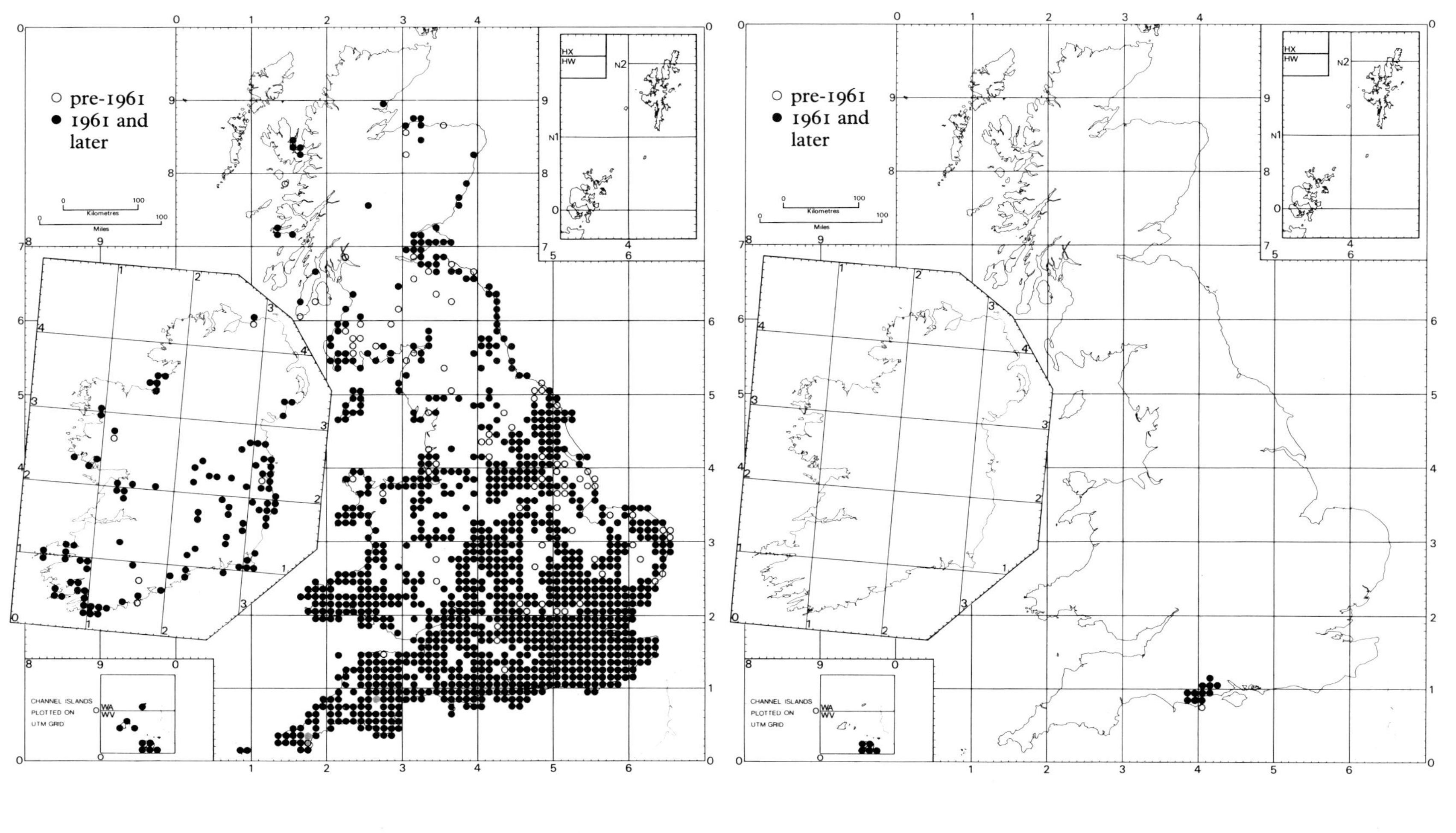

27. *Chorthippus brunneus* (p. 112)

28. *Chorthippus vagans* (p. 113)

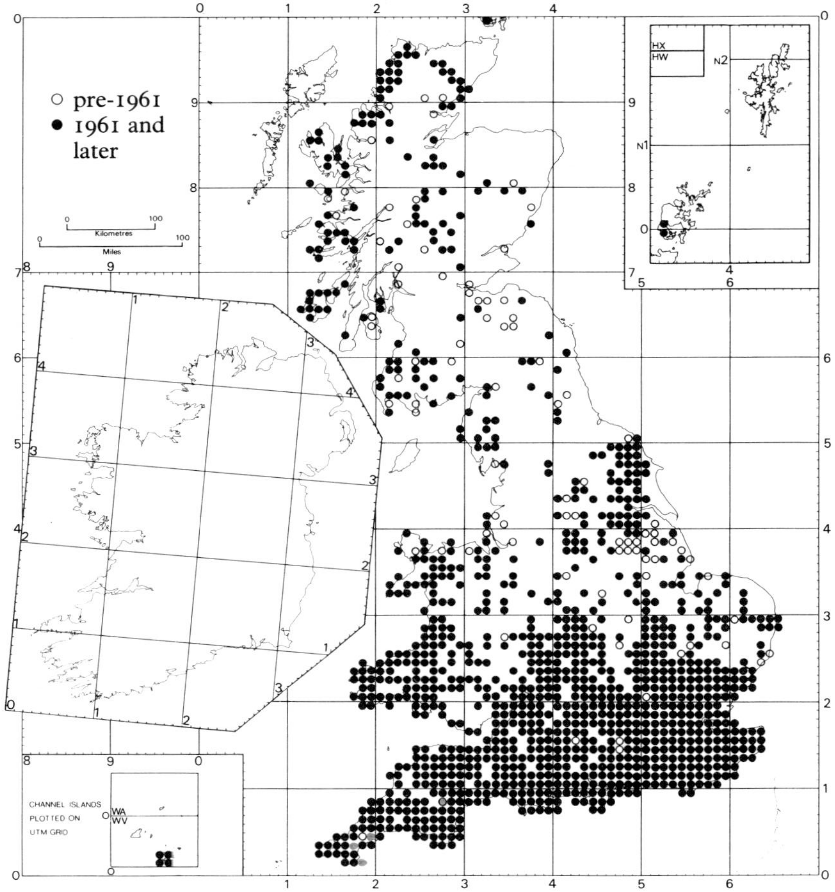

○ pre-1961
● 1961 and later

CHANNEL ISLANDS PLOTTED ON UTM GRID

29. *Chorthippus parallelus* (p. 114)

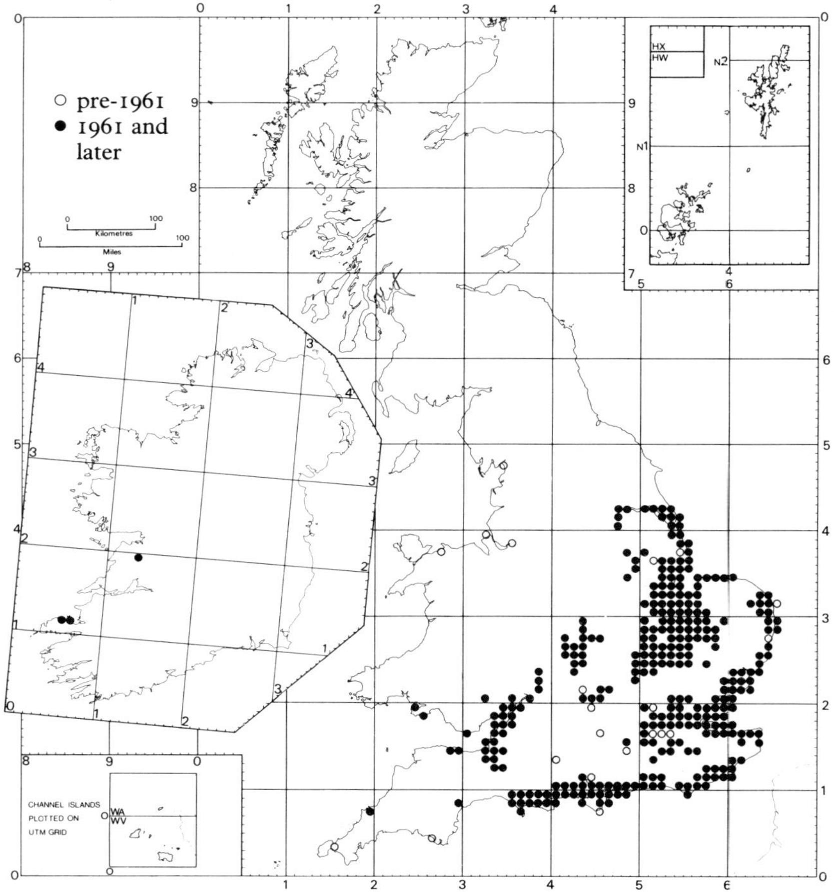

○ pre-1961
● 1961 and later

CHANNEL ISLANDS PLOTTED ON UTM GRID

30. *Chorthippus albomarginatus* (p. 115)

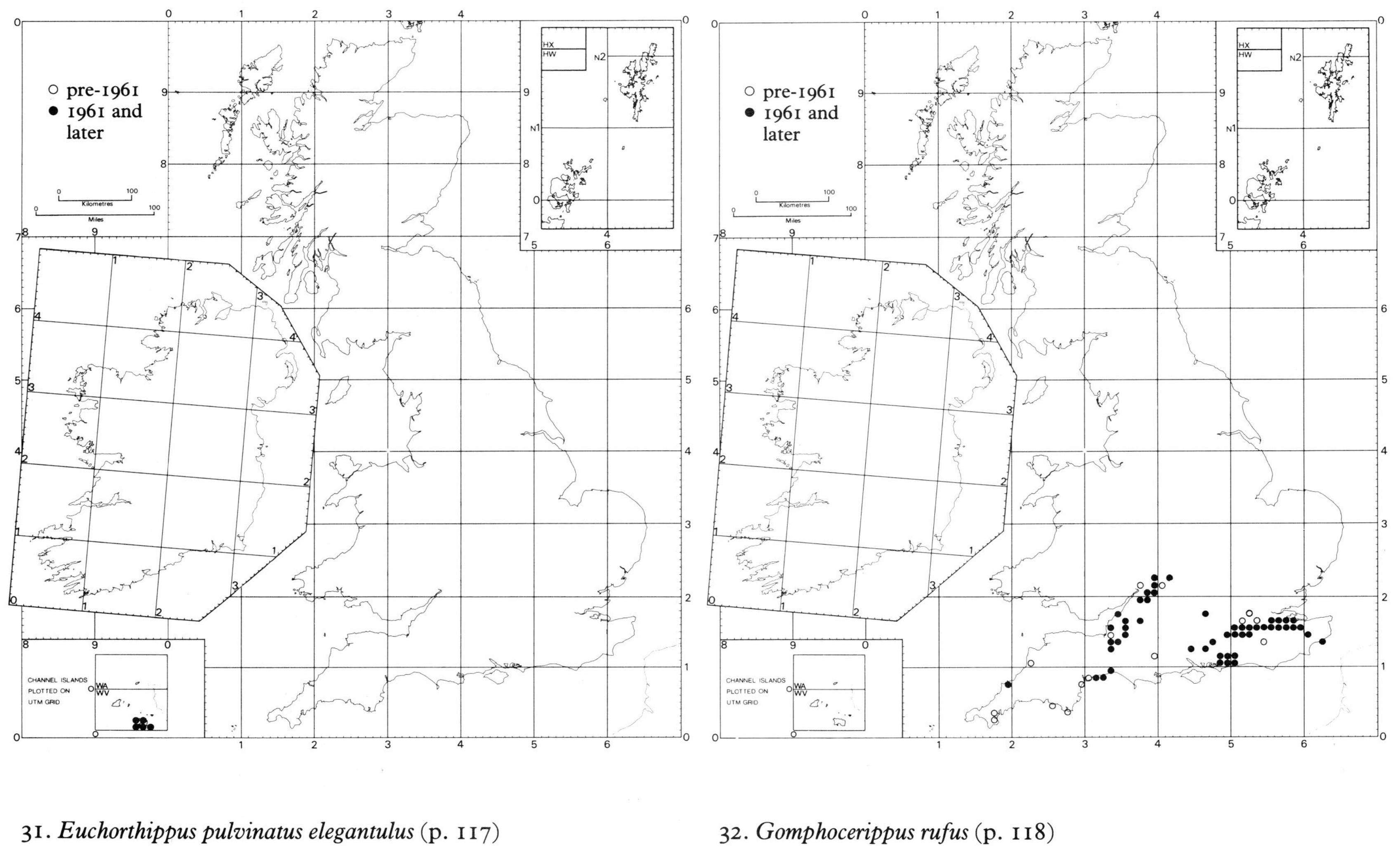

31. *Euchorthippus pulvinatus elegantulus* (p. 117)

32. *Gomphocerippus rufus* (p. 118)

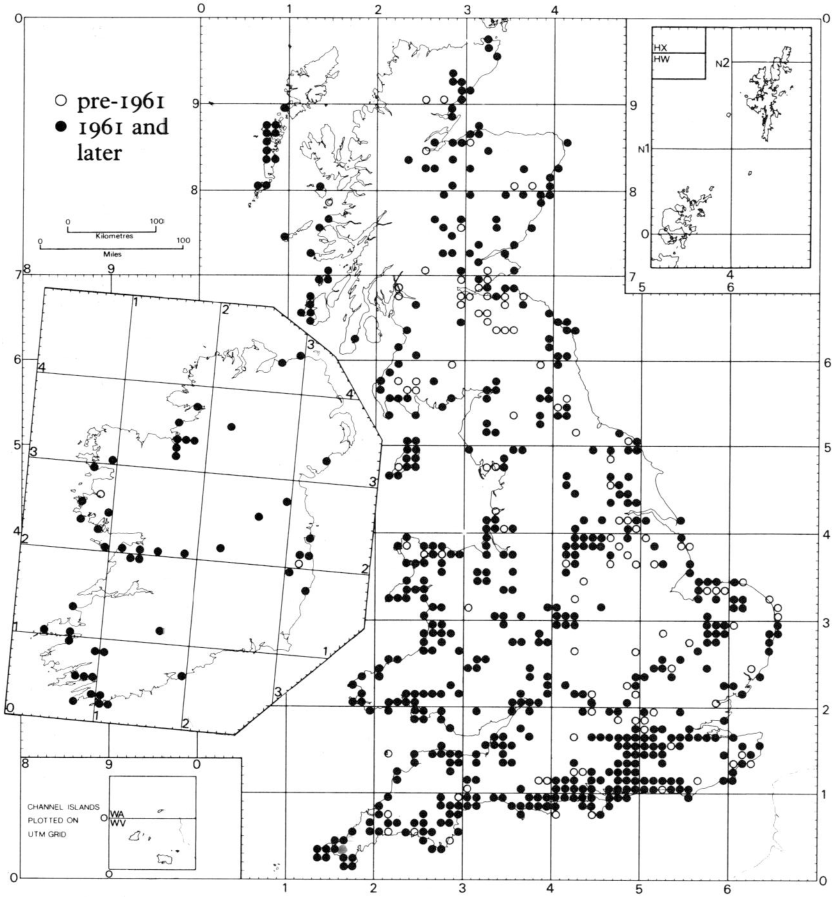

○ pre-1961
● 1961 and later

Kilometres 0 100
Miles 0 100

CHANNEL ISLANDS PLOTTED ON UTM GRID

33. *Myrmeleotettix maculatus* (p. 119)

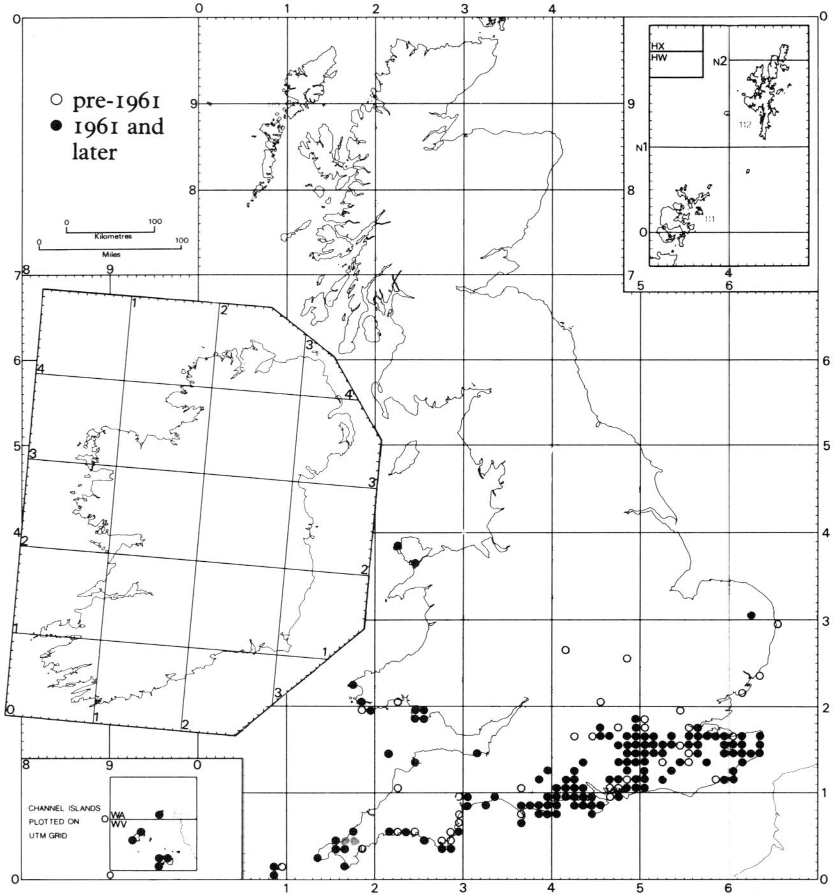

○ pre-1961
● 1961 and later

Kilometres 0 100
Miles 0 100

CHANNEL ISLANDS PLOTTED ON UTM GRID

34. Dictyoptera (native species) – all records received

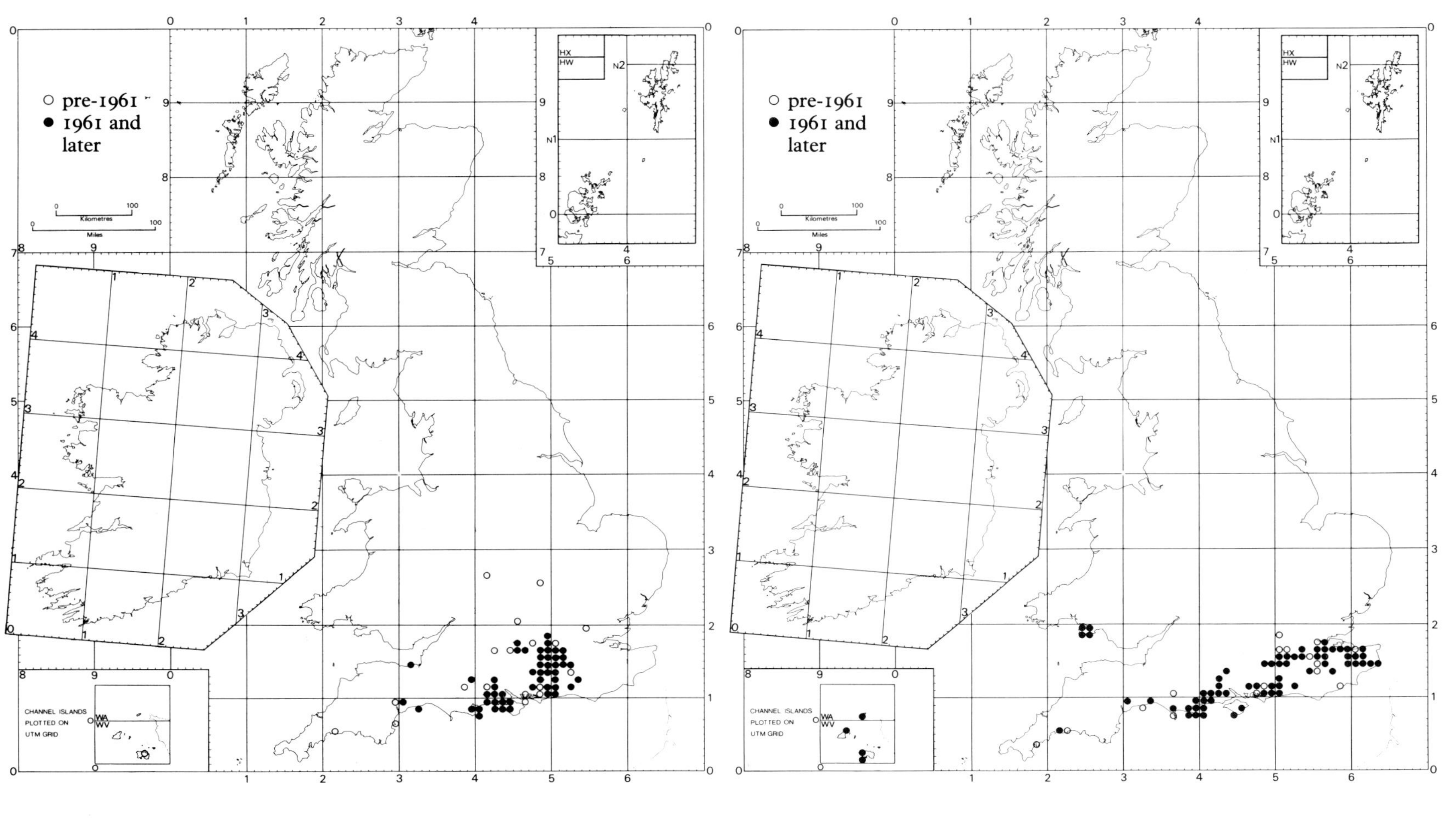

35. *Ectobius lapponicus* (p. 129)

36. *Ectobius pallidus* (p. 130)

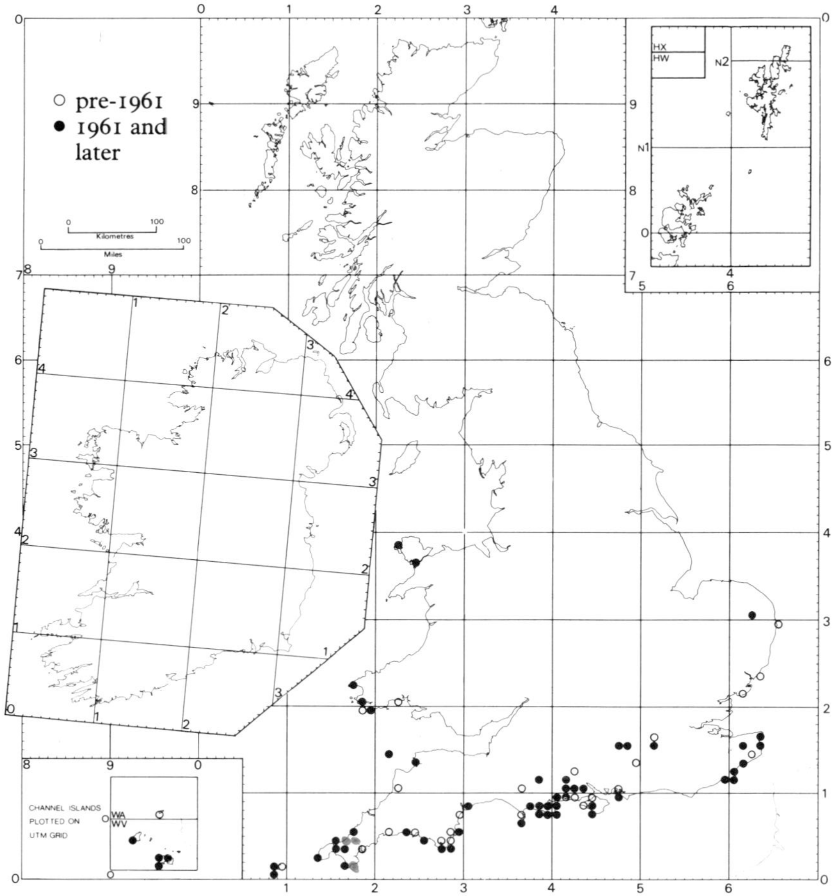

37. *Ectobius panzeri* (p. 131)

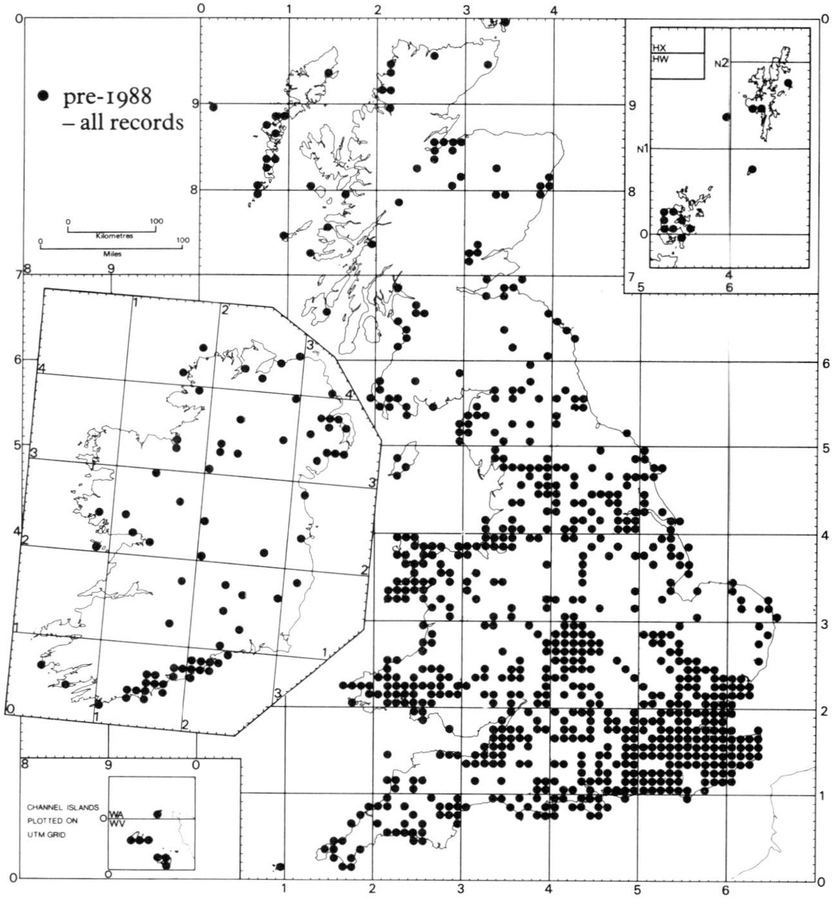

38. Dermaptera – all records received

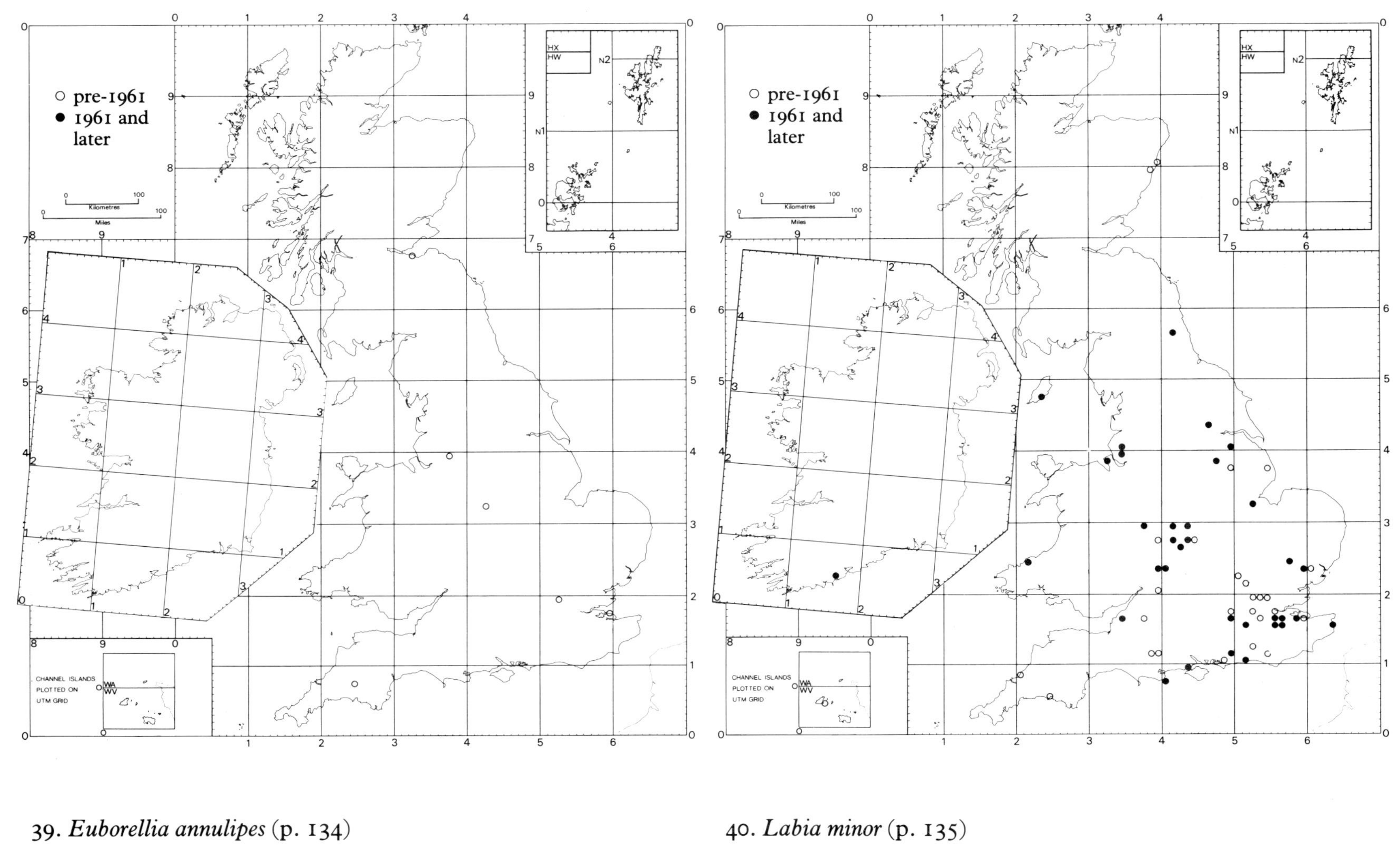

39. *Euborellia annulipes* (p. 134)

40. *Labia minor* (p. 135)

41. *Apterygida media* (p. 136)

42. *Forficula auricularia* (p. 137)

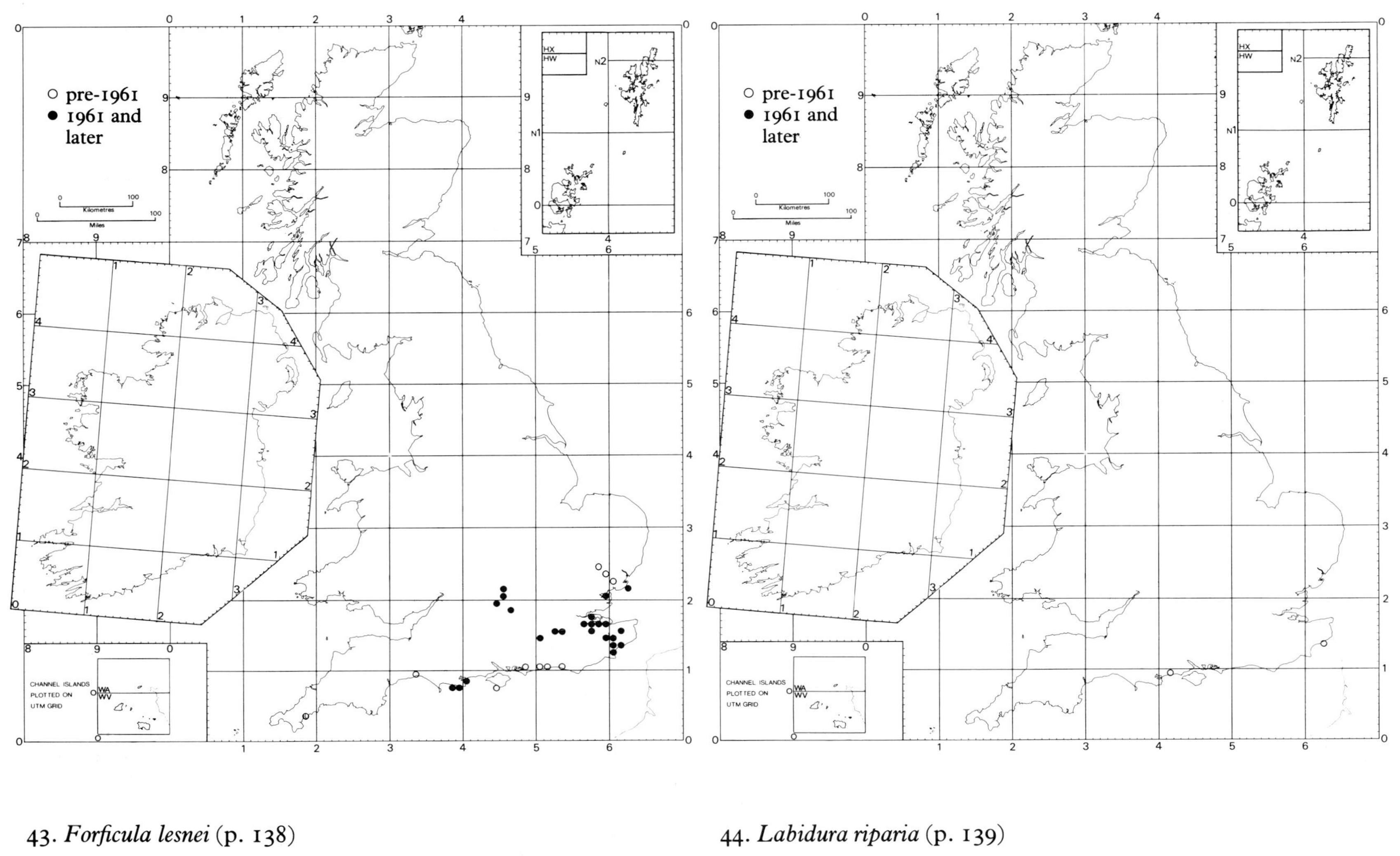

43. *Forficula lesnei* (p. 138)

44. *Labidura riparia* (p. 139)

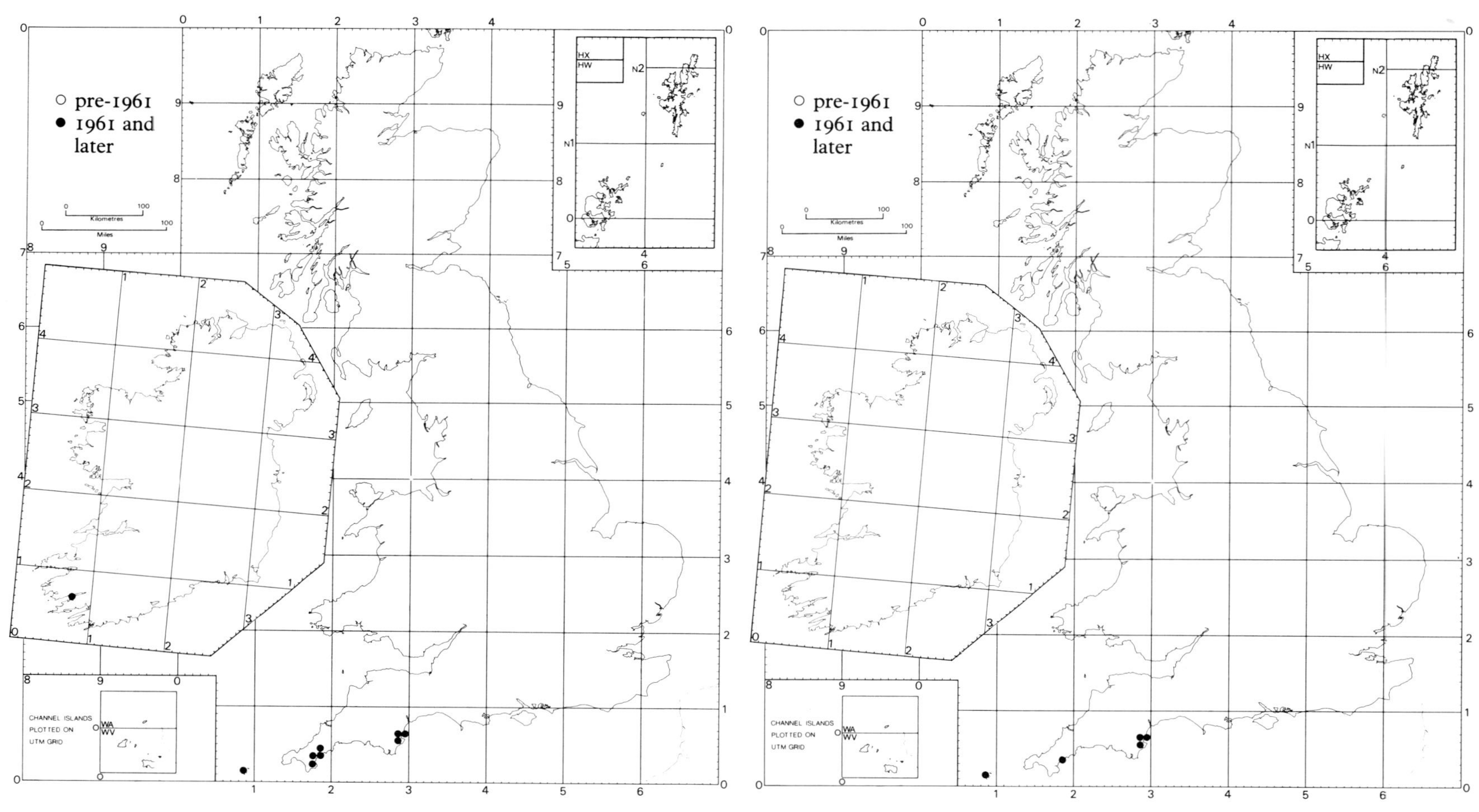

45. Phasmida – all records received

46. *Acanthoxyla geisovii* (p. 140)

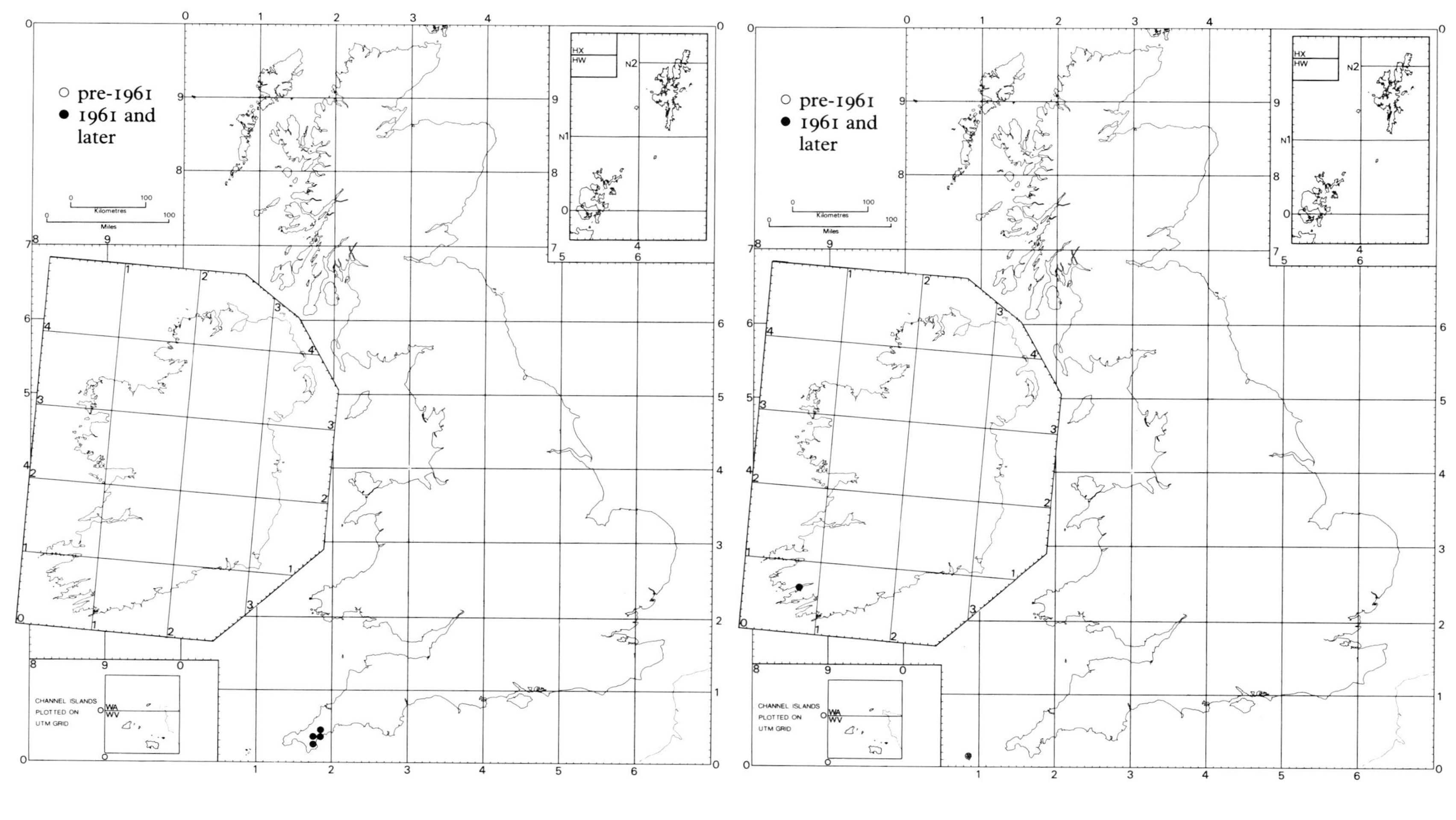

47. *Acanthoxyla inermis* (p. 142)

48. *Clitarchus hookeri* (p. 143)

APPENDIX I

Offshore Island Records (all Orders)

Island populations are always of ecological interest. The orthopterans and related insects of the British offshore islands present several features of note. The mainly nocturnal *Forficula auricularia* has an intriguingly wide distribution, reaching even remote island groups, and is clearly well suited to the damp, oceanic climate of the western and northern islands, as is apparent from its widespread populations in Shetland. It has also been found on very small islands such as the Bishops and Clerks group off the Pembrokeshire coast. It is obvious, however, that the diurnal, warmth-loving Saltatoria species are far less equipped to survive on the more northerly islands although the large population of *Myrmeleotettix maculatus* on the machairs of the Outer Hebrides is of considerable interest; and both Islay and Mull (and possibly Eigg) have conspicuously large grasshopper populations for their locations. At the opposite extreme, Orthoptera are very well represented in the Channel Islands, especially on Jersey, where *Chorthippus vagans* is a common species (J. Paul, pers. comm.). On other offshore islands around England and Wales, *Chorthippus brunneus* is evidently the species best suited to conditions on islands well separated from the mainland.

List of Offshore Islands

England and Wales

1. Holy Island
2. Isle of Wight (I.o.W.)
3. Gt. Mew Stone
4. Scilly Isles
5. Lundy
6. Steepholm
7. Caldey
8. Gateholm
9. Skokholm
10. Skomer
11. Ramsey
12. Bardsey
13. Anglesey
14. Isle of Man (I.o.M.)

Scotland

15. Arran
16. Bute
17. Islay
18. Jura
19. Colonsay
20. Mull
21. Erraid
22. Iona
23. Ulva
24. Tiree
25. Eigg
26. Rum
27. Canna
28. Skye
29. Scalpay
30. Raasay
31. Barra
32. S. Uist
33. N. Uist
34. Berneray
35. Pabbay
36. St. Kilda
37. Harris & Lewis
38. Orkneys
39. Fair Isle
40. Shetlands
41. Isle of May
42. Bass Rock

Ireland

43. Clear Island
44. Rossdohan
45. Aran Islands
46. Gorumna
47. Clare Island
48. Aran Island
49. Tory Island

Channel Islands

50. Jersey
51. Guernsey
52. Lihou & Chapelle Dom Hue
53. Sark
54. Herm
55. Alderney

It is intended that the charts of both offshore island and vice-county records should be photocopied for individual recording purposes. Symbols used are available in 'Letraset'. Space has been left for further islands to be added. The charts may not be reproduced for general use or commercially, except with the permission of the publishers.

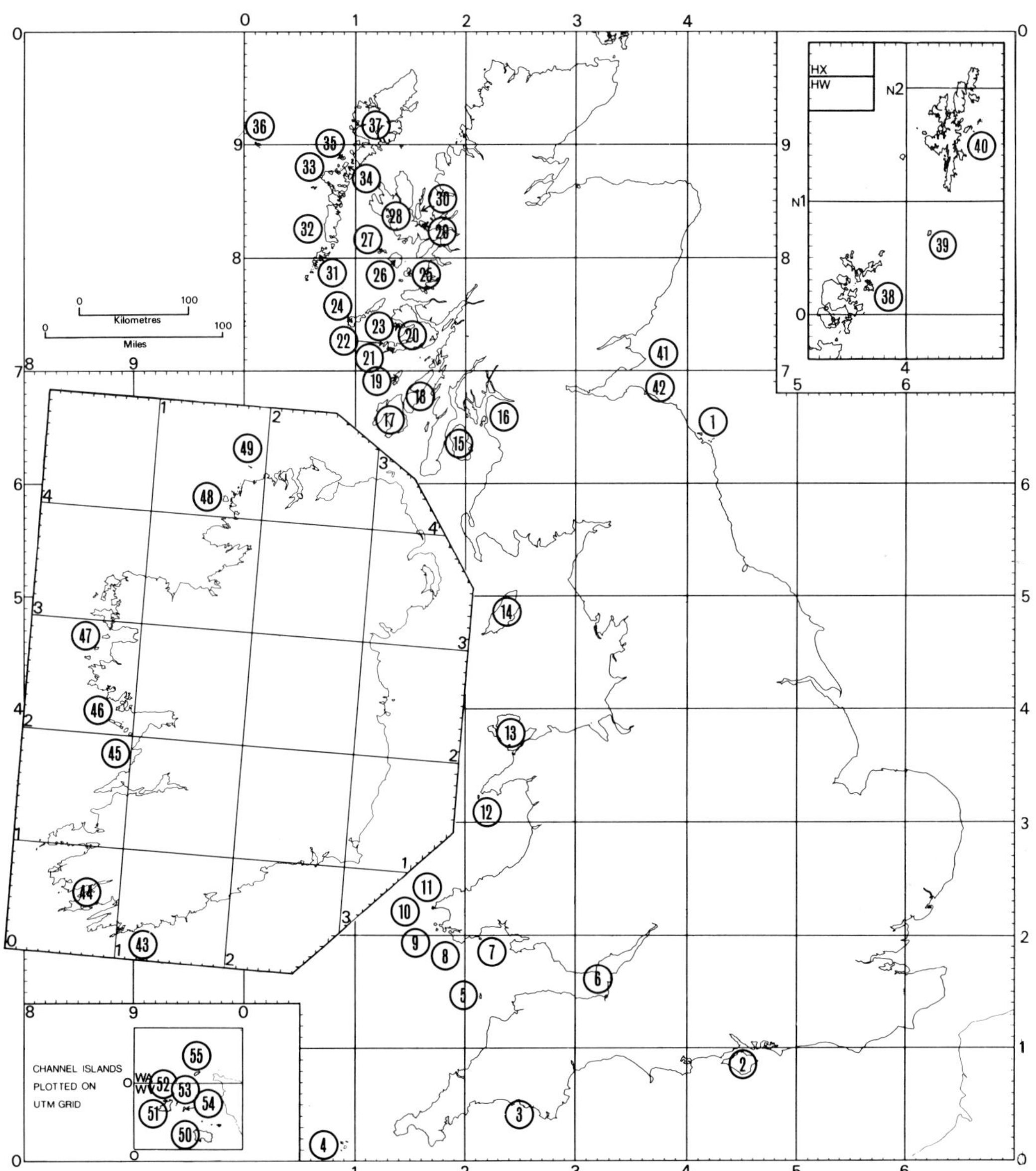

Map 49 Offshore Island Records (pp. 192–193)

Offshore Island Records

	England & Wales	1. Holy Island	2. I.o.W.	3. Gt. Mew Stone	4. Scilly Isles	5. Lundy	6. Steepholm	7. Caldey	8. Gateholm	9. Skokholm	10. Skomer	11. Ramsey	12. Bardsey	13. Anglesey	14. I.o.M.	Scotland	15. Arran	16. Bute	17. Islay	18. Jura	19. Colonsay	20. Mull	21. Erraid	22. Iona	23. Ulva	24. Tiree	25. Eigg	26. Rum	27. Canna	28. Skye	29. Scalpay	30. Raasay	31. Barra	32. S. Uist
01. *T. asynamorus*																																		
02. *M. thalassinum*			●																															
03. *T. viridissima*			●		●																													
04. *D. verrucivorus*			○																															
05. *P. griseoaptera*			●				●								●																			
06. *P. albopunctata*			●		●																													
07. *M. brachyptera*																																		
08. *M. roeselii*			●																															
09. *C. discolor*			●																															
10. *C. dorsalis*			●											●																				
11. *L. punctatissima*			●			●	●				●			●	●																			
12. *A. domesticus*			●											●	●																			
13. *G. campestris*			○																															
14. *N. sylvestris*			●																															
15. *P. squamiger*																																		
16. *G. gryllotalpa*			●																															
17. *T. ceperoi*			●																															
18. *T. subulata*			●																															
19. *T. undulata*			●		●									●	●		○		●		●	●					○	●		●			○	
20. *O. caerulescens*																																		
21. *S. grossum*																																		
22. *S. lineatus*			●																															
23. *S. stigmaticus*															●																			
24. *O. rufipes*																																		
25. *O. viridulus*			●							●	●	●		●	●		○		●	●	●	●	●	●	●	●	○	●	●	●			●	○
26. *C. brunneus*		●	●	○	●	●		●	●	●	●	●	●	●	●		○					●					○				●	●		
27. *C. vagans*																																		
28. *C. parallelus*			●					●			●			●			○	●	●	●		●		●			○	●	●	●		●		
29. *C. albomarginatus*			●																															
30. *E. p. elegantulus*																																		
31. *G. rufus*																																		
32. *M. maculatus*		●	●			○					●			●	●				●		●	●		●		●	○	●					●	●
33. *P. surinamensis*																																		
34. *B. orientalis*			●											●	○																			
35. *P. americana*																																		
36. *P. australasiae*																																		
37. *B. germanica*			●																															
38. *S. longipalpa*																																		
39. *E. lapponicus*			●																															
40. *E. pallidus*			●																															
41. *E. panzeri*			●		●	●	○							●																				
42. *E. annulipes*																																		
43. *L. minor*			○											○	●																			
44. *M. arachidis*																																		
45. *A. media*																																		
46. *F. auricularia*		●	●		●	●	●			●	●	●	●	●	●		○		●			●		●			○		●				●	●
47. *F. lesnei*			○		○		○																											
48. *L. riparia*																																		
49. *A. geisovii*					●																													
50. *A. inermis*																																		
51. *C. hookeri*					●																													
52. *C. morosus*																																		

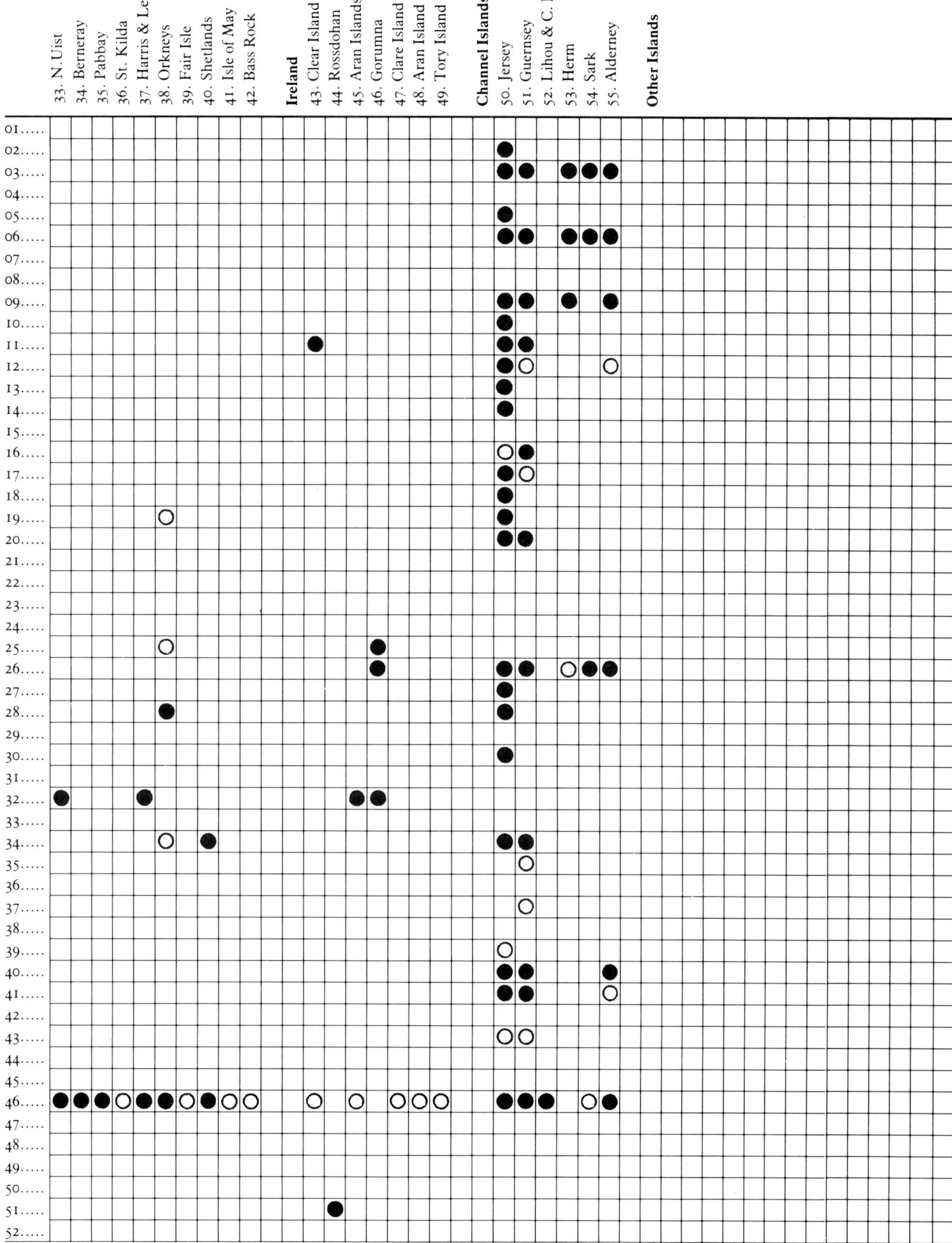

	33. N. Uist	34. Berneray	35. Pabbay	36. St. Kilda	37. Harris & Lewis	38. Orkneys	39. Fair Isle	40. Shetlands	41. Isle of May	42. Bass Rock	**Ireland**	43. Clear Island	44. Rossdohan	45. Aran Islands	46. Gorumna	47. Clare Island	48. Aran Island	49. Tory Island	**Channel Islands**	50. Jersey	51. Guernsey	52. Lihou & C. Dom Hue	53. Herm	54. Sark	55. Alderney	**Other Islands**
01.....																										
02.....																				●						
03.....																				●	●		●	●	●	
04.....																										
05.....																				●						
06.....																				●	●		●	●	●	
07.....																										
08.....																										
09.....																				●	●		●		●	
10.....																				●						
11.....												●								●	●					
12.....																				●	○				○	
13.....																				●						
14.....																				●						
15.....																										
16.....																				○	●					
17.....																				●	○					
18.....																				●						
19.....						○														●						
20.....																				●	●					
21.....																										
22.....																										
23.....																										
24.....																										
25.....						○									●											
26.....															●					●	●		○	●	●	
27.....																				●						
28.....						●														●						
29.....																										
30.....																				●						
31.....																										
32.....	●				●									●	●											
33.....																										
34.....						○		●												●	●					
35.....																					○					
36.....																										
37.....																					○					
38.....																										
39.....																				○						
40.....																				●	●				●	
41.....																				●	●				○	
42.....																										
43.....																				○	○					
44.....																										
45.....																										
46.....	●	●	●	○	●	●	○	●	○	○		○		○		○	○	○		●	●	●		○	●	
47.....																										
48.....																										
49.....																										
50.....																										
51.....													●													
52.....																										

APPENDIX II

Vice-county Records (all Orders)

Throughout the text, reference is made to numerous localities with the name of the county or vice-county in which the place occurs. For pre-1974 records, the county name given is, in most cases, that which applied before the administrative re-organization of that year. These names relate closely to the vice-county names (text fig. 56).

The two maps in Appendix IV, (text figs. 57 and 58, pp. 214-15) show, on the left, the county boundaries of Great Britain before the 1974 re-organization and, on the right, those of today. These maps are intended to be an additional aid to interpreting the distribution records for England, Wales and Scotland. County names in Ireland remain unchanged.

The Watson-Praeger vice-county system of subdividing the country into convenient recording units is based, for England, Wales and Scotland, on the method of H. C. Watson in his work, *Cybele Britannica*, Vols III and IV, published in 1852 and 1859 respectively, and, for Ireland, on that of R. L. Praeger (1901). A full definition of the vice-county boundaries of Great Britain with two folding 1:625,000 maps was published by The Ray Society (Dandy, 1969), but there has been no similar recent publication for Ireland. However, as Ireland has not suffered from administrative re-organization, the county and vice-county boundaries retain much in common. An advantage of continuing to use vice-county recording (alongside 10 km square dot-distribution recording) is that records of any age can be easily compared.

NOTE. Doubtful records, shown on the vice-county maps as ?, are not included in the charts. The vice-county maps and associated charts will inevitably be incomplete and may contain some errors or omissions of published material. Every effort has been made to make them complete, but the author (E. C. M. Haes) and publishers would welcome all additional data for these and also for the Offshore Island Records' chart, including islands not listed. These may be sent to him c/o Harley Books, Great Horkesley, Colchester, Essex CO6 4AH.

England and Wales

1 West Cornwall (with Scilly)
2 East Cornwall
3 South Devon
4 North Devon
5 South Somerset
6 North Somerset
7 North Wiltshire
8 South Wiltshire
9 Dorset
10 Isle of Wight
11 South Hampshire
12 North Hampshire
13 West Sussex
14 East Sussex
15 East Kent
16 West Kent
17 Surrey
18 South Essex
19 North Essex
20 Hertfordshire
21 Middlesex
22 Berkshire
23 Oxfordshire
24 Buckinghamshire
25 East Suffolk
26 West Suffolk
27 East Norfolk
28 West Norfolk
29 Cambridgeshire
30 Bedfordshire
31 Huntingdonshire
32 Northamptonshire
33 East Gloucestershire
34 West Gloucestershire
35 Monmouthshire
36 Herefordshire
37 Worcestershire
38 Warwickshire
39 Staffordshire
40 Shropshire (Salop)
41 Glamorgan
42 Breconshire
43 Radnorshire
44 Carmarthenshire
45 Pembrokeshire
46 Cardiganshire
47 Montgomeryshire
48 Merionethshire
49 Caernarvonshire
50 Denbighshire
51 Flintshire
52 Anglesey
53 South Lincolnshire
54 North Lincolnshire
55 Leicestershire (with Rutland)
56 Nottinghamshire
57 Derbyshire
58 Cheshire
59 South Lancashire
60 West Lancashire
61 South-east Yorkshire
62 North-east Yorkshire
63 South-west Yorkshire
64 Mid-west Yorkshire
65 North-west Yorkshire
66 Durham
67 South Northumberland
68 North Northumberland (Cheviot)
69 Westmorland with North Lancashire
70 Cumberland
71 Isle of Man

Scotland

72 Dumfries-shire
73 Kirkcudbrightshire
74 Wigtownshire
75 Ayrshire
76 Renfrewshire
77 Lanarkshire
78 Peebleshire
79 Selkirkshire
80 Roxburghshire
81 Berwickshire
82 East Lothian (Haddington)
83 Midlothian (Edinburgh)
84 West Lothian (Linlithgow)
85 Fifeshire (with Kinross)
86 Stirlingshire
87 West Perthshire (with Clackmannan)
88 Mid Perthshire
89 East Perthshire
90 Angus (Forfar)
91 Kincardineshire
92 South Aberdeenshire
93 North Aberdeenshire
94 Banffshire
95 Moray (Elgin)
96 East Inverness-shire (with Nairn)
97 West Inverness-shire
98 Argyll Main
99 Dunbartonshire
100 Clyde Isles
101 Kintyre
102 South Ebudes
103 Mid Ebudes
104 North Ebudes
105 West Ross
106 East Ross
107 East Sutherland
108 West Sutherland
109 Caithness
110 Outer Hebrides
111 Orkney Islands
112 Shetland Islands (Zetland)
113 Channel Isles

Ireland

H.1 South Kerry
H.2 North Kerry
H.3 West Cork
H.4 Mid Cork
H.5 East Cork
H.6 Waterford
H.7 South Tipperary
H.8 Limerick
H.9 Clare
H.10 North Tipperary
H.11 Kilkenny
H.12 Wexford
H.13 Carlow
H.14 Leix (Queen's County)
H.15 South-east Galway
H.16 West Galway
H.17 North-east Galway
H.18 Offaly (King's County)
H.19 Kildare
H.20 Wicklow
H.21 Dublin
H.22 Meath
H.23 West Meath
H.24 Longford
H.25 Roscommon
H.26 East Mayo
H.27 West Mayo
H.28 Sligo
H.29 Leitrim
H.30 Cavan
H.31 Louth
H.32 Monaghan
H.33 Fermanagh
H.34 East Donegal
H.35 West Donegal
H.36 Tyrone
H.37 Armagh
H.38 Down
H.39 Antrim
H.40 Londonderry

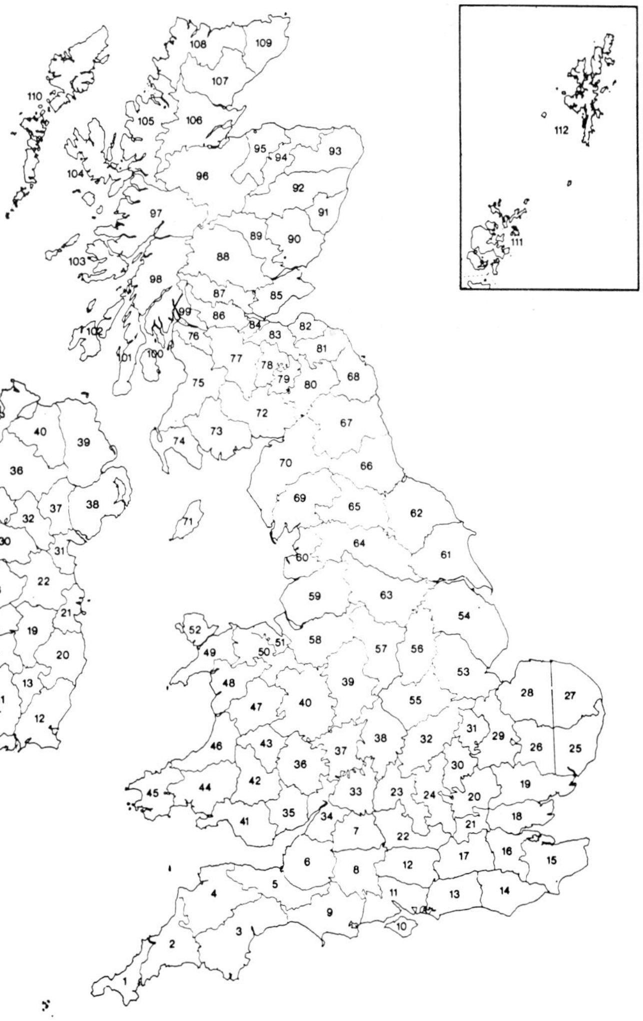

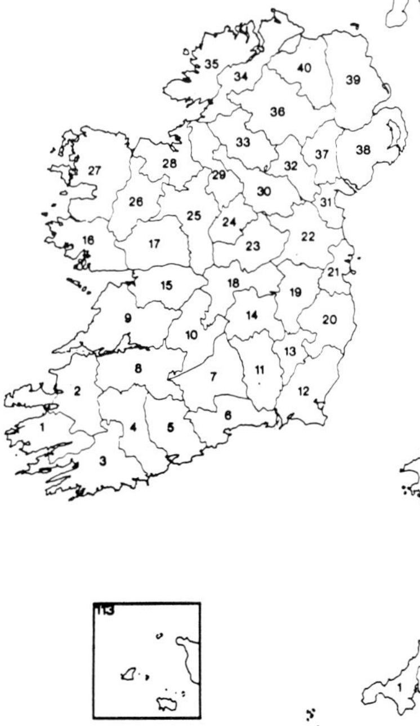

Text Figure 56
Vice-counties

Vice-county Records

	England & Wales	1. W.C'wall	2. E.C'wall	3. S.Devon	4. N.Devon	5. S.Som.	6. N.Som.	7. N.Wilts.	8. S.Wilts.	9. Dorset	10. I.o.W.	11. S.Hants.	12. N.Hants.	13. W.Sussex	14. E.Sussex	15. E.Kent	16. W.Kent	17. Surrey	18. S.Essex	19. N.Essex	20. Herts.	21. Middx.	22. Berks.	23. Oxon.	24. Bucks.	25. E.Suffolk	26. W.Suffolk	27. E.Norfolk	28. W.Norfolk	29. Cambs.	30. Beds.	31. Hunts.	32. Northants	33. E.Glos.	34. W.Glos.	35. Monmouth
01. *T. asynamorus*							○								○	●		●				○				○	○			○						
02. *M. thalassinum*		●	●	●	●	●	●	●	●	●	●	●	●	●	●	●	●	●	●	●	●	●	●	●	●	●	●	●	●	●	●	●	●	●	●	●
03. *T. viridissima*		●	●	●	●	●	●	●	○	●	●	●	○	●	●	●	●	●	●	●	○	○	●	●	●	●	●	●	○	●		●	○	●	●	●
04. *D. verrucivorus*								●		●	○	○			●	●																				
05. *P. griseoaptera*		●	●	●	●	●	●	●	●	●	●	●	●	●	●	●	●	●	●	●	●	●	●	●	●	●	●	●	●	●	●	●	●	●	●	●
06. *P. albopunctata*		●	●	●	●		●			●	●	●		●	●	●			○	○																
07. *M. brachyptera*		○	●	●	○		●	○	●	●		●	●	●	●	○	○	●					●		●			●	○		○					
08. *M. roeselii*											●	●				●	●	●	●	●	●	●	●			●										
09. *C. discolor*									●	●	●	●		●	●																					
10. *C. dorsalis*			●	●	●	●	●			●	●	●	●	●	●	●	●	●	●	●	●			○		●	●	●	●	●	●	●			●	●
11. *L. punctatissima*		●	●	●	●	●	●	●	●	●	●	●	●	●	●	●	●	●	●	●	●	●	●	●	●	●	●	●	●	●	●	●	●	●	●	●
12. *A. domesticus*		○	○	●	○	●	●		●	●	●	●	○	●	●	●	●	●	●	●	●	●	●	●	●	○	●	●	○	●	●	●	○	●	●	●
13. *G. campestris*		○	○		○					○	○	○	○	●	○			●										○	○							
14. *N. sylvestris*				●					●	○	●	●						●																		
15. *P. squamiger*										●																										
16. *G. gryllotalpa*		○	○	○	○				●	●	●	●	○	○	●		○	○	○	○		○	○					○	○	○	○				○	
17. *T. ceperoi*		●	●	●	●					●	●	●			●	●																				
18. *T. subulata*		●	●	●	●	●	●	●	●	●	●	●	●	●	●	●	●	●		○	○	○	●	●	○		●	●	○	●	●	●		●	●	●
19. *T. undulata*		●	●	●	●	●	●	●	●	●	●	●	●	●	●	●	●	●	●	●	●	○	●	●	●	●	●	●	●	●	●	●	●	●	●	●
20. *O. caerulescens*																																				
21. *S. grossum*							●			●		●						●					○					○	○	○		○				
22. *S. lineatus*		●	●	●	○		●	●	●	●	●	●	●	●	●	●	●	●			●		●	●	●	●	●	●	●	○	○			●	●	
23. *S. stigmaticus*																																				
24. *O. rufipes*		●	●	●	○		●	●	●	●		●	●	●	●	●	●	●	●		○		●	●	●						○			○	○	
25. *O. viridulus*		●	●	●	●	●	●	●	●	●	●	●	●	●	●	●	●	●	●	●	●	●	●	●	●	●	●	●	●	●	●	●	●	●	●	●
26. *C. brunneus*		●	●	●	●	●	●	●	●	●	●	●	●	●	●	●	●	●	●	●	●	●	●	●	●	●	●	●	●	●	●	●	●	●	●	●
27. *C. vagans*										●		●																								
28. *C. parallelus*		●	●	●	●	●	●	●	●	●	●	●	●	●	●	●	●	●	●	●	●	●	●	●	●	●	●	●	●	●	●	●	●	●	●	●
29. *C. albomarginatus*		●		●		●	●		○	●	●	●		●	●	●	●	●	●	●		●	○	●	●	●	●	●	●	●	●	●		●	●	●
30. *E. p. elegantulus*																																				
31. *G. rufus*		○	●	●			●			●		●	●	●	○	●	●	●					○	●										●	●	
32. *M. maculatus*		●	●	●	●	●	●	○	●	●	●	●	●	●	●	●	●	●	●	●	●	○	●	●	●	●	●	●	●	●	●	○	○	●	●	●
33. *P. surinamensis*												○		○				●	○					○												
34. *B. orientalis*		●	○	●	○	○	○	○	●	●	●	●	●	●	●	●	●	●	●	●	○	●	●	○	●	○		○	○	●	○	●	○	○	●	○
35. *P. americana*		○	○	○			○			○		○		●	○	○	○	●	○			○						●		●				●	●	○
36. *P. australasiae*		○	○							○		●	○		●	○		●	○		○	○		○	○						○				●	
37. *B. germanica*		○		○	○			○	○	○	●	○	○	●	○	●	○	●	●	○		○	○	○		○			○	●		●	○	○		
38. *S. longipalpa*				○														●																		
39. *E. lapponicus*			○	●	○	●		○	●	●	●	●	●	●	●			●	○				●	○	●								○			
40. *E. pallidus*		○	●	●	○				●	●	●	●		●	●	●	●	●				○	○						○							
41. *E. panzeri*		●	●	●	●		○			●	●	●	●	●	●	●		●	○	○						○		●	○							
42. *E. annulipes*		○		○			○									○		○				○													○	
43. *L. minor*		○	○	○	○	○	●	○	○	●	○	●	○	●	○	●	●	●	○	●	○	○	○	○		○	●	○	○	○	○		○	●	○	○
44. *M. arachidis*																○						○													○	
45. *A. media*																●	●		○	○						●	●	○		○						
46. *F. auricularia*		●	●	●	●	●	●	●	●	●	●	●	●	●	●	●	●	●	●	●	●	●	●	●	●	●	●	●	●	●	●	●	●	●	●	●
47. *F. lesnei*		○		○	○		○	○	○	●	○	○	○	○	○	●	●	●	○	●			●	●												
48. *L. riparia*										○		○				○																				
49. *A. geisovii*		●	●	●																																
50. *A. inermis*		●	●																																	
51. *C. hookeri*		●																																		
52. *C. morosus*				○														○																		

	36. Herefs.	37. Worcs.	38. Warw.	39. Staffs.	40. Salop	41. Glam.	42. Brecon	43. Radnor	44. Carm.	45. Pembs.	46. Card.	47. Mont.	48. Merion.	49. Caern.	50. Denbigh	51. Flint	52. Anglesey	53. S.Lincs.	54. N.Lincs.	55. Leics.	56. Notts.	57. Derby	58. Cheshire	59. S.Lancs.	60. W.Lancs.	61. S.E.Yorks.	62. N.E.Yorks.	63. S.W.Yorks.	64. M.-W.Yorks.	65. N.W.Yorks.	66. Durham	67. S.Northd.	68. N.Northd.	69. Westm.	70. Cumb.	71. I.o.M.	**Scotland**	72. Dumfries	73. Kirkcudbright	74. Wigtown	75. Ayrshire	76. Renfrew	77. Lanark
01.....						○														○			○		●			●										○			○		○
02.....	●	●	●	●	●	●			●	●	●	●	●	●	●	●		●	●	●	●		●	○	●			●	●						○								
03.....						●			●	●										○	○	○																					
04.....																																											
05.....	●	●	●		●	●		●	●	●	●	●	●	●	●			●	●	●	○	○	○		●	○	○							●	●	●			●				
06.....						●				●				●																													
07.....			●	●	●	●			●		●			○	●				●			○	●	●	●	○	●	●	○					●	○								
08.....											●							●	●							●																	
09.....																																											
10.....						●			●	●	●		●	●			●	●	●							●		○															
11.....	●	●	●		●	●		●	●	●	●		●	●	●		●	●	○	●	●					○		○								●			●	○			
12.....		●	●	●	●				●		○		○	●			●	●	○	○	○	●	●	●	●	●	○	●	○	○	○	○	○	○	○	●		○	○	○	○	○	○
13.....				○														○																									
14.....																																											
15.....																																											
16.....		○	○	○		○			○	○									○			○	●	○				●														○	
17.....						●			●																																		
18.....	●	●	●			○	●		●	●					●			●	○	●								○															
19.....	●	●	●	●	●	●	●		●	●	●	●	●	●	●	●	●	●	●	●	○	●	●	●	●	●	●	●	○	○	●	●	●	●	●	●		●	●	●	●		
20.....																																											
21.....																																											
22.....																																											
23.....																																				●							
24.....																																											
25.....	●	●	●	●	●	●	●	●	●	●	●	●	●	●	●	●	●	●	●	●	●	●	●	●	●	●	●	●	●	●	●	●	●	●	●	●		●	●	●	●	●	●
26.....	●	●	●	●	●	●	●	●	●	●	●	●	●	●	●	●	●	●	●	●	●	●	●	●	●	●	●	●	●	●	●	●	●	●	●	●		●	●	●	●	○	●
27.....																																											
28.....	●	●	●	●	●	●	●	●	●	●	●	●	●	●	●	●	●	●	●	●	●	●	●	●	●	●	●	●	●	●	●	●	●	●	●			●	●	●	●		●
29.....		●	●			●								○				●	●							●		●															
30.....																																											
31.....																																											
32.....	○	●	●	●	●	●	●	●	●	●	●	○	●	●	●	●	●	○	●	●	●	●	●	●	●	●	●	●	●	●	●	●	●	●	●	●		●	●	●	●	●	●
33.....																							○	○				●	○														○
34.....		●	●	○	●	○				●				●			●	●	○	○	○	○	●	●	○	○	○	●	●	○	●	●		○	○	○		○	○	○	●	○	○
35.....				○		○												○	○		○	○		○	○			●	○													○	○
36.....						○					●			●							○	○	○	●	○			●	○													○	
37.....			●	○		○													○	○	○	○	○	●	○		○	●	○		○	○			○							○	○
38.....																												●															
39.....			○																																								
40.....						●																																					
41.....									○	●							●																										
42.....				○																			○	○																			○
43.....	○	●	●	○	●	○				○	●			○			○	●	●	○	●	○	●	●	○	●	○	○	○	○	●		○	○	○	●		○				○	
44.....																							○					○															
45.....																																											
46.....	●	●	●	●	●	●	●	○	●	●	●	●	●	●	●	●	●	●	●	●	●	●	●	●	●	●	●	●	●	●	●	●	●	●	●	●		●	●	●	●	●	○
47.....																																											
48.....																																											
49.....																																											
50.....																																											
51.....																																											
52.....																																											

Vice-county Records	**Scotland** (cont'd)	78. Peebles	79. Selkirk	80. Roxburgh	81. Berwick	82. E. Lothian	83. Midlothian	84. W. Lothian	85. Fife	86. Stirling	87. W. Perth	88. Mid Perth	89. E. Perth	90. Angus	91. Kincardine	92. S. Aberdeen	93. N. Aberdeen	94. Banff	95. Moray	96. E. Inverness	97. W. Inverness	98. Argyll	99. Dunbarton	100. Clyde Is.	101. Kintyre	102. S. Ebudes	103. Mid Ebudes	104. N. Ebudes	105. W. Ross	106. E. Ross	107. E. Sutherland	108. W. Sutherland	109. Caithness	110. O. Hebrides	111. Orkneys	112. Shetlands
01. *T. asynamorus*							○																													
02. *M. thalassinum*																																				
03. *T. viridissima*																																				
04. *D. verrucivorus*																																				
05. *P. griseoaptera*																																				
06. *P. albopunctata*																																				
07. *M. brachyptera*																																				
08. *M. roeselii*																																				
09. *C. discolor*																																				
10. *C. dorsalis*																																				
11. *L. punctatissima*																																				
12. *A. domesticus*							○			●				○																						
13. *G. campestris*																																				
14. *N. sylvestris*																																				
15. *P. squamiger*																																				
16. *G. gryllotalpa*																							○													
17. *T. ceperoi*																																				
18. *T. subulata*																																				
19. *T. undulata*						○	○		●		○	●	●	●	●	●			●	●	●	○		○	○	●	●	●	●	●	○	●	○	○	○	
20. *O. caerulescens*																																				
21. *S. grossum*																																				
22. *S. lineatus*																																				
23. *S. stigmaticus*																																				
24. *O. rufipes*																																				
25. *O. viridulus*		○	○	○	○	○	●	○	●	○	●	●	●	●	●	●	●	○	●	●	●	●	●	○	●	●	●	●		●	●	○		●	○	
26. *C. brunneus*		○	○	○	●	●	●	●	●			●		●	●	●	●		●			○	○	○	●		●	●			●					
27. *C. vagans*																																				
28. *C. parallelus*		●	○	○	○	●	○	○	○	○	●	●	●	●	○	●				●	●	●	○	●	●	●	●	●	●	●	●	●	○		●	
29. *C. albomarginatus*																																				
30. *E. p. elegantulus*																																				
31. *G. rufus*																																				
32. *M. maculatus*		○	○	○	○	●	●	○	●	○	●	●	●	●	●	●	●	○	●	●	●		○		●	●	●	●	○	●	●		●	●		
33. *P. surinamensis*							○																													
34. *B. orientalis*						○	○	○	●					○		○							○												○	●
35. *P. americana*							○																													
36. *P. australasiae*							○				○																									
37. *B. germanica*							○										○	○																		
38. *S. longipalpa*																																				
39. *E. lapponicus*																																				
40. *E. pallidus*																																				
41. *E. panzeri*																																				
42. *E. annulipes*							○																													
43. *L. minor*					○	○	○		○					○	○	○																				
44. *M. arachidis*																																				
45. *A. media*																																				
46. *F. auricularia*				○		●	●		○	○	○	●	●	○	○	●	○	●	○	●	○	●	○	○	○	●	●	●	○	○	○	●	●	●	●	●
47. *F. lesnei*																																				
48. *L. riparia*																																				
49. *A. geisovii*																																				
50. *A. inermis*																																				
51. *C. hookeri*																																				
52. *C. morosus*																																				

	113. Channel Islands	Ireland	H1. S.Kerry	H2. N.Kerry	H3. W.Cork	H4. Mid Cork	H5. E.Cork	H6. Waterford	H7. S.Tipperary	H8. Limerick	H9. Clare	H10. N.Tipperary	H11. Kilkenny	H12. Wexford	H13. Carlow	H14. Leix	H15. S.E.Galway	H16. W.Galway	H17. N.E.Galway	H18. Offaly	H19. Kildare	H20. Wicklow	H21. Dublin	H22. Meath	H23. Westmeath	H24. Longford	H25. Roscommon	H26. E.Mayo	H27. W.Mayo	H28. Sligo	H29. Leitrim	H30. Cavan	H31. Louth	H32. Monaghan	H33. Fermanagh	H34. E.Donegal	H35. W.Donegal	H36. Tyrone	H37. Armagh	H38. Down	H39. Antrim	H40. Londonderry
01.....																							●																			
02.....	●			●				○			○						●					●																				
03.....	●																																									
04.....																																										
05.....	●							●																																		
06.....	●																																									
07.....																																										
08.....								●																																		
09.....	●																																									
10.....	●																																									
11.....	●		○		●		○															●	●																			
12.....	●		○	○								○					○					○							○						○	○						
13.....	●																																									
14.....	●																																									
15.....																																										
16.....	●																																									
17.....	●																																									
18.....	●									●	●				●	●	●	●	○	●	●	●	●	●	●	●	●	●	●	●					●							
19.....	●		●	●	●	●					●			●		●	●	●			●	●		○	●			●	●	●	●						●		○	●		
20.....	●																																									
21.....			●	●	●													●											●													
22.....																																										
23.....																																										
24.....																																										
25.....			●	●	●	●	●	●	●	●	●	●	●	●	●	●	●	●		●	●	●	●		●		○	●	●	●			●		●	○	●	●	●	●	●	●
26.....	●		●	●	●	●	●	●	●	●	●	○	●	●	●	●	●	●		●	●	●	●	●	●		●	●	●	●			●							●	●	
27.....	●																																									
28.....	●																																									
29.....			●								●																															
30.....	●																																									
31.....																																										
32.....			●	●	●	●	●				●	●				●	●	●				●	●	●	●				●	●					●	○	●			●	●	●
33.....																							○																			
34.....	●		○	○		○	○	○	○	○	○	○	○	○			○	○	○	○		○	●	○	○	○	○	○	●	○	○	○	○		○	○	○	○	○	○	●	○
35.....	○																						●																		○	
36.....																							●																		○	
37.....	○			○					○		○	○						○			○	○	●		○			○	○			○	○					○	○	○	○	○
38.....																							●																			
39.....	○																																									
40.....	●																																									
41.....	●																																									
42.....																																										
43.....	○		○		○	●		○					○	○								○	○													○		○	○			
44.....																							○																			
45.....																																										
46.....	●		●		●	●	●	●	●	●	●	●	●	●		●	●	○	○	●	●	●	●	○	●		●	●		●	●	●	●		●	●	●	●		●	●	●
47.....																																										
48.....																																										
49.....																																										
50.....																																										
51.....			●																																							
52.....																																										

NOTE. As dates were not given, Irish records of *B. orientalis* and *B. germanica* from Cornwell (1968b) are shown as pre-1961.

APPENDIX III

Outstanding Sites for British Orthoptera

Only a few of our British Orthoptera, Dictyoptera and Dermaptera are restricted to a single type of habitat: most are widespread over a variety of habitat (including one's own garden if one is lucky). However certain localities are outstanding, particularly for our Orthoptera. For reasons made clear by D. R. Ragge in his introductory section, the majority of these sites are concentrated south of the Thames, in southern and south-eastern England.

Any ten-kilometre square from which ten or more species of native Orthoptera have been recorded in the post-1960 period (Map 2) may be regarded as noteworthy for this group of insects. Squares with five or more species should be considered average for southern England, and noteworthy north of a line between the Humber and Dee estuaries and also for Ireland, where the paucity of species is emphasized by the apparent absence of *Chorthippus parallelus* which is so widespread in Britain.

The following twenty outstanding British localities for orthopteroids, given geographically from west to east, contain species' lists for the period from 1970 onwards.

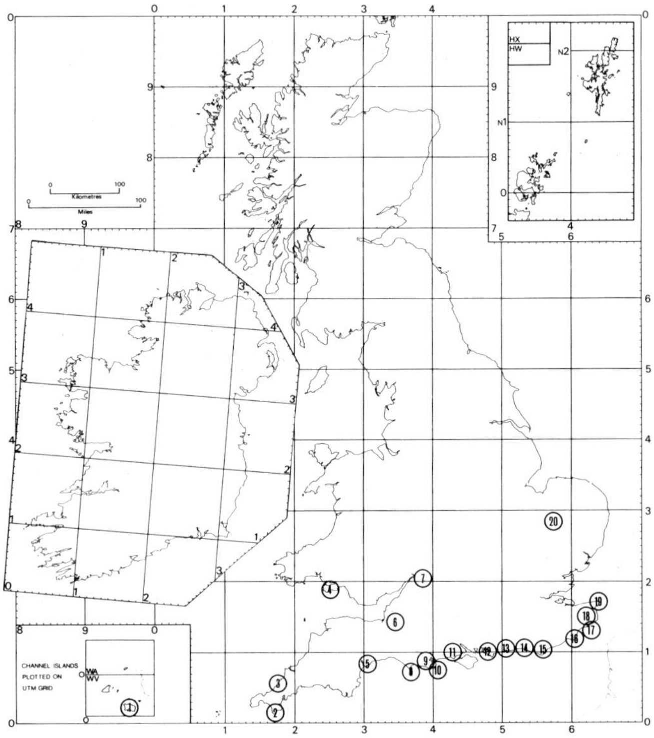

MAP 50 – Outstanding sites for British Orthoptera

1. Jersey, Channel Islands
   granite cliffs and dunes
2. The Lizard Peninsula, Cornwall
   serpentine cliffs
3. Penhale Sands, Cornwall
   dunes
4. The Gower Peninsula, Glamorgan
   cliffs, dunes and salt-marsh
5. The Pebble Heaths of East Devon
   wet and dry heathland and heathy woodland
6. The Somerset Levels
   fenland and limestone hills
7. The Central Cotswolds, Gloucestershire
   limestone hills
8. The Isle of Purbeck, Dorset
   limestone cliffs and salt-marsh
9. The Dorset Heathlands
   wet and dry heathland
10. The Purbeck Hills, Dorset
    chalk and limestone
11. The New Forest, Hampshire
    wet and dry heathland and heathy woodland
12. Chichester Harbour, West Sussex
    salt-marsh
13. The Arun Gap, West Sussex
    wooded downland
14. Castle Hill NNR and the Kingston Scarp, East Sussex
    downland
15. Deep Coombe, Lullington, East Sussex
    downland
16. Denge Marsh and Denge Beach, Kent
    shingle beach
17. Folkestone Warren, Kent
    chalk cliffs
18. Lydden and Stonewall, Kent
    downland
19. Pegwell Bay and Sandwich Dunes, Kent
    dunes and salt-marsh
20. Lakenheath and Wangford Warrens, Suffolk
    Breckland

1. JERSEY (19 species)

Main habitats for Orthoptera are coastal dunes, dry pastures and sea-cliffs. Particularly good sites include L'Ouaisné Dunes and St. Ouen's Dunes.

Tettigoniidae (6 spp.): *Meconema thalassinum*, very local in wooded localities, larger gardens and old hedges and thickets; *Tettigonia viridissima*, common and widespread in scrub and coarse herbage on dunes, cliffs, hedgerows and gardens; *Pholidoptera griseoaptera*, rather local in scrubby places and gardens; *Platycleis albopunctata*, very common on dunes and sea cliffs; *Conocephalus discolor*, very common on dunes, cliffs and coarse vegetation by roads and fields; *Leptophyes punctatissima*, widespread.

Gryllidae (2 native spp.): *Gryllus campestris*, locally common on dunes and dry banks by fields in south and south-west; *Nemobius sylvestris*, status not recorded, but present on scrubby banks and in remnant woodland in centre of island.

Tetrigidae (3 spp.): *Tetrix ceperoi*, widespread around moist areas on dunes and cliffs; *T. subulata*, present status uncertain, but much less common than the previous species; *T. undulata*, widespread but apparently not common here.

Acrididae (5 spp.): *Oedipoda caerulescens*, locally common on dunes and cliffs in south and south-west; *Chorthippus brunneus*, widespread and common in dry places; *C. vagans* reported to be the commonest grasshopper on the island; *C. parallelus*, rather local and appreciably less common than the two preceding species; *Euchorthippus pulvinatus elegantulus*, locally common on dunes in south and south-west.

Blattellidae (2 native spp.): *Ectobius pallidus*, local on dunes and rough vegetation in south and south west; *E. panzeri*, local but more widespread on dunes and cliffs.

Forficulidae (1 sp.): *Forficula auricularia*, widespread and probably common.

2. THE LIZARD PENINSULA (15 species)

The peninsula is noted for a remarkable flora, and good Orthoptera habitats here include sheltered valleys with marshes, sea-cliffs and wet and dry heathland. Particularly good sites are around Kynance Cove and Ruan Minor.

Tettigoniidae (4 spp.): *Tettigonia viridissima*, widespread and common even on exposed cliffs; *Pholidoptera griseoaptera*, as *Tettigonia viridissima*; *Platycleis albopunctata*, locally common on south-facing cliffs; *Leptophyes punctatissima*, local in scrub and rough vegetation.

Tetrigidae (3 spp.): This is an especially good area. *Tetrix ceperoi*, widespread by seepage on cliffs; *T. subulata*, locally numerous in marshy areas; *T. undulata*, widespread.

Acrididae (6 spp.): *Stenobothrus lineatus*, at least one colony, recently discovered; *Omocestus rufipes*, local colonies in heathland; *O. vividulus*, recorded in one locality, possibly overlooked elsewhere; *Chorthippus brunneus*, widespread and common; *C. parallelus*, widespread and common; *Myrmeleotettix maculatus*, very common in short vegetation on exposed cliffs and dry heathland.

Blattellidae (1 native sp.): *Ectobius panzeri*, present at Kynance Cove.

Forficulidae (1 sp.): *Forficula auricularia*, widespread.

3. PENHALE SANDS (12 species)

Main habitat for Orthoptera is around moist slacks and stabilized areas of a huge calcareous sand-dune system.

Tettigoniidae (3 spp.): *Tettigonia viridissima*, widespread and common; *Pholidoptera griseoaptera*, widespread in scrubby areas; *Platycleis albopunctata*, widespread over the dunes.

Tetrigidae (3 spp.): Another excellent site for these insects. *Tetrix ceperoi* and *T. subulata*, locally common around wet dune slacks; *T. undulata*, widespread.

Acrididae (4 spp.): *Stenobothrus lineatus*, widespread on stabilized dunes; *Chorthippus brunneus*, *C. parallelus*, widespread and common; *Myrmeleotettix maculatus*, common and widespread in short turf on stabilized dunes.

Blattellidae (1 native sp.): *Ectobius panzeri*, in at least two sites.

Forficulidae (1 sp.): *Forficula auricularia*, widespread.

4. GOWER PENINSULA (16 species)

This fascinating locality contains a remarkable variety of different and relatively unspoilt habitats. Best Orthoptera sites are probably around Oxwich Bay, but there are many other good areas over terrain which includes coastal sand-dunes, limestone and sandstone cliffs, marshland and low altitude moorland. There are also substantial areas of good broad-leaved woodland.

Tettigoniidae (7 spp.): *Meconema thalassinum*, local in wooded areas; *Tettigonia viridissima*, common and widespread on the coast; *Pholidoptera griseoaptera*, widespread and locally common; *Platycleis albopunctata*, locally common along the south coast, on dunes and cliffs; *Metrioptera brachyptera*, scattered colonies on the central moorlands (it is presently known from only four other sites in Wales); *Conocephalus dorsalis*, widespread on the landward side of salt-marshes, particularly at Llanrhidian Marsh on the north coast, and on dunes at Nicholaston and Oxwich Burrows on the south coast; *Leptophyes punctatissima*, widespread in scrub and coarse vegetation.

Tetrigidae (2 spp.): *Tetrix ceperoi*, very local on Llanrhidian Marsh and Oxwich Burrows by moist dune slacks; *T. undulata*, surprisingly local, with a few colonies mainly in old quarries and around broad-leaved woodland.

Acrididae (5 spp.): *Omocestus viridulus*, common and widespread particularly in moorland areas; *Chorthippus brunneus*, *C. parallelus*, common and widespread; *C. albomarginatus*, a few isolated colonies, around Oxwich Bay on the south coast, and at

Landimore and Llanrhidian Marsh on the north coast; *Myrmeleotettix maculatus*, widespread on cliffs and dunes.

Blattellidae (1 native sp.): *Ectobius pallidus*, widespread in copses, and on sea-cliffs and sand-dunes in its only known Welsh stations.

Forficulidae (1 sp.): *Forficula auricularia*, widespread.

5. THE PEBBLE HEATHS OF EAST DEVON (17 species)

A very distinctive district with wet and dry heathland and heathy woodland, intersected by relatively fertile stream valleys. The best sites for Orthoptera are East Budleigh, Woodbury, Harpford and Aylesbeare Commons.

Tettigoniidae (5 spp.): *Meconema thalassinum*, widespread in wooded areas, ancient hedgerows and gardens; *Tettigonia viridissima*, locally common; *Pholidoptera griseoaptera*, widespread and very common; *Metrioptera brachyptera*, common on heathland; *Leptophyes punctatissima*, widespread.

Gryllidae (1 sp.): *Nemobius sylvestris*, local in scrub, woodland margins and scrubby hedgerows.

Tetrigidae (1 sp.): *Tetrix undulata*, widespread.

Acrididae (6 spp.): *Stenobothrus lineatus*, very local on dry heathland; *Omocestus rufipes*, in at least two localities in heathy scrub in the East Budleigh area; *O. viridulus*, *Chorthippus brunneus*, *C. parallelus*, widespread and common; *Myrmeleotettix maculatus*, locally common on dry heathland.

Blattellidae (3 native spp.): *Ectobius lapponicus* and *E. pallidus*, very local on Aylesbeare Common; *E. panzeri*, on East Budleigh Common.

Forficulidae (1 sp.): *Forficula auricularia*, widespread.

6. THE SOMERSET LEVELS (16 species)

The well-known fenland is interrupted by low-lying Liassic limestone ridges (The Polden Hills) with marshland, limestone grassland, woods and scrub. Best sites for Orthoptera include Westhay Moor and Meare and Street Heath. The fenland has been severely damaged by peat extraction and pumped drainage, but surviving sites such as Westhay Moor are now nature reserves.

Tettigoniidae (5 spp.): *Tettigonia viridissima*, widespread in scrub bush over limestone and on fenland; *Pholidoptera griseoaptera*, widespread and common; *Metrioptera brachyptera*, present in several surviving fenland marshes including Street Heath and Westhay Moor; *Conocephalus dorsalis*, widespread and locally common in the fens and by drainage dykes; *Leptophyes punctatissima*, widespread.

Tetrigidae (2 spp.): *Tetrix subulata*, local but widespread in fens and by dykes; *T. undulata*, widespread in fenland and on limestone.

Acrididae (8 spp.): *Stethophyma grossum*, survives in at least one fenland site, now a nature reserve; *Stenobothrus lineatus*, extremely local, but recorded from one fenland site as well as old limestone pasture; *Omocestus rufipes*, found in one woodland site now a nature reserve – the only known station in Somerset; *O. viridulus*, widespread; *Chortippus brunneus*, *C. parallelus*, common and widespread; *C. albomarginatus*, widespread in fenland and dykes; *Gomphocerippus rufus*, very local on limestone pasture.

Forficulidae (1 sp.): *Forficula auricularia*, widespread.

7. THE CENTRAL COTSWOLDS (12 species)

The central section of the Cotswolds, between Wotton-under-Edge in the south and Birdlip in the north, is noteworthy for its Orthoptera fauna; mainly in the many steep-sided valleys over short limestone turf. The best sites are probably at Stinchcombe, near Dursley; Minchinhampton Common, Nailsworth; Randwick; and Rodborough Common.

Tettigoniidae (4 spp.): *Meconema thalassinum*, widespread and common in woodland; *Tettigonia viridissima*, very local, but with one substantial colony around Randwick; *Pholidoptera griseoaptera*, *Leptophyes punctatissima*, widespread and common.

Tetrigidae (1 sp.): *Tetrix undulata*, widespread and common.

Acrididae (6 spp.): *Stenobothrus lineatus*, widespread and locally common; *Omocestus viridulus*, widespread and very common; *Chorthippus brunneus*, *C. parallelus*, widespread and abundant; *Gomphoceripus rufus*, locally common in about ten sites; *Myrmeleotettix maculatus*, widespread and very locally common, mainly on track-sides and old quarries.

Forficulidae (1 sp.): *Forficula auricularia*, widespread and probably abundant.

8. ISLE OF PORTLAND (14 species)

The 'Isle of Portland' lies between Portland Bill and Ferry Bridge on the causeway to Weymouth. There are many good sites for Orthoptera on the limestone headland and by the salt-marsh and shingle beach at the edge of The Fleet. Most of the species are present in large populations.

Tettigoniidae (5 spp.): *Tettigonia viridissima*, common; *Pholidoptera griseoaptera*, common in scrubby areas; *Platycleis albopunctata*, common; *Conocephalus dorsalis*, present by The Fleet; *Leptophyes punctatissima*, common in scrub and coarse herbage, particularly around the old quarries.

Gryllidae (1 sp.): *Pseudomogoplistes squamiger*, persists in at least two places by the Fleet causeway.

Tetrigidae (1 sp.): *Tetrix undulata*, widespread.

Acrididae (5 spp.): *Omocestus viridulus*, scattered colonies in coarse grass on the headland; *Chorthippus albomarginatus*, present by The Fleet; *C. brunneus*, *C. parallelus*, abundant; *Myrmeleotettix maculatus*, locally common in old quarries.

Blattellidae (1 native sp.): *Ectobius panzeri*, present in several places on the headland.

Forficulidae (1 sp.): *Forficula auricularia*, widespread.

9. THE DORSET HEATHLANDS (24 species)

This area is unquestionably the prime location for Orthoptera in Britain. The habitat comprises large tracts of wet and dry heathland, broad-leaved heathy woodland, roadside scrub and salt-marsh immediately adjacent to heathland. Some parts of the area have been severely damaged by agriculture and clay-mining but there is still much of great value from Winfrith Heath in the west to Newton Heath and Littlesea by Studland Bay in the east. There are many excellent sites between these points, but the outstanding locality is Middlebere Heath National Nature Reserve, comprising an extensive and protected area of wet and dry heathland which has been examined in detail for its natural history.

Tettigoniidae (8 spp.): *Meconema thalassinum*, widespread in woodland and roadside scrub; *Tettigonia viridissima*, widespread and common in roadside scrub; *Decticus verrucivorus*, a persisting small colony on the western edge of Middlebere Heath; *Pholidoptera griseoaptera*, common in woodland and scrub; *Metrioptera brachyptera*, abundant over wet and often over dry heathland; *Conocephalus discolor*, now quite widespread over heathland; *C. dorsalis*, common in salt-marsh and present in several places on wet heathland; *Leptophyes punctatissima*, common in woodland and roadside scrub.

Tetrigidae (3 spp.): *Tetrix ceperoi*, a small colony is present at one site on Bere Heath; *T. subulata*, found at Littlesea; *T. undulata*, widespread and common.

Acrididae (9 spp.): *Stethophyma grossum*, common on quaking portions of wet heathland; *Stenobothrus lineatus*, a few small colonies recorded from dry heathland; *Omocestus rufipes*, scarce but present in scrubby heathland at the eastern side of the region; *O. viridulus*, widespread and common on grassy road margins but rare on heathland; *Chorthippus brunneus*, common on grassy roadside verges but scarce over heathland; *C. vagans*, locally common on dry heathland; *C. parallelus*, widespread and abundant; *Chorthippus albomarginatus*, common by dykes and saltmarsh; *Myrmeleotettix maculatus*, abundant on dry heathland, widespread on grassy roadside verges.

Blattellidae (3 native spp.): *Ectobius lapponicus*, very local in scrubby heathland; *E. pallidus*, widespread; *E. panzeri*, locally frequent around Littlesea.

Forficulidae (1 sp.): *Forficula auricularia*, widespread.

10. THE PURBECK HILLS (21 species)

Although immediately adjacent to the Dorset heaths this habitat is totally distinct. There is almost no heathland but large areas of chalk or limestone grassland and sea-cliffs. The Purbeck Hills stretch from where the chalk ends precipitously at Worbarrow Bay in the west to The Foreland at Studland in the east. The best sites for Orthoptera in the Purbecks are probably (west to east) Kimmeridge Bay, Chapman's Pool and Ballard Down.

Tettigoniidae (6 spp.): *Meconema thalassinum*, very local in sheltered woodland, as at Tyneham Village; *Tettigonia viridissima*, *Pholidoptera griseoaptera*, widespread and common; *Platycleis albopunctata*, common along the length of the sea-cliffs; *Conocephalus discolor*, long-known colonies at Chapman's Pool and Kimmeridge Bay, spreading elsewhere; *Leptophyes punctatissima*, widespread.

Tetrigidae (2 spp.): *Tetrix ceperoi*, local, by seepages in sea-cliffs in at least four sites; *T. undulata*, widespread, mainly on the chalk.

Acrididae (7 spp.): *Stenobothrus lineatus*, widespread and common; *Omocestus rufipes*, rare but present at one site near Langton Matravers; *O. viridulus*, widespread and common; *Chorthippus brunneus*, *C. parallelus*, abundant; *C. albomarginatus*, local, at Kimmeridge Bay and around Swanage; *Myrmeleotettix maculatus*, local, mainly in disused quarries.

Blattellidae (3 native spp.): *Ectobius lapponicus*, local at eastern end of range in scrub on chalk; *E. pallidus*, *E. panzeri*, widespread.

Labiidae (1 sp.): *Labia minor*, found at Durlston Bay, status uncertain.

Forficulidae (2 spp.): *Forficula auricularia*, widespread and common; *F. lesnei*, widespread under scrub – a good locality for this elusive species.

11. THE NEW FOREST (24 species)

The New Forest is still an outstanding locality for Orthoptera, although excessive pony-grazing during the last ten years has so affected the growth of brambles and other vegetation in the rides that the populations not only of most butterfly species, but also of Orthoptera typical of this habitat, have appreciably diminished (Tubbs, 1986). The Forest is particularly good for Orthoptera of wet and dry heathland. Amongst the best localities are, west to east, Broadbottom; Vales Moor; Castle Hill to Church Moor; Holmsley Bog and Goatspen Plain; Wilverley Bog and Denny Bog (Shatter Ford Bottom); Woodfidley Passage; Crockford Bridge; and Needs Ore.

Tettigoniidae (7 spp.): *Meconema thalassinum*, very common in all areas of broad-leaved woodland; *Pholidoptera griseoaptera*, very common until recently, but now distinctly uncommon as a result of excessive grazing though still widespread; *Metrioptera brachyptera*, abundant on wet and widespread on dry heathland; *M. roeselii*, confined to Needs Ore but numerous here; *Conocephalus discolor*, unknown until the 1970s, now widespread and locally common; *C. dorsalis*, very local – on coast at Needs Ore and in a few swamps such as Wilverley Bog; *Leptophyes punctatissima*, as *Pholidoptera griseoaptera*.

Gryllidae (1 sp.): *Nemobius sylvestris*, abundant in scrubby areas adjacent to or in clearings in broad-leaved woodland.

Gryllotalpidae (1 sp.) *Gryllotalpa gryllotalpa*, very local and uncertain, but probably still present in extreme north of Forest.

Tetrigidae (3 spp.): *Tetrix ceperoi*, *T. subulata*, probably now restricted to Crockford Bridge vicinity; *T. undulata*, widespread and common.

Acrididae (8 spp.): *Stethophyma grossum*, present in most of the larger quaking bogs; *Omocestus rufipes*, widespread and locally common; *O. viridulus*, widespread but local and now clearly affected by pony-grazing; *Chorthippus brunneus*, widespread but virtually restricted to grassy roadside verges and old pastures; rare on heathland; *C. vagans*, locally common on dry knolls west of Burley and recorded from near Lyndhurst; *C. parallelus*, widespread and locally abundant but also clearly affected by heavy grazing; *C. albomarginatus*, isolated small colonies by Ober Water and on Balmer Lawn, otherwise only on coast at the estuary of the Beaulieu River; *Myrmeleotettix maculatus*, abundant on dry heathland and present on grassy roadside verges.

Blattellidae (3 native spp.): *Ectobius lapponicus*, widespread and common; *E. pallidus*, widespread; *E. panzeri*, widespread but far less numerous that the other species; status uncertain.

Forficulidae (1 sp.): *Forficula auricularia*, widespread and probably common.

12. CHICHESTER HARBOUR (14 species)

As an orthopteran habitat, Chichester Harbour includes many good sites: at Thorney and Pilsey Islands; East Head; West Itchenor; and the environs of Chichester Yacht Basin. Within the area are large tracts of salt-marsh with adjacent rough pasture; scrub and very small areas of broad-leaved woodland; and two small but biologically rich areas of sand-dune at Pilsey Island and East Head.

Tettigoniidae (6 spp.): *Meconema thalassinum*, common in thickets and hedgerows and occasionally larger reed-beds; *Pholidoptera griseoaptera*, very common in scrub and hedgerows; *Platycleis albopunctata*, good isolated colonies on Pilsey Island and East Head; *Conocephalus discolor*, widespread and locally common; *C. dorsalis*, widespread in salt-marshes; *Leptophyes punctatissima*, widespread and common.

Tetrigidae (1 sp.): *Tetrix subulata*, present in several marshy sites near Chichester Yacht Basin.

Acrididae (5 spp.): *Stenobothrus lineatus*, persists at one site on Thorney Island; *Chorthippus brunneus*, widespread and abundant in drier habitat but scarce in vicinity of salt-marsh; *C. parallelus*, widespread and abundant; *C. albomarginatus*, abundant mainly within the confines of the salt-marsh; *Myrmeleotettix maculatus*, local on dunes and shingle.

Blattellidae (1 native sp.): *Ectobius panzeri*, rare, East Head.

Forficulidae (1 sp.): *Forficula auricularia*, widespread and abundant.

13. THE ARUN GAP (18 species)

This locality comprises Arundel Park and adjacent areas bounded by the A27 to the south, the A29 to the west, the B2139 to the north and the river Arun to the east. Important habitats for orthopteroids include chalk turf in Arundel Park and at Fairmile Bottom by the A29; grassy rides through ancient woodland and new plantations in Arundel Park and Rewell Wood; and small areas of marsh by Swanbourne Lake and the river. The area is notable for the very high population densities of most of the species of grasshopper present.

Tettigoniidae (5 spp.): *Meconema thalassinum*, widespread and common in woodland; *Pholidoptera griseoaptera*, widespread and common; *Conocephalus discolor*, present in at least three areas and locally common; *C. dorsalis*, local in marshy sites; *Leptophyes punctatissima*, widespread and common.

Gryllidae (1 sp.): *Gryllus campestris*, formerly quite widespread here but now present only in one well-known site in chalk turf.

Tetrigidae (2 spp.): *Tetrix subulata*, locally common in marshy areas; *T. undulata*, widespread and common.

Acrididae (7 spp.): *Stenobothrus lineatus*, common on chalk grassland; *Omocestus rufipes*, widespread and common in woods and plantation rides; *O. viridulus*, widespread and common; *Chorthippus brunneus*, abundant; *C. parallelus*, abundant, with a noticeably high proportion of the normally rare f. *explicatus*; *C. albomarginatus*, local in riverside pastures; *Gomphocerippus rufus*, widespread and very common; possibly the largest population in Britain.

Blattellidae (2 native spp.): *Ectobius lapponicus*, widespread; *E. pallidus*, present in at least two sites.

Forficulidae (1 sp.): *Forficula auricularia*, widespread and common.

14. CASTLE HILL N.N.R. and THE KINGSTON SCARP (13 species)

The Reserve and the connected, east-facing downland scarp above Kingston-near-Lewes include an extensive stretch of complex and very steep, cattle-grazed chalk coombs, with an old quarry and large areas of gorse and other scrub. The locality stretches from Newmarket Hill in the west to Iford Hill in the east. As at Arundel and Lullington, grasshopper populations build up into remarkably large numbers in warm summers.

Tettigoniidae (6 spp.): *Meconema thalassinum*, common in derelict orchard and churchyard at Kingston; *Tettigonia viridissima*, widespread on Castle and Newmarket Hills; *Decticus verrucivorus*, substantial numbers on Castle and Newmarket Hills, with smaller numbers above Kingston south to Iford Hill in warm summers – numbers fluctuate considerably; *Pholidoptera griseoaptera*, widespread and common in scrub; *Conocephalus discolor*, recently found near Castle Hill; *Leptophyes punctatissima*, widespread.

Tetrigidae (1 sp.): *Tetrix undulata*, widespread and common.

Acrididae (5 spp.): *Stenobothrus lineatus*, *Omocestus viridulus*, widespread and common; *Chorthippus brunneus*, abundant; *C. parallelus*, abundant, increasing to spectacular numbers in some years; *Myrmeleotettix maculatus*, very local, the best site being around the ancient earthworks and old quarry above Kingston.

Forficulidae (1 sp.): *Forficula auricularia*, common.

15. DEEP COOMBE, LULLINGTON (12 species)

This is one of the largest downland coombs in Sussex, with scrub on its steep sides and heather on its clay summits and, to the south, Lullington Heath NNR, an area of heath on blown sand. It is another site where grasshopper populations become remarkably large in warm summers. The turf is coarse and ungrazed in the valley-bottom but rabbit-grazed and stunted by the thinness of the soil on the steep slopes, providing contrasting grassland habitats.

Tettigoniidae (5 spp.): *Tettigonia viridissima*, widespread; *Decticus verrucivorus*, rare, but probably persists in very low numbers in coarse grass; *Pholidoptera griseoaptera*, common in scrub; *Conocephalus discolor*, common in long grass in valley-bottom; *Leptophyes punctatissima*, widespread.

Tetrigidae (1 sp.): *Tetrix undulata*, very common.

Acrididae (5 spp.): *Stenobothrus lineatus*, very common in short chalk turf; *Omocestus viridulus*, very common in longer grass and abundant in some years; *Chorthippus brunneus*, very common; *C. parallelus*, abundant (sometimes super-abundant!); *Myrmeleotettix maculatus*, very common in shorter turf.

Forficulidae (1 sp.): *Forficula auricularia*, widespread and common in scrub and coarse grass.

16. DENGE MARSH and DENGE BEACH (15 species)

The Dungeness area contains some of the most extraordinary scenery and natural history in this country; however the western fringe is inaccessible to the public since it lies within the Lydd ranges. The vast shingle beach with its patches of swamp and oases of stunted vegetation is very suitable for Orthoptera. Good habitat may be found as far inland as Ferryfield (Lydd) Airport.

Tettigoniidae (5 spp.): *Tettigonia viridissima*, widespread; *Pholidoptera griseoaptera*, locally common in scrub and swampy areas; *Platycleis albopunctata*, widespread and common; *Conocephalus dorsalis*, local but common in swampy areas; *Leptophyes punctatissima*, local.

Tetrigidae (3 spp.): *Tetrix ceperoi*, *T. subulata*, *T. undulata*, all recorded from Open Pits.

Acrididae (4 spp.): *Chorthippus brunneus*, abundant; *C. parallelus*, common in marshy areas but rather scarce over shingle; *C. albomarginatus*, widespread and common; *Myrmeleotettix maculatus*, widespread and very common.

Blattellidae (1 native sp.): *Ectobius panzeri*, common on shingle.

Forficulidae (2 spp.): *Forficula auricularia*, widespread; *F. lesnei*, present in vicinity of Ferryfield Airport.

17. FOLKESTONE WARREN (13 species)

The Warren lies below the cliff-top village of Capel-le-Ferne and has been famous for its insect fauna for nearly two centuries. For Orthoptera, it is probably the prime site on the North Downs, even though it is at the extreme eastern end. The habitat comprises chalk turf and cliffs, and marshy hollows and thickets on clay in the under-cliff zone by the railway.

Tettigoniidae (5 spp.): *Meconema thalassinum*, very local in taller scrub; *Tettigonia viridissima*, common; *Pholidoptera griseoaptera*, common; *Platycleis albopunctata*, very common; *Leptophyes punctatissima*, widespread in thickets.

Tetrigidae (1 sp.): *Tetrix undulata*, apparently rare, but present beside one marshy area.

Acrididae (5 spp.): *Stenobothrus lineatus*, common in short turf; *Omocestus viridulus*, common; *Chorthippus brunneus*, *C. parallelus*, abundant; *Gomphocerippus rufus*, local but there are good colonies in several places.

Forficulidae (2 spp.): *Forficula auricularia*, widespread; *F. lesnei*, recently found.

18. LYDDEN and STONEWALL (14 species)

This magnificent downland scarp includes large areas of both ungrazed and, in the Kent Naturalists' Trust's Lydden Nature Reserve, close cattle-grazed downland turf with wooded surrounds. The site is comparable to nearby Folkestone Warren in the richness and abundance of its insect fauna, which is reflected in the number of Orthoptera species present.

Tettigoniidae (5 spp.): *Meconema thalassinum*, common in woodland and taller scrub margins; *Tettigonia viridissima*, common and widespread; *Decticus verrucivorus*, a small colony present at least until 1975; *Pholidoptera griseoaptera*, *Leptophyes punctatissima*, common in scrub.

Tetrigidae (1 sp.): *Tetrix undulata*, widespread.

Acrididae (5 spp.): *Stenobothrus lineatus*, common in short turf; *Omocestus viridulus*, *Chorthippus brunneus*, *C. parallelus*, abundant; *Myrmeleotettix maculatus*, very common in short turf.

Blattellidae (1 native sp.): *Ectobius pallidus*, present in small numbers.

Forficulidae (2 spp.): *Apterygida media*, present in scrub by railway; *Forficula auricularia*, widespread and common.

19. PEGWELL BAY and SANDWICH DUNES (12 species)

This excellent locality includes very good salt-marsh habitat on both sides of the Stour estuary and extensive sand-dunes mainly on the south side. There is also good marshy habitat by the drainage dykes, and substantial areas of scrub and rough pasture. The site stretches from the Royal St. George's Golf Club links in the south to

Cliffs End in the north, with the western margin bounded by the A256.

Tettigoniidae (7 spp.): *Meconema thalassinum*, present in several places in tall scrub; *Tettigonia viridissima*, widespread; *Pholidoptera griseoaptera*, common in scrub and in rough vegetation by dykes; *Platycleis albopunctata*, very common on dunes; *Metrioptera roeselii*, common on north side of Stour estuary, but still scarce though apparently spreading to the south; *Conocephalus dorsalis*, locally common by dykes and salt-marsh; *Leptophyes punctatissima*, widespread.

Acrididae (4 spp.): *Chorthippus brunneus*, *C. parallelus*, *C. albomarginatus*, abundant; *Myrmeleotettix maculatus*, locally common on dunes on and around the golf-courses.

Forficulidae (1 sp.): *Forficula auricularia*, widespread.

20. LAKENHEATH and WANGFORD WARRENS (11 species)

Wangford Warren Nature Reserve and its environs comprise what is probably the finest piece of surviving Breckland, with large areas of rabbit-grazed turf over sand, scattered shrubs, patches of chalk flora and small areas of marshland. The fauna is distinctive, resembling that of coastal dunes. As on the southern chalk, grasshopper populations may be very large. Unfortunately, so much former Breckland has been destroyed by vast areas of conifer plantations that it is now difficult to assess the status of surviving Orthoptera because the now-isolated populations seem to be very variable in composition and probably much affected by fragmentation over the last half-century. For this reason they undoubtedly merit detailed study.

Tettigoniidae (3 spp.): *Meconema thalassinum*, local in surviving patches of broad-leaved woods and old gardens; *Pholidoptera griseoaptera*, local in damp scrubby areas and larger gardens; *Conocephalus dorsalis*, very local in marshy areas. (Bush-crickets are noticeably scarce in the Breckland).

Tetrigidae (1 sp.): *Tetrix subulata*, rare and known only from one marshy site.

Acrididae (6 spp.): *Stenobothrus lineatus*, widespread and locally common; *Omocestus viridulus*, widespread in coarse grass in rides and along roadside verges; *Chorthippus brunneus*, abundant; *C. parallelus*, widespread and locally common; *C. albomarginatus*, local in marshy areas but spreading into drier areas, just as on coastal dunes; *Myrmeleotettix maculatus*, widespread and locally abundant.

Forficulidae (1 sp.): *Forficula auricularia*, widespread.

APPENDIX IV

List of Localities, Gazetteer and County Maps

The following list includes names of all localities mentioned in the text, listed alphabetically. In most cases, a 10km square grid reference and vice-county number is given (*i.e.* Abbotsbury 30/58 VC9). However, for some larger areas, a 100km square grid reference is given (*i.e.* Anglesey 23 VC52). Irish vice-counties are indicated by the letter H instead of VC. For Vice-county map (text fig. 56), see p. 195.

Places can be located, using the grid references given, in the *AA Members Handbook*, the *Readers Digest AA Book of the Road*, the *AA Road Books* of England, Wales, Scotland and Ireland and certain other road atlases. Some atlases give a combination of letters instead of the 100km square references. These are shown on Text Figure 59, p. 215.

Abbotsbury	30/58	VC9
Abbotswood	51/50	VC14
Aberarth	22/46	VC46
Aberystwyth	22/58	VC46
Abingdon	41/49,59	VC23
Addington	51/65	VC16
Addington Hills	51/36	VC17
Adur, R.	51	VC13
Ainsdale Dunes	34/21,31	VC59
Alderney	91/50	VC113
Ambersham Common	41/91,92	VC13
Anglesey	23	VC52
Aran Island	14/61	H35
Aran Islands	03	H9
Ardnamurchan Point	17/46	VC97
Arnside	34/47	VC69
Arran, Island of	16	VC100
Arun, R.	51	VC13
Arun Gap	41/90, 51/00,01	VC13
Arundel	51/00	VC13
——— Park	51/00	VC13
Ashdown Forest	51/42,43	VC14
Ashford	51/94, 61/04	VC15
Ashley Heath	41/10	VC9
Ashtead Common	51/15	VC17

Place	Grid ref.	Vice-county
Avebury	41/16,17	VC7
Avon Forest Park	40/07	VC11
Axmouth	30/29	VC3
Aylesbeare Common	30/09	VC3
Bagfield Copse	41/22	VC8
Bagshot	41/96	VC17
Ballard Down	40/08	VC9
——— Point	40/88	VC9
Balmer Lawn	41/30	VC11
Bamburgh Dunes	46/13	VC68
Bann, R. (at Toome)	23/99	H39
Bardney	53/16	VC54
Bardsey Island	23/12	VC49
Barham	61/25	VC15
Barnstaple	21/53	VC4
Barra	08	VC110
Barton	33/79	VC59
Bass Rock	36/68	VC82
Beachamwell Warren	53/70	VC28
Beachy Head	50/59	VC14
Beaulieu River	41/30	VC10
Beccles	62/48,49	VC25
Beer Head	30/28	VC3
Belle Tout	50/59	VC14
Benacre Broad	62/58	VC25
Ben Lawers	27/64	VC88
Bere Heath	30/89	VC9
——— Wood	30/89	VC9
Berneray	08/88,98	VC110
Bernwood Forest	47/72	VC24
Berry Head	20/95	VC3
Betchworth quarries	51/25	VC17
Bideford	21/42	VC4
Birdlip	32/91	VC33
Bishops and Clerks Is.	12/62	VC45
Bisley Common/Ranges	41/95	VC17
Blackdown	41/92,93	VC13
Black Down	30/68	VC9
Blackmore	52/60	VC18
Black Ven	30/39	VC9
Blackwater, R.	20/08,18	H6
Blakeney	63/04	VC27
Blean Woods	61/15,16	VC15
Bluebell Hill	51/76	VC15
Bobbing	51/86	VC15
Bodmin Moor	20	VC2
Bolderwood	41/20	VC11
Bolt Head & Tail	20/63,73	VC3
Borth Bog N.N.R.	22/69	VC46
Botley Wood	41/50,51	VC11
Bourne Bottom	40/09	VC9
Bournemouth	40/09,19	VC9
Bovington Camp	30/88	VC9
Box Hill	51/15	VC17
Brand's Bay	40/08	VC9
Branscombe	30/18,28	VC3
Braunton Burrows	21/43	VC4
Breadalbane Mts.	27	VC88
Brean Down	31/25	VC6
Breckland	52	VCs 26, 28
Briants Puddle Heath	30/89	VC9
Bridgwater Bay	31	VCs 5, 6
Brighton	51/30	VC14
Bristol	31/57,58	VCs 6, 34
Broadbottom	41/10	VC11
Brora	29/90	VC107
Broughton Down	41/23	VC11
Browndown	40/59	VC11
Brownsea Island	40/08	VC9
Bryher	00/81	VC1
Bude	21/20	VC2
Burghead Bay	38/06,16	VC95
Burley	41/20	VC11
——— Ridge	41/20	VC11
Burnt Common	51/05	VC17
Burton Common	40/19	VC11
Bute	26	VC100
Buxted	51/42	VC14
Buxton Heath	63/12	VC27
Caldey Island	21/19	VC45
Camber Golf Course	51/92	VC14
Camel, R., Estuary	10/97	VCs 1, 2
Canford Heath	40/09	VC9
Canna	18/20	VC104
Cannock Chase	33/91, 43/01	VC39
Canterbury	61/15	VC15
Capel-le-Ferne	61/23	VC15
Cargreen	20/46	VC2
Carlisle	35/35	VC70
Carmarthen	22/42	VC44
Cashel	02/84	H16
Castlegregory	01/61	H1
Castle Hill	41/11	VC11
Castle Hill N.N.R.	51/30	VC14
Chailey Common	51/31	VC14
Chale	40/47	VC10
Challock Forest	61/05	VC15
Chapelle Dom Hue	90/27	VC113
Chapman's Pool	30/97	VC9
Chatham	51/76	VC15
Cheam	51/26	VC17
Chelmsford	52/70	VC18
Cheltenham	32/92	VC33
Chepstow	31/59	VC35
Cherhill	41/06,07	VC7
Chesil Beach	30	VC9

Cheviot Hills	36	VCs 67, 68, 70
Chichester	41/80	VC13
——— Harbour	41/70,80	VC13
——— Yacht Basin	41/80	VC13
Chilham	41/96	VC17
Chilterns, the	42,52	VCs 20, 23, 24, 30
Chinnor	42/70	VC 23
Chobham Common	41/96	VC17
Christchurch	40/19	VC9
Chudleigh	20/87	VC3
Church Moor	41/10	VC11
Church Wood	61/15,16	VC15
Clare Island	02	H27
Clashmore	20/08,18	H6
Clear Island	00/92	H3
Clee Hill	32/57,67	VC40
Cleeve Common	32/92	VC33
——— Hill	32/92	VC33
Cleveleys	34/34	VC60
Cley Marshes	63/04	VC27
Cliffs End	61/36	VC15
Clyde, R., Estuary	26	VCs 78, 99, 100
Colne, R. Estuary	62/01,02	VC19
Colonsay	16/39,49	VC102
Coombe	21/21	VC2
Coombe Hill	32/82	VC33
Conyer	51/96	VC15
Corfe Castle	30/98	VC9
Cors Goch N.R.	23/48,58	VC52
Cotswolds, the	31,32	VCs 33, 34, 37
Covert Woods	61/14	VC15
Cox Green	41/87	VC22
Crabtree Bog	41/20	VC11
Cranborne Chase	31/91	VC9
Cranborne Common	41/11	VC9
Cranes Moor	41/10	VC11
Cranham Woods	32/81,91	VC33
Criccieth	23/43,53	VC49
Crockford Bridge	40/39	VC11
Cromarty Firth	28	VCs 106, 107
Culbin Sands	28/96, 38/06	VC95
Dalby Forest	44/88	VC62
Dale	12/80	VC45
Darsham	62/46,47	VC25
Dartmoor	20	VC3
Dawlish Warren	20/97,98	VC3
Deal	61/35	VC15
Dee, R.	33	VC63
Deep Coombe	51/50	VC14
Denge Beach	61/01	VC15
——— Marsh	61/01	VC15
Denny Bog	41/30	VC11
——— Wood Inclosure	41/30	VC11
Derby Haven	24/26	VC71
Devil's Dyke	51/21	VC13
Don, R.	44	VC63
Doncaster	44/50,60	VC63
Dover	61/34	VC15
Dovey, R., Estuary	22/69	VCs 46,48
Draycott	31/45	VC6
Dreswick Point	24/26	VC71
Drummore	25/13	VC74
Duddleswell	51/42	VC14
Dungeness	61/01	VC15
Dunnet Bay	39	VC109
Durdle Door	30/88	VC9
Durlston Bay	40/07	VC9
——— Head	40/07	VC9
Dursley	31/79	VC33
Duver, The	40/68	VC10
Dyfi N.N.R.	22/69	VCs 46,48
East Boldre	40/39, 41/30	VC11
Eastbourne	50/59,69, 51/50,60	VC14
East Budleigh Common	30/08	VC3
East Burnham Common	41/98	VC24
East Fleet	30/67	VC9
East Grinstead	51/33,43	VC13
East Head	40/79	VC13
East Peckham	51/63	VC16
Edge Hill	42/34	VC38
Eigg	17/48	VC104
Elham	61/14	VC15
Elmley Island	51/96	VC15
Emer Bog	41/32	VC11
Epping Forest	51/49	VC18
Erraid	17	VC103
Exbury	41/40	VC11
Exeter	20/99	VC3
Exmoor	21	VC4
Fair Isle	67/27	VC112
Fairmile Bottom	41/90	VC13
Fairwood Common	21/59	VC41
Falmouth	10/73,83	VC1
Farley Mount	41/22	VC12
Farnham Woods	31/91	VC9
Fawley	41/40	VC11
Fen Bog N.R.	44/89	VC62
Fenn's Moss	33/43	VC50
Ferring	51/00	VC13
Ferry Bridge	30/67	VC9
Ferryfield Airport	61/02	VC15
Firth of Forth	36	VCs 82,83,85
Fishbourne	41/80	VC13
Fleet, The	30/68	VC9
Fleetwood	34/34	VC60

Folkestone	61/23	VC15
——— Warren	61/23	VC15
Fontmell Down	31/81	VC9
Foreland, The	40/08	VC9
Forest of Bere	41/61,71	VC11
Forest of Dean	32	VC32
Fort William	27/07,17	VC97
Frensham Common	41/84	VC17
Freshwater Bay	40/38	VC10
Friston Forest	50/59, 51/50	VC14
Furness	34	VC69
Fyfield Down N.N.R.	41/17	VC7
Fylingdales	44/99	VC62
Galmpton	20/85	VC3
Gateholm Island	12/70	VC45
Gatwick Airport	51/24	VC13
Glen More	26/06	VC110
Glengarriff	00/95	H3
Glenluce	25/15,25	VC74
Goatspen Plain	41/20	VC11
Godalming	41/94	VC17
Godmersham	61/05	VC15
Godwinscroft	40/19	VC9
Goldcliff	32/38	VC35
Golspie	28/89, 29/80	VC107
Gorumna Island	02/82	H16
Gower Peninsula	21	VC41
Grange Heath	30/98	VC9
Gravesend	51/67	VC16
Great Breach Wood	31/43,53	VC6
Great Haldon	20/98	VC3
Great Mew Stone	20/54	VC3
Great Ormes Head	23/76	VC49
Great Torrington Common	21/41	VC3
Greenham Common	41/46	VC22
Greenwich	51/37,47	VC16
Grizedale	34/39	VC69
Guernsey	90/27	VC113
Gugh	00/80	VC1
Guildford	41/94,95, 51/04,05	VC17
Hackhurst Downs	51/04	VC17
Halesworth	62/37	VC25
Hampstead Heath	51/28	VC21
Hamptworth Common	41/21	VC8
Hamstreet	61/03	VC15
Hankley Common	41/84	VC17
Hardwicke	32/71	VC33
Harewood Forest	41/34,44	VC12
Harlow	52/40,41	VC19
Harpenden Common	52/11	VC20
Harpford	30/09	VC3
——— Common	30/19	VC3

Harpford Wood	30/18,19	VC3
Harris	18	VC110
Hartland Moor	30/98	VC9
Harvest Slade Bottom	41/20	VC11
Harwood Dale Forest	44/99	VC62
Hatfield Moors	44/70	VC63
Haugh Woods	32/53	VC36
Haverfordwest	12/91	VC45
Hayle	10/53	VC1
Headington	42/50	VC23
Heald Wood	34/39	VC69
Helford Passage	10/72	VC1
Hell Coppice Pond	42/61	VC24
Helmsdale	39/01	VC107
Hengistbury Head	40/19	VC9
Hengwrt	23/71	VC48
Herm	90/48	VC113
Herongate	51/69	VC18
Highcliffe	40/29	VC9
High Weald	51/23,24	VCs 14, 16
Hinchelsea Bog	41/20	VC11
Hog's Back	41/94	VC17
Holmsley Bog	41/20	VC11
Holne Wood	20/67,77	VC3
Holt Heath	41/00	VC11
Holt Lowes	63/03	VC27
Holton Heath N.N.R.	30/99	VC9
Holy Island	46/16	VC68
Holy Island	23/27,28	VC52
Hordle Cliff	40/29	VC11
Horncastle	53/25	VC27
Horndean	41/61,71	VC11
Horsey	63/42	VC27
Horsford Heath	63/11	VC27
Hothfield Common	51/94	VC15
Hoy	39/29	VC111
Humber, R., Estuary	54	VCs 54, 61
Huntingdon	52/27	VC31
Hurn Airport	40/19	VC9
Hurtwood	51/04,14	VC17
Hythe	41/40	VC11
Iford Hill	51/30	VC14
Inch Point & Strand	00/69	H1
Inisheer Island	02/90	H9
Inishmore Island	02/71,80,81	H9
Inverpolly Forest	29/11	VC108
Iona	17/22	VC103
Iping Common	41/82	VC13
Ipswich	62/14	VC25
Islay	16	VC102
Iwerne Minster	31/81	VC9
Jersey	90/65	VC113
Jura	16	VC102

Keiss Links	39/35	VC109
Kenfig Burrows	21/78	VC41
Kenmare Estuary	00	H1
Keyhaven Marshes	40/39	VC11
Kidwelly	22/40	VC44
Killarney	00/98,99	H2
Kilmacolm	23/36	VC76
Kilnsea	54/41	VC61
Kimmeridge Bay	30/97	VC9
Kingley Vale	41/81	VC13
Kingsley Common	41/73	VC11
Kingston-near-Lewes	51/30	VC14
Kingston Scarp	51/30	VC14
Kintyre Peninsula	16	VC103
Knighton Heath	20/87	VC3
Kynance Cove	10/61	VC1
Ladder Chine	40/57	VC10
Lakenheath	52/78	VC26
Landford Common	41/21	VC8
Landimore Marsh	22/49	VC41
Langdale Forest	44/89,99	VC62
Langness Peninsula	24/26	VC71
Langstone Harbour	41/60	VC11
Langton Matravers	30/97,31/07	VC9
Laugharne Burrows	22/20	VC44
Leith	36/27	VC83
Leith Hill	51/14	VC17
Lewes	51/40,41	VC14
Lewis	19	VC110
Lihou	90/27	VC113
Lincoln	43/96,97	VCs 53, 54
Linwood	42/10	VC11
Littleferry	28/89	VC107
Littlesea	40/08	VC9
Little Woolden Moss	33/69	VC59
Liverpool	33/38,39,48,49	VC59
Lizard Peninsula	10/61,71	VC1
Llanbedr	23/52	VC48
Llanelli	22/50	VC44
Llanrhidian Marsh	21/49	VC41
Lleyn Peninsula	23	VC49
Lodge Hill	42/70	VC24
Longdon Marsh	32/83	VC37
L'Ouaisné	90/54	VC113
Lough Bunny	11/39	H9
Lough Conn	13/10,11,20	H27
Lough Cullin	13/20	H11
Lough Erne	23	H33
Lough Neagh	23/99	H36–40
Luckett	20/37	VC2
Luccombe Bay	40/57	VC10
——— Chine	40/57	VC10
Ludham	63/31	VC10

Lullington	51/50	VC14
——— Heath N.N.R.	51/50	VC14
Lulworth Cove	30/87	VC9
Lundy Island	21/14	VC4
Luton	52/02	VC30
Lydd	61/02	VC15
Lydden	61/24	VC15
Lyme Regis	30/39	VC9
Lymington	40/39	VC11
Lyndhurst	41/20	VC11
——— Hill	41/20	VC11
Lynher, R., Estuary	20/35,45	VC2
Machynlleth	23/70	VC46
Machrihanish	16/62	VC101
Magor	32/48	VC35
Maidenhead	41/88	VC22
Malling Down	51/42	VC14
Maltby	43/59	VC63
Malvern Hills, the	32/73,74	VC37
Man, Isle of	24,25	VC71
Margam Burrows	21/78	VC41
Margate	61/37	VC15
Marlborough Deeps	40/29	VC11
Marloes	12/70	VC45
Matley Bog	41/30	VC11
——— Passage	41/30	VC11
May, Isle of	36/69	VC85
Meadhaydown Woods	20/88	VC3
Meall nan Tarmachan Mt.	27/53	VC88
Meare	31/44	VC6
Meathop Moss	34/47,48	VC69
Menai Strait	23/46,56,57	VCs 49, 52
Mendips, the	31	VC6
Merriott	31/41	VC5
Middlebere Heath N.N.R.	30/98	VC9
Midhurst	41/82	VC13
Mildenhall	52/77	VC25
Milford	41/94	VC17
Milford Haven	12/80,90	VC45
Milford-on-Sea	40/29	VC11
Mill Hill	51/29	VC21
Minchinhampton Common	32/80	VC34
Minehead Warren	21/94	VC5
Minster	51/97	VC15
Moneypenny House	51/92	VC14
Monmouth	32/51	VC35
Montrose Dunes	37/75,76	VC90
Moray Firth	28	VCs 95, 96, 106
Mordiford N.R.	32/53	VC36
Mull, Island of	17	VC103

Nailsworth	31/89	VC34
Needs Ore Point	40/49	VC11
Newborough Warren N.N.R.	23/46	VC52
New Forest	40,41	VC11
Newmarket Hill	51/07	VC14
Newport	31/28,38	VC35
Newport Bay	22/04	VC45
Newton Abbot	20/87	VC3
Newton Common	63/21	VC27
Newton Heath	40/08	VC9
Newton St. Faith	63/21	VC27
Newtown Bay	40/49	VC10
Nicholaston Burrows	21/58	VC41
Nicholls Moss	34/48	VC69
Nigg	28/87	VC106
Noar Hill N.R.	41/73	VC11
Nomansland	41/21	VC11
Norfolk Broads, the	63/31,41,42	VC27
North Downs, the	51,61	VCs 15, 16, 17
North Uist	08	VC110
North York Moors	44,45	VC62
Nutley	51/42	VC14
Ober Water	41/20	VC11
Ockham Common	51/05	VC17
Old Grimsby	00/81	VC1
Old Winchester Hill N.N.R.	41/62	VC11
Open Pits	61/01	VC15
Orford Ness	62/44	VC25
Orkney Islands	39,30	VC111
Orsett	51/68	VC18
Osmington	30/78	VC9
Ouse Gap	51/40,41	VC14
Overton	33/34	VC50
Overton Cliff	21/48	VC41
Oxshott	51/16	VC17
Oxwich Bay	21/58	VC41
——— Burrows	21/58	VC41
——— Point	21/58	VC41
Pabbay	08/88,89	VC110
Pagham Harbour	40/89	VC13
Paignton	20/86	VC3
Paine's Wood	41/90	VC13
Pakefield	62/58,59	VC25
Pangbourne	41/67	VC22
Parkhurst Forest	40/49	VC10
Path Hill	41/67	VC23
Pegwell Bay	61/36	VC15
Pembroke	12/90	VC45
Pencarrow Head	20/15	VC2
Pengwern Common	21/59	VC45
Penhale Point	10/75	VC1
Penhale Sands	10/75	VC1
Penkridge Bank	43/01	VC39
Pennines, the	34, 35, 44, 45	VCs 59,63–67, 69, 70
Penrith	35/52,53	VC69
Petersfield	41/72	VC11
Picket Post	41/10	VC11
Pilsey Island	41/70	VC13
Plymouth Sound	20/45	VC3
Plympton	20/55	VC3
Pokesdown	40/19	VC9
Polden Hills, the	31/43	VC6
Poldhu	10/61	VC1
Polegate	51/50	VC14
Polzeath	10/97	VC2
Poole Harbour	30/98, 40/08	VC9
Porlock Weir	21/84	VC5
Porth Mellin	10/83	VC2
Portishead Down	31/47	VC6
Portland Bill	30/66,67,77	VC9
Portsdown	41/60	VC11
Portsea Island	41/60	VC11
Portsmouth	40/69, 41/60	VC11
Preston	34/52,53	VC60
Pulborough	51/01	VC13
Purbeck Hills, the	30/88,98	VC9
Pwlldu Head	21/58	VC41
Pwllheli	23/33	VC49
Quantock Hills, the	31/13,23	VC5
Queenborough	51/97	VC15
Queen Elizabeth Forest	41/71	VC11
Quennevais	90/54	VC113
Raasay Island	18/53,54	VC104
Radipole Lake	30/67,68	VC9
Ramsey Island	12/62,72	VC45
Randwick	32/80	VC33
Ranmore Common	51/15	VC17
Ravenshall Wood	25/55	VC73
Rendlesham Forest	62/34,35	VC25
Rewell Wood	41/90	VC13
Richmond Park	51/17,27	VC17
Riddlesdown	51/36	VC17
Ringwood	41/10	VCs 9, 11
Riverstick	10/65	H4
Roach, R., Estuary	51/99	VC18
Robin Hood's Bay	45/90	VC62
Rochester	51/76	VC16
Rocken End	40/47	VC10
Rockford Common	41/10	VC11
Rodborough Common	32/80	VC34
Roe Inclosure	41/10,20	VC11
Romney Marsh	61/02,03	VC15
Rossdohan Island	00/76	H1

Ross Dunes	46/13	VC68
Rosturk	02/89	H27
Rother, R. (East)	51	VC14
Rotherham	43/49	VC63
Rough Hill	42/34	VC23
Roundway Hill	41/06	VC7
Rousdon Cliffs	30	VC3
Royal St. George's G.C.	61/35	VC15
Ruan Minor	10/71	VC1
Rum	17, 18	VC104
St. Bee's Head	25/91	VC70
St. Boniface Down	40/57	VC10
St. Bride's Bay	12	VC45
——— Head	12/71	VC45
St. Catherine's Hill	41/42	VC11
St. Catherine's Hill	40/91	VC11
St. Catherine's Point	40/47	VC10
St. Germans	20/35	VC2
St. Govan's Head	11/99	VC45
St. Helen's	40/68	VC10
St. Kilda	09/09	VC110
St. Leonard's Forest	51/13,23	VC13
St. Margaret's Bay	61/34	VC15
St. Mary's	00/81,91	VC1
St. Mawes	10/83	VC2
St. Ouen's Dunes	90/55	VC113
——— Pond	90/55	VC113
Samarès Marsh	90/64	VC113
Sandhurst	41/86	VC22
Sandwich Bay	61/35,36	VC15
Sark	90/47	VC113
Saxa Voe	69/61	VC112
Scalby	53/09	VC62
Scalpay	18/27	VC110
Scilly Isles	00/80,81,91	VC1
Seaford Head	50/49	VC14
Selborne Common	41/73	VC12
Send	51/05	VC17
Sennen Cove	10/32	VC1
Setley Common	40/39, 41/30	VC11
Seven Sisters	50/59	VC14
Shabbington Woods	42/61	VC24
Shapwick	31/43	VC6
Shatter Ford Bottom	41/30	VC11
Sheet	41/72	VC11
Sheffield	43/38,39	VC63
Sheppey, Isle of	51,61	VC15
Shetland Islands	41, 42	VC112
Sholing	41/41	VC11
Shoreham Bank	51/20	VC13
Sidmouth	30/18	VC3
Silverdale	34/47	VC60
Silwood Park	41/96	VC22
Sinclair's Bay	39/35	VC109
Skeffling	54/31	VC61
Skokholm Island	12/70	VC45
Skomer Island	12/70	VC45
Skye, Island of	18	VC104
Slepe Heath	30/98	VC9
Slimbridge	32/70	VC34
Slindon	41/90	VC13
Slough	41/97,98	VC22
Sludge Beds N.R.	02/98	VC3
Snitterfield	42/25	VC38
Somerset Levels, the	31	VC6
Sopley Common	46/19	VC9
Southampton	41/31,41	VC11
South Downs, the	41,51	VCs 13, 14
South Foreland, the	61/34	VC15
South Stack	23/28	VC52
South Uist	08	VC110
Spurn Head	54/31,41	VC61
Stackpole	11/99	VC45
Staines	51/07	VC21
Stannington	43/38	VC63
Stanpit Marsh	40/19	VC9
Stedham	41/82	VC13
Steepholm	31/26	VC6
Stinchcombe	31/79	VC34
Stirling	26/79	VC86
Stockbridge Down	41/33	VC11
——— Fen	41/33	VC11
Stoke Common	41/98	VC24
Stokeford Heath	30/88	VC9
Stoke Point	20/54	VC3
Stonewall	51/54	VC15
Stour, R., Estuary	61/36	VC15
Stratford-upon-Avon	42/15	VC38
Street	31/43	VC6
Strensall Common	44/65,66	VC62
Striber's Moss	34/38	VC69
Stubby Copse Inclosure	41/30	VC11
Studland Bay	40/08	VC9
——— Heath	40/08	VC9
Sutton Common	62/34	VC25
Swale, The	61/06	VC15
Swanage	40/07	VC9
Swanbourne Lake	51/00	VC13
Swannington Bottom Plantation	63/11	VC27
Swansea	21/96	VC41
Tal-y-Bont	22/86	VC46
Talbot Heath	40/09	VC9
Tamar, R., Estuary	20/45,46	VCs 1, 2

Tamar, R., Valley	20, 21	VCs 1, 2
Tarbert	16/86	VC101
Telscombe Cliffs	51/40	VC14
Tewkesbury	32/83	VC33
Thetford	52/87,88	VC28
——— Warren	52/88	VC28
Three Dubs Crags	34/39	VC69
Thorne Moors	44/71	VC63
——— Waste	44/71	VC63
Thorney Island	41/70	VC13
Thursley Common N.N.R.	41/94	VC17
Tilford	41/84	VC17
Tiree	07/94	VC103
Tollard Royal	31/91	VC8
Tollesbury	52/91	VC18
Torquay	20/96	VC3
Torrs Warren	25/15	VC74
Tory Island	14/84	H35
Totland Bay	40/38	VC10
Totteridge	51/29	VC21
Totton	41/31	VC11
Tresco	00/81	VC1
——— Abbey	00/81	VC1
Trevose Head	10/87	VC1
Tyneham	30/88	VC9
Tywyn Point	22/30	VC44
Uckfield	51/42	VC14
Ulva	17/33,34,43,44	VC103
Unst	69/50,51,60,61	VC112
Vale	90/38	VC113
Vales Moor	41/10	VC11
Ventnor	40/57	VC10
Wadebridge	10/98	VCs 1, 2
Walland Marsh	51/92, 61/02	VC15
Walney Island	34/16,17,26	VC69
Wangford Warren	52/78	VC26
Wareham	30/98	VC9
Warwick	42/26	VC38
Wash, The	53	VCs 28, 53, 54
Waterford	21/61	H6
Watersfield	51/01	VC13
Weald, The	41, 51, 61	VCs 13–17
Wedmore	31/44	VC6
Weeting Heath	52/78	VC28
Wells Marshes	53/94	VC28
Wem Moss	33/43	VC40
Wembury Bay	20/54	VC3

West Bay	30/49	VC9
Westend Common	41/94,95	VC17
Westhall	62/48	VC25
Westhay Moor	31/44	VC6
West Itchenor	41/70	VC13
Westleton Heath	62/46	VC25
West Walk	41/51,61	VC11
Wey, R.	41, 52	VC17
Weymouth	30/67,68	VC9
Whale Chine	40/47	VC10
Whitecliff Bay	40/68	VC10
White Downs	51/14	VC17
Whiteford Burrows	21/49	VC41
Whiteparish Common	41/22	VC7
Whixall Moss	33/43	VC40
Wick Copse	42/50	VC23
Wight, Isle of	40	VC10
Wilverley Bog	41/20	VC11
Wimbledon Common	51/27	VC17
Winchester	41/42,43	VC11
Windrush, R.	42	VCs 23, 33
Windsor Forest	41/97	VC22
——— Great Park	41/97	VC22
Winfrith Heath	30/88	VC9
Winterton-on-Sea	63/41	VC27
Wisley Common	51/03	VC17
Witchett Pool	22/20	VC44
Witford/Crymlyn Burrows	21/79	VC44
Witney	42/30,31	VC23
Woburn	42/93	VC30
Woking	41/95, 51/05	VC17
Wolferton	53/62	VC28
Woodbridge	62/24	VC25
Woodbury Common	30/08	VC3
Woodfidley	41/30	VC11
Woolmer Forest	41/73,83	VC12
Worbarrow Bay	31/79	VC9
Worthing	51/10	VC13
Wotton-under-Edge	31/79	VC34
Wraysbury	41/97, 51/07	VC22
Wye & Crundale N.N.R.	61/04	VC15
Wyre Forest	32/77	VC37
Yarner Wood N.N.R.	20/77	VC3
Yateley Common	41/85	VC12
York	44/55,65	VC62

England

1 Bedfordshire
2 Berkshire
3 Buckinghamshire
4 Cambridgeshire
5 Cheshire
6 Cornwall and Scilly Isles
7 Cumberland
8 Derbyshire
9 Devon
10 Dorset
11 Durham
12 Essex
13 Gloucestershire
14 Greater London
15 Hampshire and Isle of Wight
16 Herefordshire
17 Hertfordshire
18 Huntingdonshire
19 Isle of Man
20 Kent
21 Lancashire
22 Leicestershire
23 Lincolnshire
24 Norfolk
25 Northamptonshire
26 Northumberland
27 Nottinghamshire
28 Oxfordshire
29 Rutland
30 Shropshire
31 Somerset
32 Staffordshire
33 Suffolk
34 Surrey
35 Sussex
36 Warwickshire
37 Westmorland
38 Wiltshire
39 Worcestershire
40 Yorkshire

Wales

41 Anglesey
42 Breconshire
43 Caernarvonshire
44 Cardiganshire
45 Carmarthenshire
46 Denbighshire
47 Flintshire
48 Glamorgan
49 Merionethshire
50 Monmouthshire
51 Montgomeryshire
52 Pembrokeshire
53 Radnorshire

Scotland

54 Aberdeenshire
55 Angus
56 Argyll
57 Ayrshire
58 Banffshire
59 Berwickshire
60 Bute
61 Caithness
62 Clackmannanshire
63 Dumfries-shire
64 Dunbartonshire
65 East Lothian
66 Fifeshire
67 Inverness-shire
68 Kincardineshire
69 Kinross
70 Kirkcudbrightshire
71 Lanarkshire
72 Midlothian
73 Moray
74 Nairn
75 Orkney
76 Peebleshire
77 Perthshire
78 Renfrewshire
79 Ross and Cromarty
80 Roxburghshire
81 Selkirkshire
82 Shetland
83 Stirlingshire
84 Sutherland
85 West Lothian
86 Wigtownshire

Northern Ireland

87 Antrim
88 Armagh
89 Down
90 Fermanagh
91 Londonderry
92 Tyrone

Republic of Ireland

93 Carlow
94 Cavan
95 Clare
96 Cork
97 Donegal
98 Dublin
99 Galway
100 Kerry
101 Kildare
102 Kilkenny
103 Laois
104 Leitrim
105 Limerick
106 Longford
107 Louth
108 Mayo
109 Meath
110 Monaghan
111 Offaly
112 Roscommon
113 Sligo
114 Tipperary
115 Waterford
116 Westmeath
117 Wexford
118 Wicklow

Text Figure 57

Pre-1974 county boundaries

England

1 Avon
2 Bedfordshire
3 Berkshire
4 Buckinghamshire
5 Cambridgeshire
6 Cheshire
7 Cleveland
8 Cornwall
9 Cumbria
10 Derbyshire
11 Devon
12 Dorset
13 Durham
14 Essex
15 East Sussex
16 Gloucestershire
17 Greater London
18 Greater Manchester
19 Hampshire
20 Hereford and Worcester
21 Hertfordshire
22 Humberside
23 Isle of Wight
24 Kent
25 Lancashire
26 Leicestershire
27 Lincolnshire
28 Merseyside
29 Norfolk
30 North Yorkshire
31 Northamptonshire
32 Northumberland
33 Nottinghamshire
34 Oxfordshire
35 Salop
36 Somerset
37 South Yorkshire
38 Staffordshire
39 Suffolk
40 Surrey
41 Tyne and Wear
42 Warwickshire
43 West Sussex
44 West Midlands
45 West Yorkshire
46 Wiltshire

Wales

47 Clwyd
48 Dyfed
49 Gwent
50 Gwynedd
51 Mid Glamorgan
52 Powys
53 South Glamorgan
54 West Glamorgan

Scotland

55 Borders
56 Central
57 Dumfries and Galloway
58 Fife
59 Grampian
60 Highland
61 Lothian
62 Orkney
63 Shetland
64 Strathclyde
65 Tayside
66 Western Isles

Text Figure 58 (left)
Post 1974/75 county and regional boundaries

Text Figure 59 (below)
Numerical equivalents of the 100km sq. reference letters of the National, Irish and Channel Islands (UTM) Grids

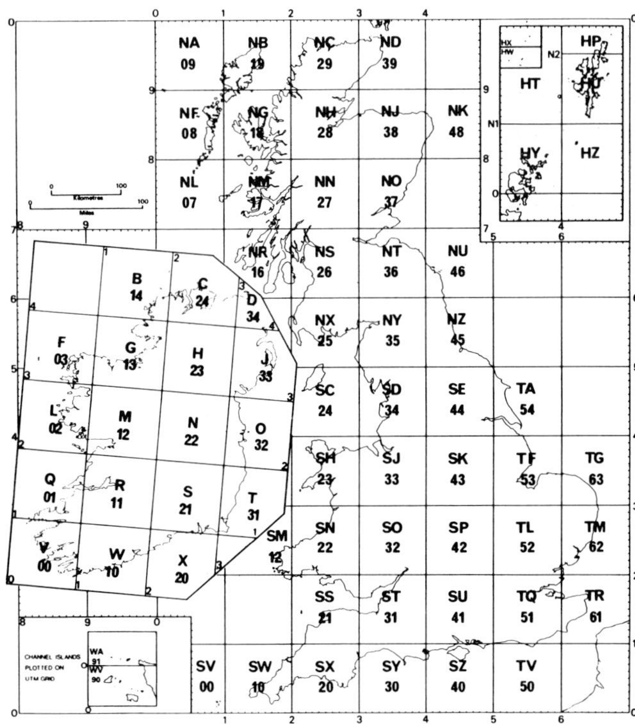

APPENDIX V

Welsh, Scottish and Irish Names for Orthopteroids

The following list of native-language names for orthopteroids has been assembled from a variety of sources. Though, no doubt, incomplete, it is included here for general interest. Any additional local, dialect or other names would be welcomed by the publishers.

(i) Welsh

In addition to the local names for grasshoppers and the mole-cricket given elsewhere in the book, the following 'standardized' list of names has been compiled by Mr. David Davies of Cymdeithas Edward Llwyd (The Edward Lloyd Society – the Welsh-language natural history society) for eventual publication in the Society's journal, *Y Naturiaethwr*, and is reproduced here with his permission.

Saltatoria	
Tachycines asynamorus	Cricedyn Hirgorn Di-adain
Meconema thalassinum	Cricedyn Hirgorn y Dderwen
Tettigonia viridissima	Cricedyn Hirgorn Mawr Gwyrdd
Decticus verrucivorus	Dafad-frathwr
Pholidoptera griseoaptera	Cricedyn Hirgorn Tywyll
Platycleis albopunctata	Cricedyn Hirgorn Llwyd
Metrioptera brachyptera	Cricedyn Hirgorn y Gors
M. roeselii	Cricedyn Hirgorn Roesel
Conocephalus discolor	Hirben Hir-adain
C. dorsalis	Hirben Byr-adain
Leptophyes punctatissima	Cricedyn Hirgorn Brith
Acheta domesticus	Cricedyn yr Aelwyd
Gryllus campestris	Cricedyn y Maes
Nemobius sylvestris	Cricedyn y Coed
Pseudomogoplistes squamiger	Cricedyn Cennog
Gryllotalpa gryllotalpa	Rhinc y Tes
Tetrix ceperoi	Sioncyn-gwair Arfor
T. subulata	Sioncyn-gwair Main
T. undulata	Sioncyn-gwair Cyffredin
Stethophyma grossum	Ceiliog-rhedyn Marn y Gors
Stenobothrus lineatus	Ceiliog-rhedyn Rhesog
S. stigmaticus	Ceiliog-rhedyn Brith Lleiaf
Omocestus rufipes	Ceiliog-rhedyn y Coed
O. viridulus	Ceiliog-rhedyn Gwyrdd Cyffredin
Chorthippus brunneus	Ceiliog-rhedyn y Maes
C. vagans	Ceiliog-rhedyn y Grug
C. parallelus	Ceiliog-rhedyn y Ddôl
C. albomarginatus	Ceiliog-rhedyn Bach y Gors
Gomphocerippus rufus	Ceiliog-rhedyn y Garreg-galch
Myrmeleotettix maculatus	Ceiliog-rhedyn Brith
Dictyoptera	
Blatta orientalis	Cocrotsien Cyffredin
Pycnoscelus surinamensis	Cocrotsien Surinam

Periplaneta americana	Cocrotsien America
P. australasiae	Cocrotsien Awstralia
Blattella germanica	Cocrotsien yr Almaen
Supella longipalpa	Cocrotsien Rhwymyn Gwelw
Ectobius lapponicus	Cocrotsien Dywyll
E. pallidus	Cocrotsien Felenddu
E. panzeri	Cocrotsien Leiaf
Dermaptera	
Forficula auricularia	Chwilen Glust
Phasmida	
Acanthoxyla geisovii	Pryfyn Pric Pigog
Clitarchus hookeri	Pryfyn Pric Llyfn
Carausius morosus	Pryfyn Pric Labordai

(ii) Scottish

The following Scots dialect and *Gaelic names have been gleaned from the reference works listed below.

Saltatoria spp. (grasshoppers)	gerslouper or cricket *fionnan-feòir *dreòlan-teasbhuidh
(green jumping)	*leumnach uaine
(locust)	*locust
Gryllidae (crickets)	cracket *greollán *cuileag-theallaich
Dermaptera (earwigs)	horn-, horny-, hornie- or horned-golach or goloch forky-golach forkit- or forky-tail forker or horner *fiolan or fiolan-gòbhlach or gòbhlag

Reference works:

A pronouncing Gaelic Dictionary, 1872. MacLachlan & Stewart, Edinburgh.
Chambers Scots Dialect Dictionary, 1911. Edinburgh.
The New English-Gaelic Dictionary, 1981. Gairm Publications, Glasgow.
Concise Scots Dictionary, 1985. Aberdeen University Press, Aberdeen.

(iii) Irish

These names have been kindly supplied by Dr D. C. F. Cotton.

Acheta domesticus (house-cricket)	criogar
Saltatoria spp. (grasshoppers)	dreolín teaspaigh
Locusta migratoria (migratory locust)	lócaiste
Blattodea (cockroach)	ciaróg dhobh
Forficula auricularia (common earwig)	gailseach
Phasmida (stick-insect)	cipíneach

References

The following list of references includes some books and papers to which the authors have referred, and which have also been used in the compilation of the maps, but which have not been cited in the text. These works, indicated by an asterisk, may be of value and interest as further reading. Some of the sources given are of unpublished data.

All abbreviations comply with the principles adopted in the third edition (1980) of the *Serial Publications in the British Museum (Natural History) Library*.

*ALLAN, P. B. M., 1955. Something about the Mole-Cricket. *Entomologist's Rec. J. Var.* **67**: 21.

ANDERSON, R., 1977. *Metrioptera roeselii* (Hagenbach) (Orthoptera: Tettigoniidae) new to Ireland. *Ir. nat. J.* **19**: 17.

ANDO, Y. & HARTLEY, J. C., 1982. Biology of a long winged form of *Conocephalus discolor* (Thunberg). *Entomologia exp. appl.* **32**: 238–241.

APPLETON, D., DICKSON, R. & ELSE, G. R., 1975. *The Insects of the Forest of Bere*. Fareham.

ASHBY, G. J., 1972. The House Cricket. In *The UFAW handbook on the care and management of laboratory animals* (4th edn), pp. 588–589. Churchill Livingstone, Edinburgh & London.

ASKEW, R. R., 1974. Insects from Bardsey Island. *Entomologist's Gaz.* **25**: 45–46.

BAINS, J. MAINWARING, 1940. Orthoptera of the Hastings District. *Hastings E. Suss. Nat.* **6**: 27–33.

BAYNES, E. S. A., 1955. Report on migrant insects in Ireland for 1954. *Ir. nat. J.* **11**: 286–287.

BALDOCK, D. W., 1977. *Chorthippus albomarginatus* (De Geer) Orth.: Acrididae) in South Kerry. *Entomologist's mon. Mag.* **112**: 144.

———, 1985. Provisional Atlas of Orthoptera and native Dictyoptera in Surrey 1975–85. Unpublished.

*BATE, J., 1969. On some aspects of the biology of *Acheta domesticus* (Insecta: Orthoptera) with reference to the infestation of refuse tips. *Pedobiologia* **9**: 300–322, 16 figs.

BEATSON, S. H. & DRIPS, J. S., 1972. Long-term survival of cockroaches out of doors. *Envir. Hlth.* **80**: 340–341, 2 figs.

BEGON, M., 1983. Grasshopper populations and weather: the effects of insolation on *C. brunneus*. *Ecol. Ent.* **8**: 361–370.

BELLMANN, H., 1988. *A field guide to the grasshoppers and crickets of Britain and northern Europe*. 213 pp., 147 col. pls, figs. Collins, London.

BERKENHOUT, J., 1789. (2nd edn) *Synopsis of the Natural History of Great Britain and Ireland*: **1**: *Comprehending the Animal and Fossil Kingdom*. 334 pp. T. Cadell, London.

BERNAYS, E. A. & CHAPMAN, R. F., 1970. Food selection by *Chorthippus parallelus* (Zetterstedt) (Orthoptera: Acrididae) in the field. *J. Anim. Ecol.* **39**: 383–394.

BLAIR, K. G., 1936. *Conocephalus fuscus* Fab., a grasshopper new to Britain. *Entomologist's mon. Mag.* **72**: 273–274.

———, 1941. *Tetrix ceperoi* I. Bolivar in Britain (Orth.) *J. Soc. Br. Ent.* **2**: 116–117.

BOHN, H., 1985. *Blatta furcata* (Karny) the nearest relative of the oriental cockroach (*Blatta orientalis* L.) (Insecta: Blattodea: Blattidae). *Israel J. Zool.* **33**: 39–50.

BOND, K. G. M. & BLACKITH, R. E., 1987. A desert locust of the solitary phase in Ireland. *Ir. Nat. J.* **22**: 356–358.

BOWEN, H. J. M. & WILLIAMSON, M. H., 1950. *Mogoplistes squamiger* Fisch. (Orth. Gryllidae) in Dorset. *Entomologist's mon. Mag.* **86**: 81.

*BRINDLE, A., 1971. The Grasshoppers, Earwigs and Cockroaches of Lancashire and Cheshire. *Lancashire and Cheshire Fauna Society* Publication No. **59**. Annual Report: 23–31.

———, 1973. The Dermaptera of Africa. Part I. *Annls Mus. r. Afr. cent. Sér* 8vo (Zool.) **205**: 1–335.

———, 1977. British Earwigs (Dermaptera). *Entomologist's Gaz.* **28**: 29–37, 7 figs.

———, 1978. The Dermaptera of Africa. Part II. *Annls Mus. r. Afr. cent. Sér* 8vo (Zool.) **225**: [i] + 1–204.

BRITTEN, H., 1933. Insects new to Lancashire and Cheshire during 1932. *Rep. Lancs. Chesh. Fauna Comm.* pp. 33–37.

BROCK, P. D., 1985a. The Phasmid Rearer's Handbook (Stick Insects and Leaf Insects). *Amat. Ent.* **20**: ii + 41 pp.

———, 1985b. New Zealand Phasmids established in south-west England: a Brief Account with notes on their distribution. *Bull. amat. Ent. Soc.* **44**: 133–136, 1 pl.

———, 1986. A third New Zealand stick insect (Phasmatodea) established in the British Isles, with notes on the other species, including a correction. *In* Mazzini, M. & Scali, V. [Eds] *1st International Symposium on Stick Insects*. University of Siena (1985) pp. 125–132.

BROUGH, P., GIBBONS, R. & POPE, C., 1986. *The Nature of Hampshire and the Isle of Wight*. pp. 26, 54, 66. Barracuda, Buckingham.

BROUGHTON, W. B., 1976. Proposal for a new term 'echeme' to replace 'chirp' in animal acoustics. *Physiol. Ent.* **1**: 103–106.

BROWN, A. J. & SEARLE, C. A., 1974. The native Orthoptera of the New Forest. *Entomologist's Gaz.* **25**: 285–292, 16 figs.

*BROWN, E. S., 1950. Notes on the taxonomy, British distribution and ecology of *Tetrix subulata* (L.) and *T. ceperoi* I. Bolivar (Orthopt., Tetrigidae). *J. Soc. Br. Ent.* **3**: 189–200. 3 figs.

BROWN, V. K., 1969. *Aspects of the biology and growth of three species of* Ectobius *(Dictyoptera: Blattidae)*. Unpublished PhD thesis, University of London.

———, 1973a. Collection and culture of field-dwelling cockroaches for experimental purposes. *Entomologist* **106**: 114–117.

———, 1973b. Aspects of the reproductive biology of three species of *Ectobius* (Dictyoptera: Blattidae). *Entomologia exp. appl.* **16**: 213–222.

———, 1973c. The overwintering stages of *Ectobius lapponicus* (L.) (Dictyoptera: Blattidae). *J. Ent.* (A) **48**: 11–24.

———, 1973d. A key to the nymphal instars of the British species of *Ectobius* Stephens (Dictyoptera: Blattidae). *Entomologist* **106**: 202–209.

———, 1973e. The biology and development of *Brachygaster minutus* Olivier (Hymenoptera: Evaniidae), a parasite of the oothecae of *Ectobius* spp. (Dictyoptera: Blattidae). *J. nat. Hist.* **7**: 665–674.

———, 1978. Variations in voltinism and diapause intensity in *Nemobius sylvestris* (Bosc) (Orthoptera: Gryllidae). *Ibid.* **12**: 461–472.

———, 1980. Developmental strategies in *Ectobius pallidus* (Dictyoptera: Blattidae). *Int. J. Invertebr. Reprod.* **2**: 85–93.

———, 1981. Notes and key to the oothecae of the British *Ectobius* (Dictyoptera: Blattidae). *Entomologist's mon. Mag.* **116** (1980): 151–154.

———, 1983. *Grasshoppers*. Naturalist's Handbooks **2**. 65 pp. Cambridge University Press, Cambridge.

BRYAN, M. D., 1987. Island interludes – Guernsey and the Isle of Mull in 1986. *Entomologist's Rec. J. Var.* **99**: 125–128.

BULL, C. M., 1979. The function of complexity in the courtship of the grasshopper *Myrmeleotettix maculatus*. *Behaviour* **69**: 201–216.

BURR, M. D., 1897. *British Orthoptera*, iv + 69 pp., 6 pls. The Economic and Educational Museum, Huddersfield.

———, 1899. The Orthoptera of the Channel Islands. *Entomologist's Rec. J. Var.* **11**: 245–246.

———, 1907. Orthoptera in East Kent in 1907. *Ibid.* **19**: 252–254.

———, 1936. *British Grasshoppers and their Allies, A Stimulus to their Study*, xvi + 162pp. + 2 pp. addendum, 6 pls, 56 figs., 40 maps. Philip Allan & Co., London. [republished the same year by Janson & Sons, London.]

———, 1939a. An Earwig Problem. Why do the forceps of earwigs vary? *Discovery, Lond.* **2**: 340–345.

———, 1939b. Another Earwig Problem. Do Earwigs Fly? *Ibid.* **2**: 407–411.

*BURTON, J. F., 1959. Notes on Orthoptera for 1958 from Breconshire, Kent and Oxfordshire. *Entomologist's Rec. J. Var.* **71**: 76–77.

*———, 1961. Notes on Orthoptera in Southern England in 1960. *Ibid.* **73**: 64–66.

*———, 1964. Orthoptera Notes from S. W. Britain, 1963. *Ibid.* **76**: 136–139.

———, 1965. Notes on the Orthoptera of the Isle of Man with special reference to *Stenobothrus stigmaticus* (Rambur) (Acrididae). *Entomologist's mon. Mag.* (1964) **100**: 193–197, 1 pl.

*———, 1971a. Some Notes on Welsh Orthoptera with some first county records. *Nature Wales* **12**: 267–268.

*———, 1971b. Some records of Grasshoppers (Acrididae) in S.W. Ireland. *Entomologist's Rec. J. Var.* **83**: 392–393.

———, 1981. A Survey of the Saltatoria of the Bristol Area and N. Somerset. *Entomologist's Rec. J. Var.* **93**: 77–80, 167–171.

———, 1982. A Survey of the Saltatoria of the Bristol Area and N. Somerset. *Ibid.* **94**: 11–15.

*———, 1983. The Great Green Bush-cricket: *Tettigonia viridissima* L. and Speckled Bush-cricket: *Leptophyes punctatissima* (Bosc) in Pembrokeshire. *Ibid.* **95**: 123.

BUTLIN, R. K., HEWITT, G. M. & WEBB, S. F., 1985. Sexual selection for intermediate optimum in *Chorthippus brunneus* (Orthoptera: Acrididae). *Anim. Behav.* **33**: 1281–1292.

———, Woodhatch, C. W. & Hewitt, G. M., 1987. Male spermatophore investment increases female fecundity in a grasshopper. *Evolution* **41**: 221–225.

BUXTON, J. H. & MADGE, D. S., 1974. Artificial incubation of eggs of the Common Earwig, *Forficula auricularia* (L.). *Entomologist's mon. Mag.* **110**: 55–57.

CAMERON, E., 1957. On the parasites and predators of the cockroach. II. – *Evania appendigaster* (L.). *Bull. ent. Res.* **48**: 199–209.

CAMPION, H., 1923. Records of two British Orthoptera. *Entomologist* **56**: 262.

*CARLBERG, U., 1983. Bibliography of Phasmida (Insecta) I. 1970–1979. *Spixiana* **6**: 27–43.

———, 1985. Bibliography of Phasmida (Insecta) II. (1960–1969). *Beitr. Ent.* **35**: 3–12.

———, 1986. Phasmida: a biological review (Insecta). *Zool. Anz.* 216: 1–18.

———, 1986. Bibliography of Phasmida (Insecta) III. 1950–1959. *Beitr. Ent.* **36**: 255–260.

———, 1987a. Bibliography of Phasmida (Insecta) IV. 1940–1949. *Beitr. Ent.* **37**: 197–202.

———, 1987b. Bibliography of Phasmida (Insecta) V. 1930–1939. *Beitr. Ent.* **37**: 535–546.

———, 1987. Bibliography of Phasmida (Insecta) VI. 1980–1984. *Spixiana* **10**: 147–156.

CARPENTER, G. H., 1899. Notes: Zoology: Insects: Noteworthy Irish Orthoptera. *Ir. Nat.* **8**: 249.

CASSIDY, M. D., 1978. Development of an induced food plant preference in the Indian Stick-insect, *Carausius morosus*. *Ent. exp. appl.* **24**: 87–93.

CEJCHAN, A., 1977. The postembryonic development of the bush crickets *Tettigonia cantans* (Fuessly), *Decticus verrucivorus* (L.) and *Metrioptera brachyptera* (L.) (Orthoptera: Tettigonioidea, Tettigoniidae). *Acta ent. Mus. natn. Pragae* Supp. **8**, 88 pp.

*CHAPMAN, K. H., 1952. Ecological studies on solitary Acrididae in England and South Africa. *J. ent. Soc. S. Afr.* **15**: 165–203.

CHINERY, M., 1986. *Insects of Britain and Western Europe*. 320pp., many col. pls, text figs. Collins, London.

CHOPARD, L., 1951. *Faune de France* **56**, *Orthoptéroïdes*. 359 pp, 531 figs. Paul Lechevalier, Paris.

*CLARK, E. J., 1948. Studies in the ecology of British Grasshoppers. *Trans. R. ent. Soc. Lond.* **99**: 173–222, 1 fig.

CLARK, J. T., 1974. *Stick and Leaf Insects*. viii + 65 pp. Barry Shurlock, Winchester.

*CLARK, J. T., 1977. A male of the Stick insect *Carausius morosus* Sinéty (Phasmida, Phasmatidae). *Entomologist's mon. Mag.* **112**: 139–143.

COLLINS, G.B., 1949. *Roeseliana roeselii* (Hag.) (Orth., Tettigoniidae) in Surrey. *Entomologist's mon. Mag.* **85**: 50.

*COMONT, J. C., 1985. Orthoptera of Pembrokeshire (V.C. 45). A tetrad survey to 1984. Unpublished.

COPSON, P., 1984. *Distribution Atlas: Orthopteroids in Warwickshire.* Warwick Museum, Warwick.

CORNWELL, P. B., 1968a. *The Cockroach.* Vol. 1: a laboratory insect and an industrial pest. 391pp. Hutchinson, London.

———, 1968b. The incidence of German and Oriental Cockroaches in Ireland. *Ir. Nat. J.*. **16**: 97–100.

COTTON, D. C. F., 1980. Distribution records of Orthoptera (Insecta) from Ireland. *Bull. Ir. biogeog. Soc.* **4**: 13–22.

———, 1982. A Synopsis of the Irish Orthoptera. *Entomologist's Gaz.* **33**: 243–254.

COWLEY, J., 1949. Orthoptera from Somerset. *J. Soc. Brit. Ent.* **3**: 46–47.

CUMMING, R., 1978. Mimicry in nymphal Dark Bush Cricket. *Bull. amat. Ent. Soc.* **37**: 190–191.

CURRIE, P. W. E., 1953. The 'Drumming' of *Meconema thalassinum* Fabr. *Entomologist's Rec. J. Var.* **65**: 93–94.

CURTIS, J., 1825. *British Entomology*, **2**. Pls 51–98. Sherwood, Gilbert and Piper, London.

———, 1829[–31]. *A Guide to an Arrangement of British Insects.* pp. vi [+1–128, with numbered double columns: 1–256. Orthoptera on columns 79–81]. Westley & Davis, London.

*DALE, C. W., 1895. Notes on Orthoptera. *Entomologist* **28**: 333–334.

DALTON, R. F., 1953. Arthropods (except Lepidoptera) *In* Lang, W.D., Benham, E. & Dalton, R.F., Report on Dorset Natural History for 1952. *Proc. Dorset nat. Hist. archaeol. Soc.* **74**: 111–120.

DANDY, J. E., 1969. *Watsonian Vice-counties of Great Britain.* 38pp, 2 maps. The Ray Society, London.

*DAVIES, M., 1987. Grasshoppers, Crickets and Bush-crickets in Devon. *Nature in Devon.* **8**: 45–64.

DEWHURST, C. F., 1978. Acrididae killed by the fungus *Entomophthora grylli* Fres. in Kenya. *Entomologist's mon. Mag.* **113**: 168.

DIRSH, V. M., 1973. Genital organs in Acridomorphoidea (Insecta) as taxonomic character. *Z. zool. Syst. EvolForsch.* **11**: 133–154.

———, 1975. *Classification of the Acridomorphoid Insects.* viii + 171 pp. E. W. Classey, Faringdon.

DIVER, C. & DIVER, P., 1933. Contributions towards a Survey of the Plants and Animals of South Haven Peninsula, Studland Heath, Dorset, 3. Orthoptera. *J. anim. Ecol.* **2**: 36–69, 2 pls, 1 fig.

DOLLING, W. R., 1968. *Decticus verrucivorus* (Linnaeus) (Orthoptera, Tettigoniidae) in Kent. *Entomologist.* **101**: 168.

DONOVAN, E., 1792–1813. *The Natural History of British Insects.* Vols. 1–16. Rivington, London.

DOUGLAS, M. J., 1973. *Stenobothrus lineatus* (Panz.) (Orth., Acrididae) in West Suffolk. *Entomologist's mon. Mag.* **108**: 218.

DUNN, E. & KEVAN, D. K. MCE., 1955. Two alien Orthopteroid insects from Edinburgh. *Entomologist's Rec. J. Var.* **67**: 35–36.

EASTOP, V. F., 1953. An apparently undescribed structure in the Dermaptera. *Proc. R. ent. Soc. Lond.* **28**: 45–46.

ELIAS, T., 1985. Arolwg Enwau Creaduriaid, Eisteddfod y Rhyl 1985 (Survey of Creatures' Names, Rhyl Eisteddfod 1985, in Welsh) in *Y Naturiaethur*, journal of Cymdeithas Edward Llwyd, No. **16** July 1986, pp. 6–7.

ELLIS, A. E., 1943. Miscellaneous observations. Animals: Orthoptera. *Trans. Norfolk Norwich Nat. Soc.* **15**: 373.

EVANS, I. M., 1970. *Pholidoptera griseoaptera* (Degeer) (Orth: Tettigoniidae) new to Leicestershire. *Entomologist's mon. Mag.* **106**: 66.

FARROW, R. A., 1963. A comparative study of the biology of *Tetrix ceperoi* (Bolivar) and *T. subulata* (L.). Unpublished thesis for diploma. Imperial College, University of London.

FINCHER, F., 1964. *Leptophyes punctatissima* (Bosc) (Orth., Tettigoniidae) in Worcestershire. *Entomologist's mon. Mag.* **100**: 98.

FORSTER, J. R., 1770. *A Catalogue of British Insects.* 16pp. Eyres, Warrington.

FOWLES, A. P., 1986a. *Dyfed Invertebrate Group Newsletter* **1** 7–12, 18 figs.

———, 1986b. *Ibid.* **4**: [2].

———, 1987. *Ibid.* **7**: 7.

———, 1988. *Ibid.* **9**: 3.

FRAZER, W. R., 1944. First authentic record of *Chorthippus vagans* Ev. (Orthopt., Acrididae) in Britain. *J. Soc. Br. Ent.* **2**: 224.

———, 1949. *Chorthippus vagans* von Eversm. (Orthopt., Acrididae) in Hampshire and Dorset. *Ibid.* **3**: 59–60.

FULTON, B. B., 1924. The European earwig. *Stn Bull. Ore. agric. Exp. Stn.* **207**: 29 pp.

GABBUTT, P. D., 1954. Notes on the mating behaviour of *Nemobius sylvestris* (Bosc) (Orth., Gryllidae). *Br. J. Anim. Behav.* **2**: 84–88.

*G[ARRAD], L. S., 1969. Bush-crickets in the Isle of Man. *J. Manx Mus.* **7**: 120, 1 pl.

GENT, P. J., 1966. A cockroach new to Northamptonshire. *Entomologist's Rec. J. Var.* **78**: 256.

*GEORGE, R. S., 1965. Synopsis of the Information available concerning Dictyoptera, Orthoptera and Dermaptera in Gloucestershire. *Proc. Cotteswold Nat. Fld Club* **31**: 196–203.

GODWIN, H., 1956. *The History of the British Flora.* viii, 384pp., 119 figs, 26 pls, Cambridge University Press, Cambridge.

GOOD, J. A., 1979. The lesser earwig *Labia minor* L. (Dermaptera: Labiidae) in Ireland. *Ir. Nat. J.* **19**: 448.

*———, 1982a. Notes on the biogeography and ecology of the common earwig, *Forficula auricularia* (Dermaptera), in Ireland. Part 1: Distribution. *Ibid.* **20**: 496–497.

*———, 1982b. Part 2: Life cycle. *Ibid.* **20**: 543–546.

GOODHUE, R. D., [1980]. *Irish household pests.* Irish Environmental Library No. 69, Folens, Dublin.

———, Greer Walker, M. & Blackith, R. E., 1964. The Distribution of Irish Orthopteroids. *Entomologist's mon. Mag.* **100**: 165–167.

*GOODLIFFE, F. D., 1938. Tetrigidae and Acrididae (Orth.) in North Wales. *J. Soc. Br. Ent.*. **1**: 126.

GOROKHOV, A. V., 1984. A contribution to the taxonomy of modern Grylloidea (Orthoptera) with a description of new taxa. [in Russian] *Zool. Zh.* **63**: 1641–1651.

GRAYSON, F. W. L. & HASSALL, M., 1985. Effects of rabbit grazing on population variables of *Chorthippus brunneus* (Orthoptera). *Oikos* **44**: 27–34.

*GREEN, J., 1953. Orthoptera in Carmarthenshire. *Entomologist's mon. Mag.* **89**: 17.

GREENSLADE, R. M., 1942. Cepero's ground-hopper, *Tetrix ceperoi* (Bolivar) on Sheppey. *Entomologist's Rec. J. Var.* **54**: 30.

GURNEY, A. B., 1960. *Meconema thalassinum*, a European katydid new to the United States. *Proc. ent. Soc. Wash.* **62**: 95–96.

———, 1965. Two new cockroaches of the genera *Pelmatosilpha* and *Henschoutedenia*, with a key to the West Indian species of *Pelmatosilpha* (Dictyoptera: Blattaria). *Proc. R. ent. Soc. Lond.* (B) **34**: (1–2), 5–11.

GWYNNE, D. T., 1986. Courtship feeding in katydids (Orthoptera: Tettigoniidae): investment in offspring or in obtaining fertilizations? *Am. Nat.* **128**: 342–352.

———, BOWEN, B. J. & CODD, C. G. 1984. The function of the katydid spermatophore and its rôle in fecundity and insemination (Orthoptera: Tettigoniidae). *Aust. J. Zool.* **32**: 15–22.

——— & MORRIS, G. K. [Eds] 1983. *Orthopteran Mating Systems.* Sexual competition in a diverse group of insects. xvii + 376 pp. Westview Press, Boulder, Colorado.

*HAES, E. C. M., 1972. The Distribution of native Dictyoptera in Sussex. *Entomologist's Gaz.* **23**: 167–168, 1 pl., 1 fig.

*———, 1973. The Distribution of native Saltatoria in Sussex (1965–70). *Ibid.* **24**: 29–46, 2 pls, 21 figs.

———, 1975. The Field Cricket in Britain. *Country-Side* **22**: 430–433, 1 pl.

———, 1976. Orthoptera in Sussex. *Entomologist's Gaz.* **27**: 181–202, 21 figs.

———[Ed.], 1979. Provisional atlas of the insects of the British Isles. Part 6. Orthoptera. (2nd edn) 40pp. Inst. of Terrestrial Ecology, Huntingdon.

———, 1979–1988. *Orthoptera Recording Scheme Newsletters* 1–13. Biological Records Centre, Huntingdon.

———, 1982. Orthoptera in Highland Scotland. *Entomologist's Rec. J. Var.* **94**: 6–8.

———, 1984. An apparent spread of *Conocephalus discolor* (Thunberg) (Orthop.:Tettigoniidae) in the New Forest and Dorset. *Entomologist's Gaz.* **35**: 64–65.

——— & ELSE, G. R., 1975. Confirmation of *Metrioptera roeselii* (Hagenbach) (Orth., Tettigoniidae) in Hampshire. *Entomologist's mon. Mag.* **111**: 183–184.

HARDAS, S. G., 1960. The dorsal metathoracic spines of *Labidura riparia* Pallas (Labiduridae, Dermaptera) and their functional significance. *J. Zool. Soc. India* **12**: 133–136.

*HARDING, P. T., 1981. A review of Irish records of *Leptophyes punctatissima* (Bosc) (Orthoptera: Tettigoniidae). *Ir. Nat. J.* **20**: 256–257.

HARTLEY, J. C., 1962. The egg of *Tetrix* (Tetrigidae, Orthopterra), with a discussion on the probable significance of the anterior horn. *Q. Jl microsc. Sci.* **103**: 253–259.

———, 1964. The structure of the eggs of the British Tettigoniidae (Orthoptera). *Proc. R. ent. Soc. Lond.* (A) **39**: 111–117.

——— & Robinson, D. J., 1976. Acoustic behaviour in both sexes of the speckled bush-cricket *Leptophyes punctatissima. Physiol. Ent.* **1**: 21–25.

*——— & WARNE, A. C., 1972a. New Vice-County Records for Tettigoniidae (Orth.) in England and Wales. *Entomologist's mon. Mag.* **108**: 11.

——— & ———, 1972b. The developmental biology of the egg stage of Western European Tettigoniidae (Orthoptera). *J. Zool., Lond.* **168**: 267–298.

——— & ———, 1973. The distribution of *Pholidoptera griseoaptera* (DeGeer) (Orthoptera: Tettigoniidae) in England and Wales related to accumulated temperatures. *J. anim. Ecol.* **42**: 531–537.

HARZ, K., 1969. *Die Orthopteren Europas.* The Orthoptera of Europe **I**. Series Ent. 5, xx + 749 pp. W. Junk, The Hague.

———, 1975. *Die Orthopteren Europas.* The Orthoptera of Europe **II**. Series Ent. 11, [viii +] 939 pp. W. Junk, The Hague.

——— & Kaltenbach, A. 1976. *Die Orthopteren Europas.* The Orthoptera of Europe **III**. Series Ent. 12, 434 pp. W. Junk, The Hague.

HASSALL, M. & GRAYSON, F. W. L., 1987. The occurrence of an additional instar in the development of *Chorthippus brunneus* (Orthoptera: Gomphocerinae). *J. nat. Hist.* **21**: 329–337.

HAWKINS, R. D., 1984. *Acheta domesticus* L. (The house-cricket) living out-doors in Surrey. *Entomologist's Rec. J. Var.* **96**: 129.

HEATH, G. L., 1980. Rearing and studying the Praying Mantids. AES leaflet no. **36**: 16 pp.

HELVERSEN, D. VON & HELVERSEN, O. VON, 1983. II.3. Species recognition and acoustic localization in Acridid grasshoppers: a behavioral approach. In *Neuroethology and Behavioural Physiology* pp. 95–107 (Eds Huber, F. and Markl, H.). Springer-Verlag, Berlin.

HENSON, H., 1951. The wings of *Forficula auricularia* Linn. (Dermaptera). *Proc. R. ent. Soc. Lond.* (A) **26**: 135–142.

HERTER, K., 1965. Die Fortpflanzungsbiologie des Ohrwurmes *Forficula auricularia* L. *Zool. Jb.* **92**: 405–466.

HINCKS, W. D., 1949. Dermaptera and Orthoptera. *Handbk Ident. Br. Insects.* **1** (5), 20 pp., 74 figs (Royal Ent. Soc. of London).

HORRELL, E. C., 1905. *Leucophaea surinamensis* Linn. in Essex. *Entomologist* **38**: 92.

HUDSON, W. H., 1903. *Hampshire Days.* 316pp, 16pl. Longmans, London.

*INGRISCH, S., 1983. Zum Einfluss der Feuchte auf die Schlupfrate und Entwichlungsdauer der Eier mitteleuropaischer Feldheuschrecken (Orthoptera, Acrididae). *Dt. ent. Z.* **30**: 1–15.

———, 1984a. The influence of environmental factors on dormancy and duration of egg development in *Metrioptera roeseli* (Orthoptera: Tettigoniidae). *Oecologia* **61**: 254–258.

———, 1984b. Embryonic development of *Decticus verrucivorus* (Orthoptera: Tettigoniidae). *Entomologia gen.* **10**: 1–9.

———, 1985. Effect of hibernation length on termination of diapause in European Tettigoniidae (Insecta: Orthoptera). *Oecologia* **65**: 376–381.

———, 1986a. The plurennial life cycles of the European Tettigoniidae (Insecta: Orthoptera) 1. The effect of temperature on embryonic development and hatching. *Ibid.* **70**: 606–616.

———, 1986b. The plurennial life cycles of the European Tettigoniidae (Insecta: Orthoptera) 2. The effect of photoperiod on the induction of an initial diapause. *Ibid.* **70**: 617–623.

———, 1986c. The plurennial life cycles of the European Tettigoniidae (Insecta: Orthoptera) 3. The effect of drought and the variable duration of the initial diapause. *Ibid.* **70**: 624–630.

JANSSEN, D., 1977. Some notes on *Conocephalus discolor.* (Orthoptera: Tettigoniidae). *Bull. amat. Ent. Soc.* **36**: 43–44.

JONES. M. D. R., 1966. The acoustic behaviour of the bush cricket *Pholidoptera griseoaptera.* 1. Alternation, synchronism and rivalry between males. *J. Exp. Biol.* **45**: 15–30.

KELLY-STEBBINGS, A. F. & HEWITT, G. M., 1972. The laboratory breeding of British Gomphocerine grasshoppers (Acrididae: Orthoptera). *Acrida* **1**: 233–245.

*KENNARD, H. A., 1975. Orthoptera: 27th Report of the Entomological Section. *Rep. Trans. Devon Ass. Advmt Sci.* **107**: 184–186.

KEVAN, D. K. McE., 1951. *Tachycines asynamorus* Adelung (Orth., Gryllacridoidea) in Glasgow. *Entomologist's mon. Mag.* **87**: 116.

———, 1952. A Summary of the Recorded Distribution of British Orthopteroids. *Trans. Soc. Br. Ent.* **11**: 165–180.

———, 1953a. Notes on the distribution of British Orthopteroids. *J. Soc. Br. Ent.* **4**: 119–122.

*———, 1953b. Additional Notes on the Distribution of British Orthoptera. *Ibid.* **4**: 183–185.

———, 1954. Further Notes on the Distribution of British Orthopteroids. *Ibid.*, **5**: 65–71.

———, 1955. The Home of the House Cricket, *Acheta domesticus* (L.) (Orth., Gryllidae). *Entomologist's mon. Mag.* **91**: 263.

*———, 1956. The Known Distribution of British Orthopteroids, Fourth Supplement. *Ibid.* **5**: 187–192.

*———, 1957. Wiltshire Orthopteroids. *Entomologist* **90**: 12–16.

*———, 1958. Derbyshire Orthopteroids. *The Gnat* **1**: 5.

———, 1961. A Revised Summary of the Known Distribution of British Orthopteroids. *Trans. Soc. Br. Ent.*, **14**: 187–205.

———, 1977. The Higher Classification of Orthopteroid Insects: A General View; *and* Appendix: Suprafamilial classification of "orthopteroid" and related insects; a draft scheme for discussion and consideration. *Mem. Lyman ent. Mus. Res. Lab.* **4**: 1–31 & (1)–(26).

———, 1980a. Names involving the Madeira and Surinam cockroaches (Dictuoptera, Blattodea, Nauphoetidae). *Entomologist's Rec. J. Var.* **92**: 77–82.

———, 1980b. The Orthopteroid insects of the Bermudas. *Mem. Lyman ent. Mus. Res. Lab.* **8**: vi + 182.

———, 1982a. Orthoptera. *In* Parker, S. P. [Ed.], *Synopsis and Classification of Living Organisms.* pp. 352–379. McGraw Hill, New York.

———, 1982b. Phasmatoptera. *In* Parker, S. P. [Ed.], *Synopsis and Classification of Living Organisms.* pp. 379–383. McGraw Hill, New York.

———, 1986. A rationale for the classification of orthopteroid insects – the saltatorial orthopteroids or grigs – one order or two? *Proc. Pan Amer. Acridol. Soc.* (**1985**): 49–67.

KING, J. J., 1901. *Fauna, Flora & Geology of the Clyde Area* (Glasgow Handbook) (Orthoptera, p. 314).

KIRBY, W. F., 1910. An undetermined species of Stick-insect found in Devonshire. *Zoologist,* ser. IV, **14**: 197–198.

LAMB, R. J., 1976. Parental behaviour in the Dermaptera with special reference to *Forficula auricularia.* (Dermaptera; Forficulidae). *Can. Ent.* **108**: 609–619.

LANSBURY, I., 1965. Notes on the Hemiptera, Coleoptera, Diptera and other invertebrates of the Burren, Co. Clare, and Inishmore, Aran Islands. *Proc. R. Ir. Acad.* **64**: 89–115.

LE SUEUR, F., 1976. *A Natural History of Jersey.* 221pp., 1 pl., 18 figs. Phillimore, London & Chichester.

LEAR, N. W., 1985. Orthoptera in and around the New Forest. *Bull. amat. Ent. Soc.* **44**: 20.

LIMBERT, M., 1986. The Orthoptera of Thorne Moors. *Sorby Rec.* **24**: 35–38.

LINNAEUS, C., 1758. *Systema Naturae,* 10th ed. **1**, [iv +] 824pp. Holmiae.

LISKE, E. & DAVIS, W. J., 1987. Courtship and mating behaviour of the Chinese raying mantis, *Tenodera aridifolia sinensis.* *Anim. Behav.* **35**: 1524–1537.

*LUCAS, W. J., 1899. *Mecostethus grossus.* *Entomologist,* **32**: 169–171.

*———, 1919. Notes on British Orthoptera in 1918. *Entomologist* **52**: 172.

———, 1920. *A Monograph of the British Orthoptera*. 264pp, 25 figs, 25 pls. Ray Society, London.

*———, 1921. Notes on British Orthoptera, 1920. *Entomologist* **54**: 95.

*———, 1922. Notes on British Orthoptera in 1921. *Ibid.* **55**: 200.

*———, 1924. Notes on British Orthoptera (including Dermaptera) in 1923. *Ibid.* **57**: 154.

*———, 1925a. Notes on British Orthoptera (including Dermaptera) in 1924. *Ibid.* **58**: 85.

*———, 1925b. British Orthoptera in the Dale Collection. *Entomologist's mon. Mag.*, **61**: 248.

*———, 1928. Notes on British Orthoptera, including Dermaptera, in 1927. *Entomologist* **61**: 79.

*———, 1931. Notes on British Orthoptera in 1930. *Ibid.* **64**: 121.

McDermott, C., 1957. *Pholidoptera griseoaptera* (Degeer) in Yorkshire. *Entomologist's Rec. J. Var.* **69**: 287.

McLachlan, R., 1887. *Periplaneta australasiae* F. at Belfast. *Entomologist's mon. Mag..* **23**: 235.

Marrable, D. M., 1980. Reproductive biology and nymphal development of British Tettigoniidae (Orthoptera). Ph.D. thesis, University of London.

Marshall, F. R., 1969. Orthoptera on Lundy. *Rep. Lundy Field Soc.* **20**: 33.

Marshall, J. A., 1974. The British Orthoptera since 1800. *In* Hawksworth, D.L. (Ed.), *The Changing Flora and Fauna of Britain*, Systematics Association Special Volume no. **6**: 307–322.

———, 1984. Orthopterists meeting. *Antenna* **8**: 75–76.

Mason, D., 1985. *Hospitals can damage your health.* 16pp. The British Pest Control Association, London.

Mason, J. L., 1971. *Decticus verrucivorus* (L.), The Wart-biter (Orth., Tettigoniidae) new to North Wiltshire (V.C.7). *Entomologist's mon. Mag.* **107**: 126.

Menzies, I. S., 1946. *Conocephalus fuscus* F. (Orth.: Tettigoniidae) in Sussex. *Entomologist's mon. Mag.* **82**: 39.

——— & Airy Shaw, H. K., 1947. *Roeseliana roeselii* Hagenb. (Orth., Tettigoniidae), not *Platycleis occidentalis* Zeuner, in Surrey. *Ibid.* **83**: 151.

*Miller, E. I., 1889. British Orthoptera. *Entomologist* **22**: 195–198.

Moffet [as Moufet], T., 1634. *Theatrum Insectorum*. Cotes, London.

Monk, K. A., 1983. Morphological variation in relation to habitat in some British grasshoppers. *J. nat. Hist.* **17**: 75–85.

Morgan, I. K., 1984. *Llanelli Naturalist Newsletter*, Dec. 1984.

———, 1985. *Llanelli Naturalist Newsletter*, March 1985.

Mourier, H., 1986. Notes on the life history of *Labia minor* (L.) (Dermaptera), a potential predator of housefly eggs and larvae (Diptera, *Musca domestica* L.). *Ent. Meddr* **53**: 143–148.

O'Connor, J. P., 1981. A 1937 record of *Tachycines asynamorus* Adelung (Orthoptera) from Ireland. *Entomologist's mon. Mag.* **116**: 116: 245.

*——— & Nash, R., 1979. Record of six insect species (Coleoptera; Orthoptera) recently imported into Ireland. *Ir. Nat. J.* **19**: 433–434.

——— & O'Connor, M. A., 1985. *Pholidoptera griseoaptera* (Degeer) (Orthoptera: Tettigoniidae) new to Ireland. *Entomologist's Gaz.* **36**: 229–232.

——— & ———, 1988. *Meconema thalassinum* (DeGeer) (Orthoptera: Meconematidae) new to eastern Ireland. *Ir. Nat. J..* **22**: 455.

Ollason, J. G., 1972. A statistical description of structural variation in the erci of the common earwig (Forficula auricularia). *J. Zool. Lond.* **167**: 153–160.

O'Mahony, E., 1950. *Prolabia arachidis* (Yers.), an introduced earwig in Ireland. *Entomologist's mon. Mag.* **86**: 359.

*Parfit, E., 1881. The Fauna of Devon: Orthoptera, Euplerop-tera & Homoptera. *Trans. Devon Ass.*, p. 370.

*Parsons, A. J., 1977. Notes on some invertebrates of Steep Holm. *Proc. Bristol Nat. Soc.* **37**: 98.

Paul, J., 1985. British Orthoptera in 1984. *Entomologist's Rec. J. Var.* **97** 122–126.

———, 1986a. A macropterous specimen of *Conocephalus dorsalis* (Latr.) (Orth. Tettigoniidae) from dry limestone downland. *Entomologist's mon. Mag.* **122**: 30.

———, 1986b. *Pholidoptera griseoaptera* (Deg.) (Orth. Tettigoniidae) in Cumbria and Scotland. *Ibid.* **122**: 41.

———, 1986c. *Metrioptera brachyptera* (L.) (Orth. Tettigoniidae) from Staffordshire. *Ibid.* **122**: 42.

———, 1987. *Conocephalus discolor* (Thunb.) (Orthoptera) new to Wiltshire and other notes on British Orthoptera in 1985. *Entomologist's Rec. J. Var.* **99**: 107–109.

———, 1988a. Colour and pattern variation in *Tetrix ceperoi* Bolivar (Orthoptera: Tetrigidae): an aid to identification. *Entomologist's Gaz.* **39**: 133–139.

———, [1988b.] (In press) *Grasshoppers and Crickets of Berkshire, Buckinghamshire and Oxfordshire*. Pisces, Oxford.

Payne, K., 1972. A survey of the *Spartina*-feeding insects in Poole Harbour, Dorset. *Entomologist's mon. Mag.* **108**: 66–79.

*Payne, R. G., 1983. The Grasshoppers and Crickets of Essex. *S. Essex Naturalist* **1980–81**: 11–26.

Payne, R. M., 1955a. *Decticus verrucivorus* (L.) (Orth., Tettigoniidae) in Sussex. *Entomologist's mon. Mag.* **91**: 263.

*———, 1955b. *Stenobothrus lineatus* Panz. in Hertfordshire. *Entomologist's Rec. J. Var.* **67**: 244.

*———, 1956. Macrolabic *Forficula auricularia* L. (Derm., Forficulidae) and some Orthoptera in N.E. Yorks. *Ibid.* **92**: 383.

*———, 1958a. The Distribution of grasshoppers and allied insects in the London area. *Lond. Nat.* (1957) **37**: 102–115.

*———, 1958b. *Stenobothrus lineatus* (Panzer) (Orth., Acrididae in Bucks. *Ibid.* **94**: 16.

*PAYNE, R. M., 1959. *Stenobothrus lineatus* (Panzer) and other grasshoppers (Orth., Acrididae) in Breckland. *Entomologist's mon. Mag.* **95**: 48.

———, 1969. A disappointing day at Porthgwarra. *Entomologist's Rec. J. Var.* **81**: 91–92.

PELHAM-CLINTON, E. C., 1971. *Chorthippus parallelus* (Zetterstedt) (Orth. Acrididae) in Orkney. *Entomologist's mon. Mag.* **106**: 185.

PHILLIPS, M. L., 1983. Parasitism of the common earwig *Forficula auricularia* [Dermaptera: Forficulidae] by Tachinid flies in an apple orchard. *Entomophaga* **28**: 89–96.

PICKARD, B. C., 1954. *Grasshoppers and crickets of Great Britain and the Channel Islands.* 131 pp., 39 figs. Privately published, Ilkley.

*———, 1955. The status of *Chorthippus mollis* (Charpentier) in Jersey, Channel Isles (Saltatoria, Acrididae). *Entomologist* **88**: 137–138.

———, 1956a. *Mogoplistes squamiger* (Fisch.), *Conocephalus discolor* (Thun.) and *Chorthippus vagans* (Eversmann) (Orth., Saltatoria) in Dorset. *Entomologist's mon. Mag.* **92**: 6.

———, 1956b. *Gryllus campestris* L. in Britain (Orth. Gryllidae). *Entomologist* **87**: 230–231.

PITKIN, L. M., 1976. A comparative study of the stridulatory files of the British Gomphocerinae (Orthoptera: Acrididae). *J. nat. Hist.* **10**: 17–28.

PORT, G. R. & THOMPSON, J. R., 1980. Outbreaks of insect herbivores on plants along motorways in the United Kingdom. *J. appl. Ecol.* **17**: 649–656.

PRAEGER, R. L., 1901. Irish topographical botany. *Proc. R. Irish Acad.* 3rd Series, Vol. VII. clxxxviii + 410 pp., 8 maps.

RAGGE, D. R., 1954. The Distribution of *Chorthippus vagans* (Eversmann) in Dorset and Hampshire (Orth: Acrididae). *Entomologist* **87**: 230–231.

*———, 1955a. Recent Records of the Mole-Cricket from Hampshire and Surrey. *Entomologist's Rec. J. Var.* **67**: 161.

———, 1955b. Rediscovery of *Decticus verrucivorus* (L.) (Orth: Tettigoniidae) in Dorset. *Entomologist* **88**: 260–261.

———, 1956. Some notes on the field cricket *Gryllus campestris* L. (Orth. Gryllidae). *Ibid.* **89**: 300–301.

———, 1963. First record of the grasshopper *Stenobothrus stigmaticus* (Rambur) (Acrididae) in the British Isles, with other new distribution records and notes on the origin of the British Orthoptera. *Ibid.* **96**: 211–217, 1 fig.

———, 1965. *Grasshoppers, Crickets and Cockroaches of the British Isles.* xii + 299pp, 22pls, 130 figs, Warne, London.

———, 1973. The British Orthoptera: A Supplement. *Entomologist's Gaz.* **24**: 227–245.

———, 1977. Classification of Tettigonioidea. *Mem. Lyman. ent. Mus. Res. Lab.* **4**: 44–46.

———, 1986. The songs of the western European grasshoppers of the genus *Omocestus* in relation to their taxonomy (Orthoptera: Acrididae). *Bull. Br. Mus. nat. Hist.* (Ent.) **53**: 213–249.

———, 1987a. The songs of the western European grasshoppers of the genus *Stenobothrus* in relation to their taxonomy (Orthoptera: Acrididae). *Ibid.* (Ent.) **55**: 393–424.

———, 1987b. Speciation and biogeography of some southern European Orthoptera, as revealed by their songs. *In* Baccetti, B. M. [Ed.] *Evolutionary Biology of Orthopteroid Insects.* 612 pp. Ellis Horwood, Chichester.

——— & Reynolds, W. J., 1984. The taxonomy of the western European grasshoppers of the genus *Euchorthippus*, with special reference to their songs (Orthoptera: Acrididae). *Bull. Br. Mus. nat. Hist.* (Ent.) **49**: 103–151.

RANDS, D. G., 1978. The Distribution of Common Bush-crickets and Grasshoppers in Bedfordshire. *Bedfordshire Nat.*, **32**: 25–30, 10 figs. [Supplementary distribution records have been published annually in subsequent volumes.]

———, 1979. Orthoptera in the Isle of Wight, 1978–79. Unpublished maps.

REHN, J. A. G., 1945. Man's uninvited fellow-traveler – the cockroach. *Scient. Mon., N.Y.* **61**: 265–276.

RENTZ, D. C., 1972. The lock and key as an isolating mechanism in katydids. *Am. Scient.* **60**: 750–755.

RENTZ, D. C. F., 1980. Comments on the Classification of the Orthopteran Family Tettigoniidae, with a Key to Subfamilies and Description of Two New Subfamilies. *Aust. J. Zool.* (1979) **27**: 991–1013.

———, 1985. A Monograph of the Tettigoniidae of Australia. **1**: *The Tettigoniinae* with an appendix by D.H. Colless. x + 384 pp. Commonwealth Scientific and Industrial Research Organisation, Canberra.

RICHARDS, O. W. & WALOFF, N., 1954. Studies on the biology and population dynamics of British grasshoppers. *Anti-Locust Bull.* **17**: 182pp, 4pls, 67 figs.

RIDE, W. D. L., SABROSKY, C. W., BERNARDI, G. & MELVILLE, R. V. [Editorial Committee], 1985. *International Code of Zoological Nomenclature.* 3rd Edn. xx + 338pp. International Trust for Zoological Nomenclature in association with BM(NH), London.

RITCHIE, M. G., BUTLIN, R. K. & HEWITT, G. M., 1987. Causation, fitness effects and morphology of macropterism in *Chorthippus parallelus* (Orthoptera: Acrididae). *Ecol. Ent.* **12**: 209–218.

RIVERS, C. F., 1953. A New Zealand Stick Insect in South Devon. *Bull. Amat. Ent. Soc.* **12**: 92–94.

ROBERTS, H. R., 1941. Nomenclature in the Orthoptera concerning genotype designations. *Trans. Am. ent. Soc.* **67**: 1–34.

ROBINSON, D. J., 1980. Acoustic communication between the sexes of the bush cricket, *Leptophyes punctatissima*. *Physiol. ent.* **5**: 183–189.

ROCHFORD, P. J., 1972. The American Cockroach. In *The UFAW handbook on the care and management of laboratory animals* (4th edn), pp. 575–581. Churchill Livingstone, Edinburgh & London.

ROTH, L. M., 1967. The evolutionary significance of rotation of the otheca in the Blattaria. *Psyche* **74**: 85–103.

———, 1985. A taxonomic revision of the genus *Blattella*

Caudell (Dictyoptera, Blattaria: Blattellidae). *Entomologica scand.* Supplement no. **22**: 1–221pp.

———, Niegisch, W. D. & Stahl, W. H., 1956. Occurrence of 2-Hexenal in the cockroach *Eurycotis floridana*. *Science* **123**: 670–671.

*Ryle, G. B., 1959. Orthoptera (Saltatoria) in Wales and Monmouthshire. *Entomologist's mon. Mag.* **95**: 72.

Sakai, S., 1982. A new proposed classification of the Dermaptera with special reference to the check list of the Dermaptera of the world. *Bull. Daito Bunka Univ.* **20**: 1–108.

Samways, M. J., 1974. A simple but effective device for capturing Tettigoniidae (Orth.) and other insects. *Entomologist's mon. Mag.* **109**: 168–171.

Sanger, K. & Helfert, B., 1976. Vergleichende Untersuchungen ber Anzahl und Dauer der Larvenstadien von Tettigoniiden (Orthoptera: Saltatoria). 1 Teil. *Zool. Anz., Jena* **196**: 28–42.

Sellick, J. T. Clark, 1988. The capitula of phasmid eggs: an update with a review of the current state of phasmid ootaxonomy. *Zool. J. Linn. Soc.* **93**: 273–282, 3 figs.

Shaw, E., 1889. Synopsis of the British Orthoptera. *Entomologist's mon. Mag.* **25**: 354–359; 365–372; 409–421; 450–455.

———, 1890. Synopsis of the British Orthoptera. *Ibid.* **26**: 56–64; 94–97; 167–176.

Sheppard, D. & Campbell, J. M., 1984. *An atlas of Oxfordshire Orthoptera*. Oxfordshire Museums Occasional Paper no. 5. 23pp. Oxfordshire County Council.

Shirt, D. B. (Ed.), 1987. *British Red Data Books: 2. Insects*. xliv + 402 pp. Nature Conservancy Council, Peterborough.

Sinety, L. de, 1901. Recherches sur la biologie et l'anatomie des phasmes. *Cellule* **19**: 117–278, 5 pls.

Skelton, M. J., 1973. Orthoptera distribution maps scheme. Progress report. April 1973. *Entomologist's Gaz.* **24**: 223–226.

———, (Ed.) 1978. *Provisional Atlas of the Insects of the British Isles.* Part **6** Orthoptera, Inst. of Terrestrial Ecology, Huntingdon.

*———, 1985. Orthoptera in the London Area. Unpublished data.

Skidmore, P., Limbert, M. & Eversham, B. C., 1987. The insects of Thorne Moors. *Sorby Rec.* **23** (Supplement) 1985: 96; 98–100; 106.

*Sopp, E. J. B., 1905. A preliminary list of Orthoptera of Lancashire & Cheshire. *Rep. Lancs. Chesh. nat. Hist. Soc.* **1904**: 44–56.

Speight, M. C. D., 1976. Irish Orthoptera: some distribution records, including a first record of *Tachycines asynamorus* Adelung (Rhaphidophoridae). *Ir. nat. J.* **18**: 272–273.

Stearn, W. T., 1973. *Botanical Latin.* 2nd edn. xiv + 566 pp., David & Charles, Newton Abbot.

*Stelfox, A. W., 1947. On the distribution in Ireland of our largest grasshopper *Mecostethus grossus* L. *Ir. nat. J.* **9**: 37–38.

Stephens, J.F. 1835–37. *Illustrations of British Entomology*, **6**. 240 pp., 7pls. [1835. Orthoptera: pp. 3–48, pl. 28.]. Baldwin & Cradock, London.

Stubbs, A. E., 1967. The Wood Cricket, *Nemobius sylvestris* (Bosc) (Orthoptera: Gryllidae) in Surrey. *Entomologist* **100**: 284.

———, 1969. *Tetrix subulata* (L.) (Orthoptera: Tetrigidae) in Pembrokeshire. *Entomologist's Rec. J. Var.* **81**: 249–250.

*Swain, H. D., 1958. A new record of *Metrioptera brachyptera* (L.) f. *marginata* (Thunberg) (Orth.: Tettigoniidae). *Entomologist's Gaz.* **9**: 62, 1 pl.

Tawfik, M. F. S., Abul-Nasr, S. & El-Husseini, M. M., 1972. The biology of *Labidura riparia* Pallas. *Bull. Soc. ent. Egypte* **56**: 75–92.

*Taylor, E., 1954. A further record of *Mogoplistes squamiger* Fisch. (Orth., Gryllidae) in Dorset. *Entomologist's mon. Mag.* **90**: 300.

Tubbs, C. R., 1986. *The New Forest.* 300 pp., 20 pls, 42 figs. (New Naturalist) Collins, London.

Turk, S. M., 1985. Two New Zealand stick-insects naturalised in mainland Cornwall. *Entomologist's Rec. J. Var.* **97**: 129–130.

Uvarov, B. P., 1921. A new genus and species of Orthoptera found in a greenhouse in England. *Entomologist's mon. Mag.* **57**: 206–209.

———, 1922. A grasshopper new to Britain. *Ibid.* **58**: 211.

———, 1940. *Tetrix ceperoi* I. Bolivar, new to British Fauna (Orthoptera, Tetrigidae). *J. Soc. Br. Ent.* **2**: 72–75.

———, 1944. A New Zealand Phasmid (Orthoptera) established in the British Isles. *Proc. R. ent. Soc. Lond.* B. **13**: 94–96.

———, 1949. The migratory Locust in England in 1947 and 1948. *Ibid.* A. **24**: 20–25.

———, 1950. A second New Zealand stick-insect (Phasmatodea) established in the British Isles. *Ibid.*, B. **19**: 174–175.

Vickery, V. R., 1965. Factors governing the distribution and dispersal of the recently introduced grasshopper *Met. roeselii* (Hgb.) (Orthoptera: Ensifera). *Ann. Soc. Ent.* Quebec, **10**: 165–171.

——— & Kevan, D. K. McE., 1967. Records of the Orthopteroid Insects in Ontario. *Proc. ent. Soc. Ont.* **97**: 13–68.

Wake, A. J., 1984. *The Grasshoppers and Crickets of Essex. A provisional Atlas.* 26 pp. Colchester & Essex Museums, Colchester.

———, 1988. Provisional Maps of Orthoptera and Dermaptera in Essex. Unpublished.

Wall, R. & Begon, M., 1986. Population density, phenotype and mortality in the grasshopper *Chorthippus brunneus*. *Ecol. Ent.* **11**: 445–456.

Waloff, N., 1950. The egg pods of British short-horned grasshoppers (Acrididae). *Proc. R. ent. Soc. Lond.* (A) **25**: 115–126.

Waloff, Z. V., 1940. The distribution and migrations of *Locusta* in Europe. *Bull. ent. Res.* **31**: 211–246.

*WALTERS, M. P., 1968. Zoological notes: Common cockroach *Blatta orientalis* L. *Ir. nat. J.* **16**: 80.

WARNE, A. C., 1972. Embryonic development and the systematics of the Tettigoniidae (Orthoptera: Saltatoria). *Int. J. Insect Morph. Embryol.* **1**: 267–287, 6 figs.

_______ & Hartley, J.C. 1975. The distribution and dispersal of *Conocephalus dorsalis* (Latreille) (Tettigoniidae) in the British Isles. *Entomologist's Gaz.* **26**: 127–132.

WATERSTON, A. R., 1981. Present knowledge of the non-marine invertebrate fauna of the Outer Hebrides. *Proc. R. Soc. Edinb.* **79**B: 238.

WELSTEAD, A. R. & WELSTEAD, N. I., 1985. *Orthoptera of the New Forest and its Environs.* Species distribution maps 1980–85. 16 pp. Privately published. Hythe.

WESTWOOD, J. O. 1838. *Introd. Mod. Classif. Ins.* **1**(viii): 401–462.

WHITE, A., 1855. *List of the specimens of British Animals in the collection of the British Museum.* Part XIV. Nomenclator of Anoplura, Euplexoptera and Orthoptera. London: British Museum (Natural History). 17 pp.

WHITE, G. 1789. *The Natural History and Antiquities of Selborne.* 468 pp. B. White & Son, London.

*WHITELEY, D., 1974. An introduction to the Orthoptera of the Sheffield area. *Sorby Rec.* **13**: 7–11.

_______, 1981. Grasshoppers, Crickets and Cockroaches (Orthoptera) in the Sheffield area 1976–1980. *Ibid.* **19**: 68–75.

_______, (Ed.), 1985. *The Natural History of the Sheffield Area and the Peak District.* 256pp. Sorby Natural History Society, Sheffield.

WIDGERY, J. P., 1978. Roesel's Bush-cricket *Metrioptera roeselii* in Regent's Park. *Lond. Nat.* **57**: 57–58, 1 pl.

*WISE, A. J., 1966. The macropterous form (f. *marginata*) of *Metrioptera brachyptera* (L.) (Orthoptera: Tettigoniidae) in Hampshire. *Entomologist* **99**: 151.

WOOD, J. G., 1872. *Insects at Home.* xx + 670 pp. Longmans, London.

*WOOTTON, A., 1966. House and Mole Crickets in Buckinghamshire. *Entomologist* **99**: 304.

YAGER, D. D. & HOY, R. R., 1987. The cyclopean ear: a new sense for the praying mantis. *Science* **231**: 727–729.

ZETTERSTEDT, J. W., 1821. *Orthoptera Sveciae.* 132pp. Lundae.

ZEUNER, F. E., 1940a. The Orthoptera Saltatoria of Jersey, Channel Islands. *Proc. R. ent. Soc. Lond.* (B) **9**: 105–110.

_______, 1940b. *Phlugiolopsis henryi* n.g., n.sp., a new Tettigoniid, and other Saltatoria (Orthop.) from the Royal Botanic Gardens, Kew. *J. Soc. Br. Ent.* **2**: 76–84.

COLOUR PLATES

Plate 1: Tettigonioidea: Rhaphidophoridae, Tettigoniidae

Figs 1–6, 8, 10, × 2; 7, 9, × 1

1 *Tachycines asynamorus* Adelung ♀
Greenhouse Camel-cricket
Page 78

2 *Meconema thalassinum* (De Geer) ♂
Oak Bush-cricket
Page 80

3 *Meconema thalassinum* (De Geer) ♂
detail: cerci
Oak Bush-cricket
Page 80

4 *Meconema thalassinum* (De Geer) ♀
Oak Bush-cricket
Page 81

5 *Tettigonia viridissima* (Linnaeus) ♂
Great Green Bush-cricket
Page 81

*6 *Tettigonia viridissima* (Linnaeus) ♀
Great Green Bush-cricket
Page 81

7 *Tettigonia viridissima* (Linnaeus) nymph
(nat. size)
Great Green Bush-cricket
Page 81

8 *Decticus verrucivorus* (Linnaeus) ♂
Wart-biter
Page 82

9 *Decticus verrucivorus* (Linnaeus) nymph
(nat. size)
Wart-biter
Page 82

10 *Decticus verrucivorus* (Linnaeus) ♀
Wart-biter
Page 82

*see also silhouette (natural size)

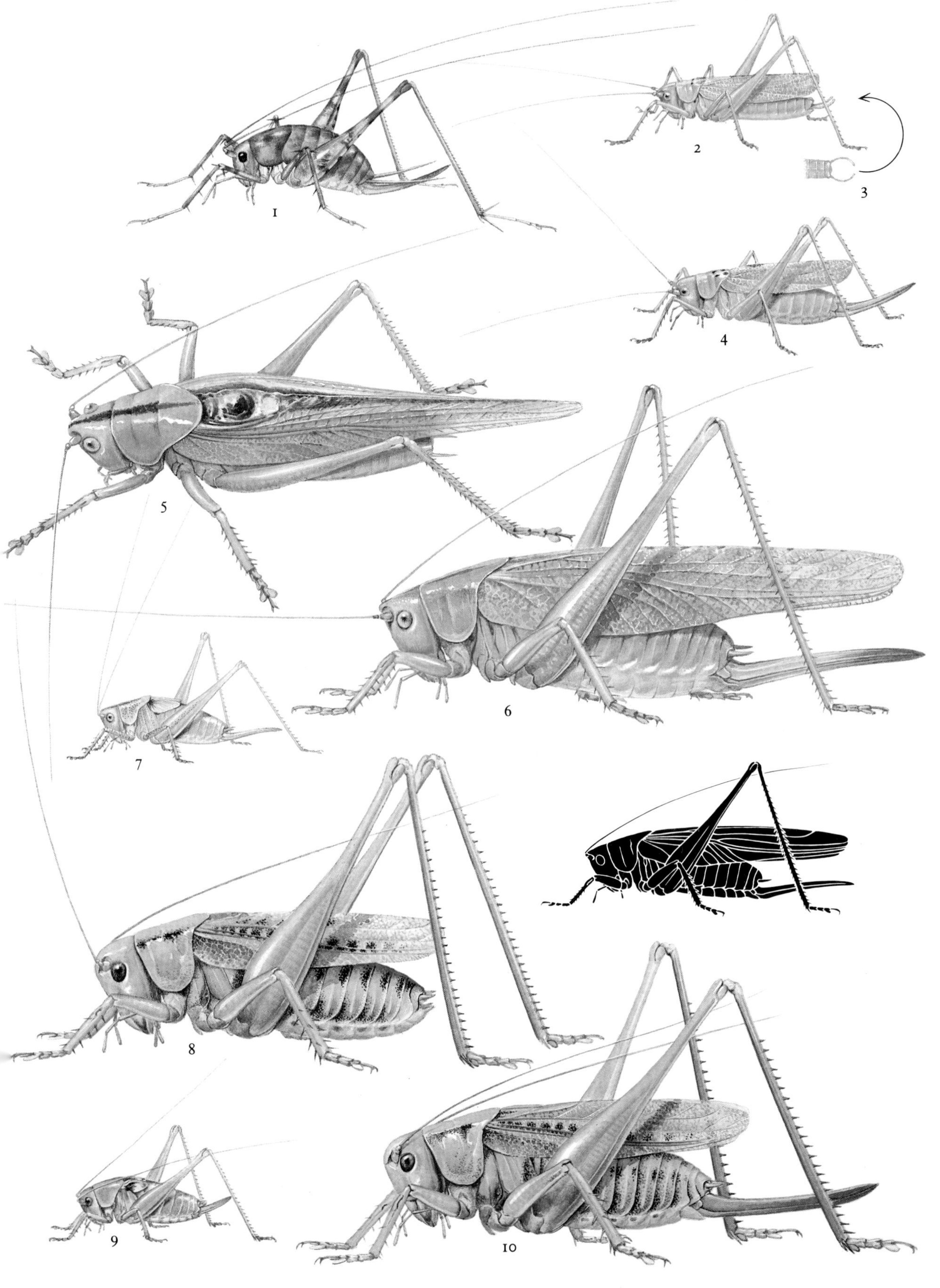

Plate 1: Rhaphidophoridae, Tettigoniidae

Figs 1–6, 8, 10, x2; 7, 9, x1

Plate 2: Tettigonioidea: Tettigoniidae

Figs 1–6, 9–16, × 2; 7, 8 × 1

1 *Pholidoptera griseoaptera* (De Geer) ♂
Dark Bush-cricket
Page 84

2 *Pholidoptera griseoaptera* (De Geer) ♀
Dark Bush-cricket
Page 84

3 Lycosid spider (*Pardosa lugubris* (Walckenaer))
mimicked by nymph of *P. griseoaptera* (fig. 4)
Pages 38, 84

4 *Pholidoptera griseoaptera* (De Geer) nymph
Dark Bush-cricket
Page 84

5 *Platycleis albopunctata* (Goeze) ♂
Grey Bush-cricket
Page 85

6 *Platycleis albopunctata* (Goeze) ♀
Grey Bush-cricket
Page 85

7 *Platycleis albopunctata* (Goeze) ♂
young adult, green stage (nat. size)
Grey Bush-cricket
Page 85

8 *Platycleis albopunctata* (Goeze) nymph
(nat. size)
Grey Bush-cricket
Page 85

*9 *Metrioptera brachyptera* (Linnaeus) ♂
Bog Bush-cricket
Page 86

10 *Metrioptera brachyptera* (Linnaeus)
detail: pronotum
Bog Bush-cricket
Page 86

11 *Metrioptera brachyptera* (Linnaeus) ♀
Bog Bush-cricket
Page 86

12 *Metrioptera brachyptera* (Linnaeus) ♂
macropterous form, f. *marginata* (Thunberg)
Bog Bush-cricket
Page 86

13 *Metrioptera roeselii* (Hagenbach) ♂
Roesel's Bush-cricket
Page 87

14 *Metrioptera roeselii* (Hagenbach)
detail: pronotum
Roesel's Bush-cricket
Page 87

*see also silhouette (natural size)

15 *Metrioptera roeselii* (Hagenbach) ♀
Roesel's Bush-cricket
Page 87

16 *Metrioptera roeselii* (Hagenbach) ♀
macropterous form, f. *diluta* (Charpentier)
Roesel's Bush-cricket
Page 87

Plate 2: Tettigoniidae

Figs 1–6, 9–16, x2; 7, 8, x1

Plate 3: Tettigonioidea: Tettigoniidae; Grylloidea: Gryllidae

Figs 1–14, × 2

1 *Conocephalus discolor* (Thunberg) ♂
Long-winged Cone-head
Page 89

2 *Conocephalus discolor* (Thunberg) ♀
Long-winged Cone-head
Page 89

3 *Conocephalus discolor* (Thunberg) ♂
brown extra-macropterous form
Long-winged Cone-head
Page 89

4 *Conocephalus dorsalis* (Latrcillc) ♂
Short-winged Cone-head
Page 91

5 *Conocephalus dorsalis* (Latreille) ♀
brown variety
Short-winged Cone-head
Page 91

6 *Conocephalus dorsalis* (Latreille) ♀
macropterous form, f. *burri* Ebner
Short-winged Cone-head
Page 91

7 *Leptophyes punctatissima* (Bosc) ♂
Speckled Bush-cricket
Page 92

8 *Leptophyes punctatissima* (Bosc) nymph
Speckled Bush-cricket
Page 92

9 Juvenile capsid bug (*Calocoris* sp.)
mimicked by nymph of *L. punctatissima* (fig. 8)
Pages 38, 92

*10 *Leptophyes punctatissima* (Bosc) ♀
Speckled Bush-cricket
Page 92

11 *Acheta domesticus* (Linnaeus) ♂
dorsal view
House-cricket
Page 94

12 *Acheta domesticus* (Linnaeus) ♀
lateral view
House-cricket
Page 94

13 *Gryllus campestris* Linnaeus ♂
Field-cricket
Page 95

14 *Gryllus campestris* Linnaeus ♀
Field-cricket
Page 95

*see also silhouette (natural size)

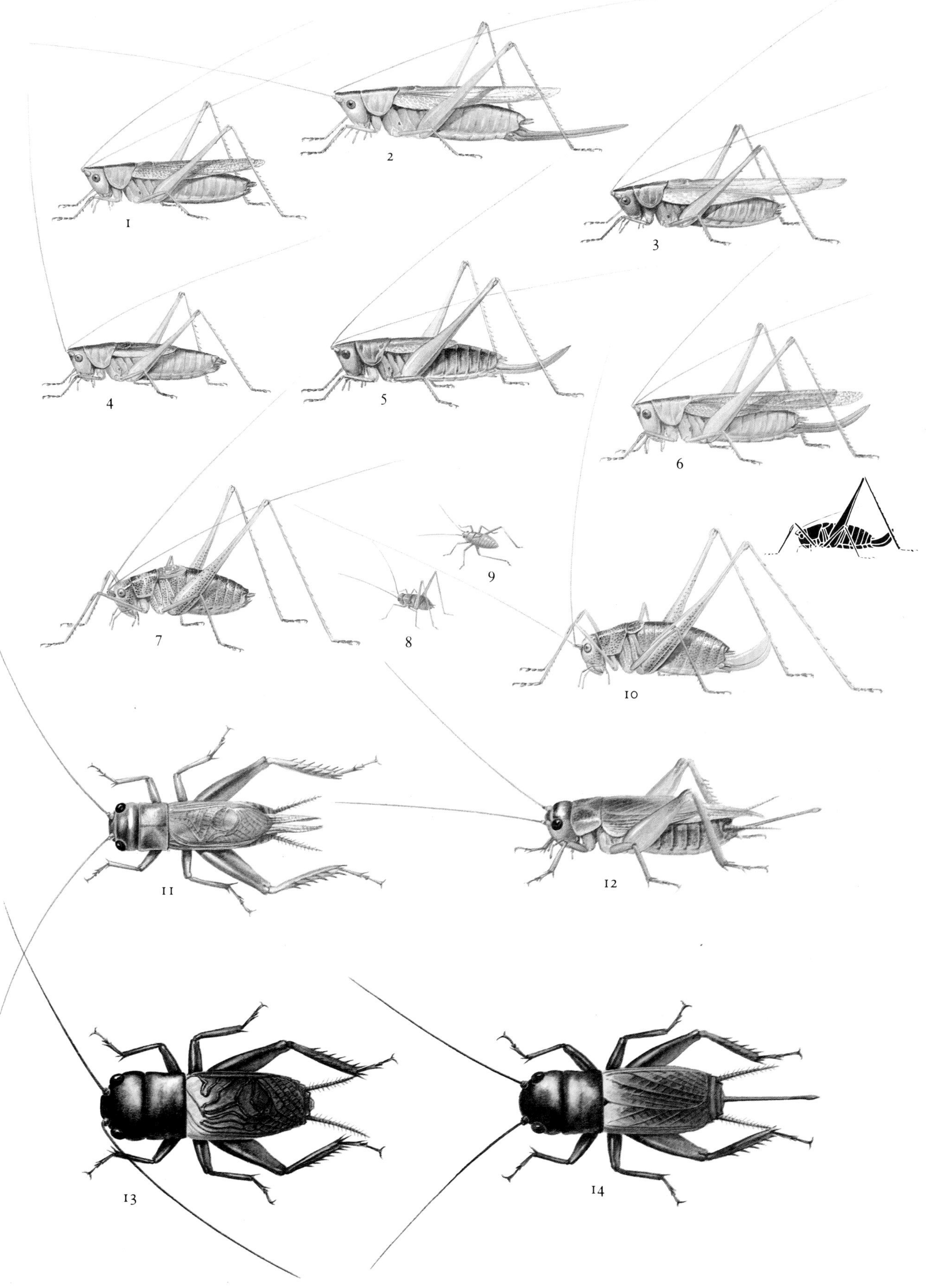

Plate 3: Tettigoniidae, Gryllidae

Figs 1–14, x2

Plate 4: Grylloidea: Gryllidae, Gryllotalpidae; Acridoidea: Tetrigidae

Figs 1–6, × 2; 7–18 × 3

1 *Nemobius sylvestris* (Bosc) ♂
Wood-cricket
Page 96

*2 *Nemobius sylvestris* (Bosc) ♀
Wood-cricket
Page 96

3 *Pseudomogoplistes squamiger* (Fischer) ♂
Scaly Cricket
Page 97

4 *Pseudomogoplistes squamiger* (Fischer) ♀
Scaly cricket
Page 97

5 *Gryllotalpa gryllotalpa* (Linnaeus) ♂
dorsal view
Mole-cricket
Page 98

6 *Gryllotalpa gryllotalpa* (Linnaeus) ♀
lateral view
Mole-cricket
Page 98

7 *Tetrix ceperoi* (Bolivar) ♂
dorsal view
Cepero's Ground-hopper
Page 100

*8 *Tetrix ceperoi* (Bolivar) ♀
lateral view
Cepero's Ground-hopper
Page 100

9 *Tetrix ceperoi* (Bolivar) ♀
greenish variety, lateral view
Cepero's Ground-hopper
Page 100

10 *Tetrix ceperoi* (Bolivar),
detail: head, lateral and dorsal views
Cepero's Ground-hopper
Page 100

11 *Tetrix subulata* (Linnaeus) ♂
dorsal view
Slender Ground-hopper
Page 101

12 *Tetrix subulata* (Linnaeus) ♀
lateral view
Slender Ground-hopper
Page 101

13 *Tetrix subulata* (Linnaeus) ♀
short-winged form, f. *bifasciata* Herbst
Slender Ground-hopper
Page 101

14 *Tetrix subulata* (Linnaeus)
detail: head, lateral and dorsal views
Slender Ground-hopper
Page 101

15 *Tetrix undulata* (Sowerby) ♂
dorsal view
Common Ground-hopper
Page 103

16 *Tetrix undulata* (Sowerby) ♀
lateral view
Common Ground-hopper
Page 103

17 *Tetrix undulata* (Sowerby) ♀
mottled variety, lateral view
Common Ground-hopper
Page 103

18 *Tetrix undulata* (Sowerby)
detail: head, lateral and dorsal views
Common Ground-hopper
Page 103

*see also silhouette (natural size)

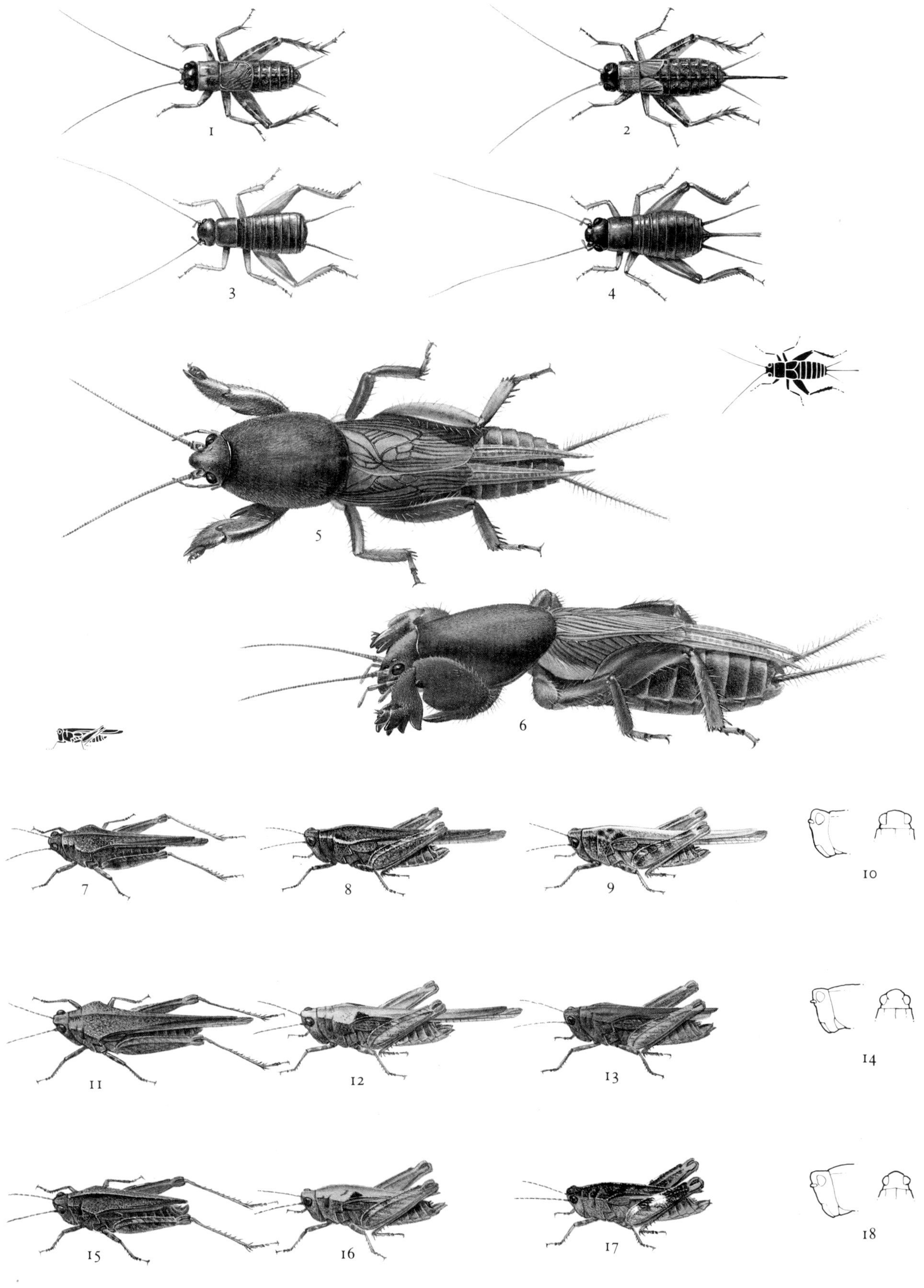

Plate 4: Gryllidae, Gryllotalpidae, Tetrigidae

Figs 1–6, x2; 7–18, x3

Plate 5: Acridoidea: Acrididae; Mantodea: Mantidae

Figs 1–5, × 1.5

1 *Schistocerca gregaria* (Forskål) ♀
swarming phase
Desert Locust
Page 147

2 *Locusta migratoria* (Linnaeus) ♂
solitary phase
Migratory Locust
Page 146

3 *Locusta migratoria* (Linnaeus) ♀
swarming phase
Migratory Locust
Page 146

*4 *Anacridium aegyptium* (Linnaeus) ♀
Egyptian Grasshopper
Page 146

5 *Mantis religiosa* (Linnaeus) ♀
Praying Mantis
Page 148

*see also silhouette (natural size)

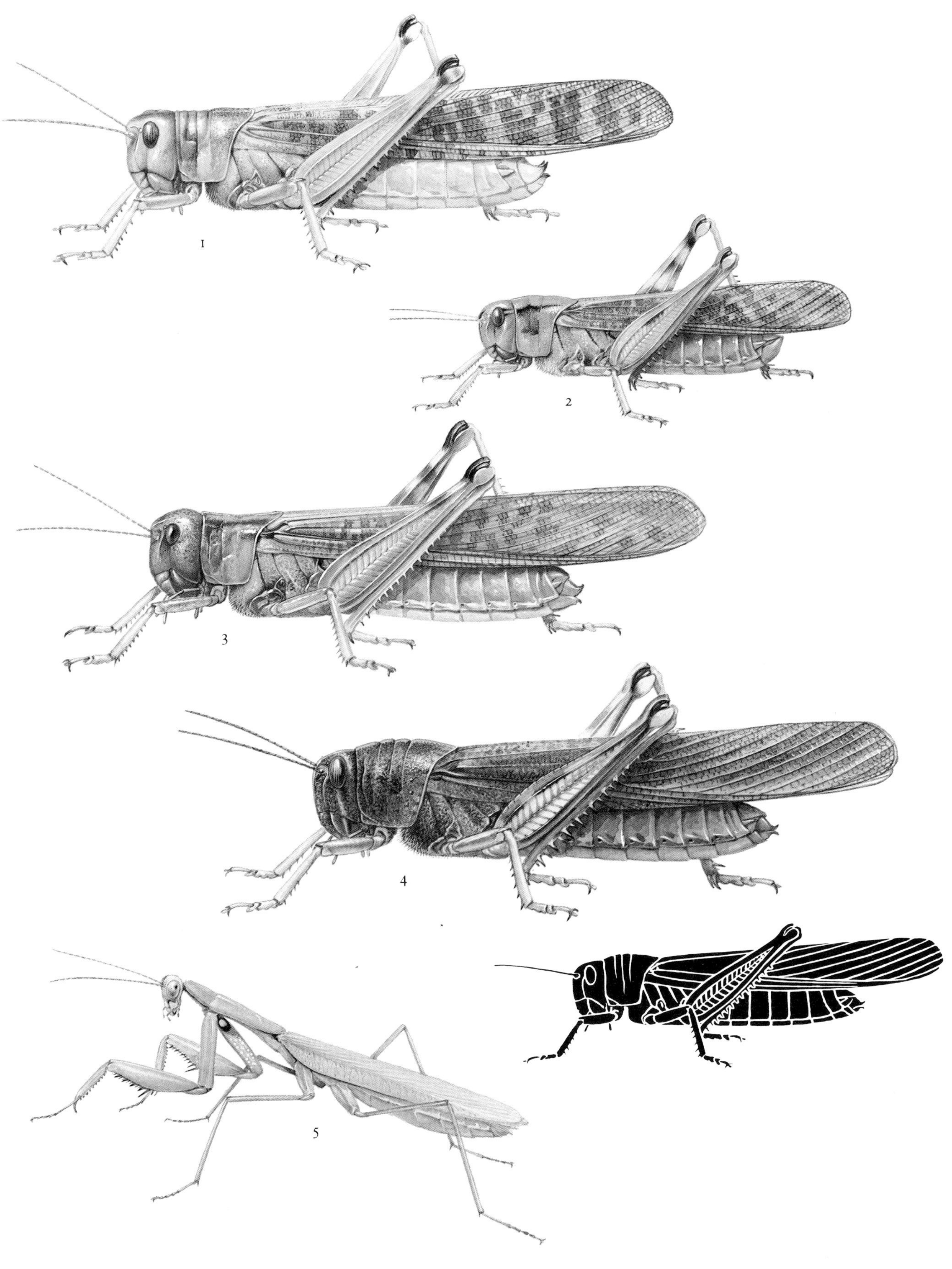

Plate 5: Acrididae, Mantidae

Figs 1–5, x1·5

Plate 6: Acridoidea: Acrididae

Figs 1–21, × 2

1 *Oedipoda caerulescens* (Linnaeus) ♂
Blue-winged Grasshopper
Page 105

2 *Oedipoda caerulescens* (Linnaeus)
in flight
Blue-winged Grasshopper
Page 105

3 *Stethophyma grossum* (Linnaeus) ♂
Large Marsh Grasshopper
Page 106

4 *Stethophyma grossum* (Linnacus) ♀
Large Marsh Grasshopper
Page 106

5 *Stethophyma grossum* (Linnaeus) ♀
purple variety
Large Marsh Grasshopper
Page 106

6 *Stenobothrus lineatus* (Panzer) ♂
Stripe-winged Grasshopper
Page 107

*7 *Stenobothrus lineatus* (Panzer) ♀
Stripe-winged Grasshopper
Page 107

8 *Stenobothrus lineatus* (Panzer) ♀
purple variety
Stripe-winged Grasshopper
Page 107

9 *Stenobothrus lineatus* (Panzer)
detail: pronotum
Stripe-winged Grasshopper
Page 107

10 *Stenobothrus stigmaticus* (Rambur) ♂
Lesser Mottled Grasshopper
Page 108

11 *Stenobothrus stigmaticus* (Rambur) ♀
Lesser Mottled Grasshopper
Page 108

12 *Stenobothrus stigmaticus* (Rambur)
detail: pronotum
Lesser Mottled Grasshopper
Page 108

13 *Omocestus rufipes* (Zetterstedt) ♂
lateral view
Woodland Grasshopper
Page 109

14 *Omocestus rufipes* (Zetterstedt) ♂
ventral view
Woodland Grasshopper
Page 109

15 *Omocestus rufipes* (Zetterstedt) ♀
Woodland Grasshopper
Page 109

16 *Omocestus rufipes* (Zetterstedt)
detail: pronotum
Woodland Grasshopper
Page 109

17 *Omocestus rufipes* (Zetterstedt)
detail: head, frontal view
Woodland Grasshopper
Page 109

18 *Omocestus viridulus* (Linnaeus) ♂
Common Green Grasshopper
Page 110

19 *Omocestus viridulus* (Linnaeus) ♀
Common Green Grasshopper
Page 110

20 *Omocestus viridulus* (Linnaeus) ♀
purple variety
Common Green Grasshopper
Page 110

21 *Omocestus viridulus* (Linnaeus)
detail: pronotum
Common Green Grasshopper
Page 110

*see also silhouette (natural size)

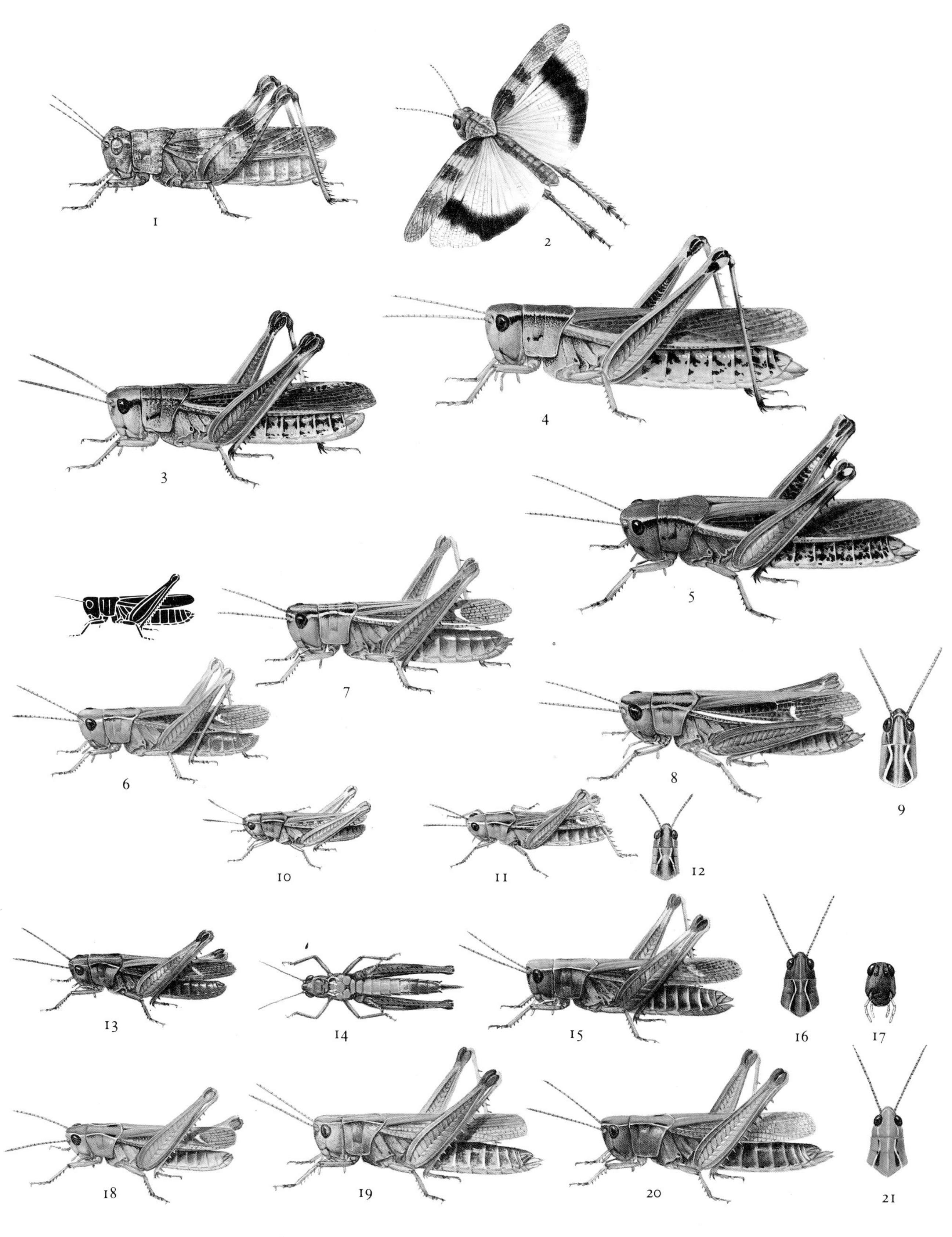

Plate 6: Acrididae

Figs 1–21, x2

Plate 7: Acridoidea: Acrididae

Figs 1–25, × 2

1 *Chorthippus brunneus* (Thunberg) ♂
Field Grasshopper
Page 112

2 *Chorthippus brunneus* (Thunberg) ♀
Field Grasshopper
Page 112

3 *Chorthippus brunneus* (Thunberg) ♀
green variety
Field Grasshopper
Page 112

4 *Chorthippus brunneus* (Thunberg),
detail: pronotum
Field Grasshopper
Page 112

5 *Chorthippus vagans* (Eversmann) ♂
Heath Grasshopper
Page 113

6 *Chorthippus vagans* (Eversmann) ♀
Heath Grasshopper
Page 113

7 *Chorthippus vagans* (Eversmann),
detail: pronotum
Heath Grasshopper
Page 113

8 *Chorthippus parallelus* (Zetterstedt) ♂
Meadow Grasshopper
Page 114

*9 *Chorthippus parallelus* (Zetterstedt) ♀
Meadow Grasshopper
Page 114

10 *Chorthippus parallelus* (Zetterstedt) ♀
purple variety
Meadow Grasshopper
Page 114

11 *Chorthippus parallelus* (Zetterstedt) ♀
macropterous form, f. *explicatus* (Sélys)
Meadow Grasshopper
Page 114

12 *Chorthippus parallelus* (Zetterstedt)
detail: pronotum
Meadow Grasshopper
Page 114

13 *Chorthippus albomarginatus* (De Geer) ♂
Lesser Marsh Grasshopper
Page 115

14 *Chorthippus albomarginatus* (De Geer) ♀
Lesser Marsh Grasshopper
Page 115

15 *Chorthippus albomarginatus* (De Geer)
detail: pronotum
Lesser Marsh Grasshopper
Page 115

16 *Euchorthippus pulvinatus elegantulus*
Zeuner ♂
Jersey Grasshopper
Page 117

17 *Euchorthippus pulvinatus elegantulus*
Zeuner ♀
Jersey Grasshopper
Page 117

18 *Euchorthippus pulvinatus elegantulus*
Zeuner
detail: pronotum
Jersey Grasshopper
Page 117

19 *Gomphocerippus rufus* (Linnaeus) ♂
Rufous Grasshopper
Page 118

20 *Gomphocerippus rufus* (Linnaeus) ♀
Rufous Grasshopper
Page 118

21 *Gomphocerippus rufus* (Linnaeus)
detail: pronotum
Rufous Grasshopper
Page 118

22 *Myrmeleotettix maculatus* (Thunberg) ♂
Mottled Grasshopper
Page 119

23 *Myrmeleotettix maculatus* (Thunberg) ♀
green variety
Mottled Grasshopper
Page 119

24 *Myrmeleotettix maculatus* (Thunberg) ♀
brown variety
Mottled Grasshopper
Page 119

25 *Myrmeleotettix maculatus* (Thunberg)
dctail: pronotum
Mottled Grasshopper
Page 119

*see also silhouette (natural size)

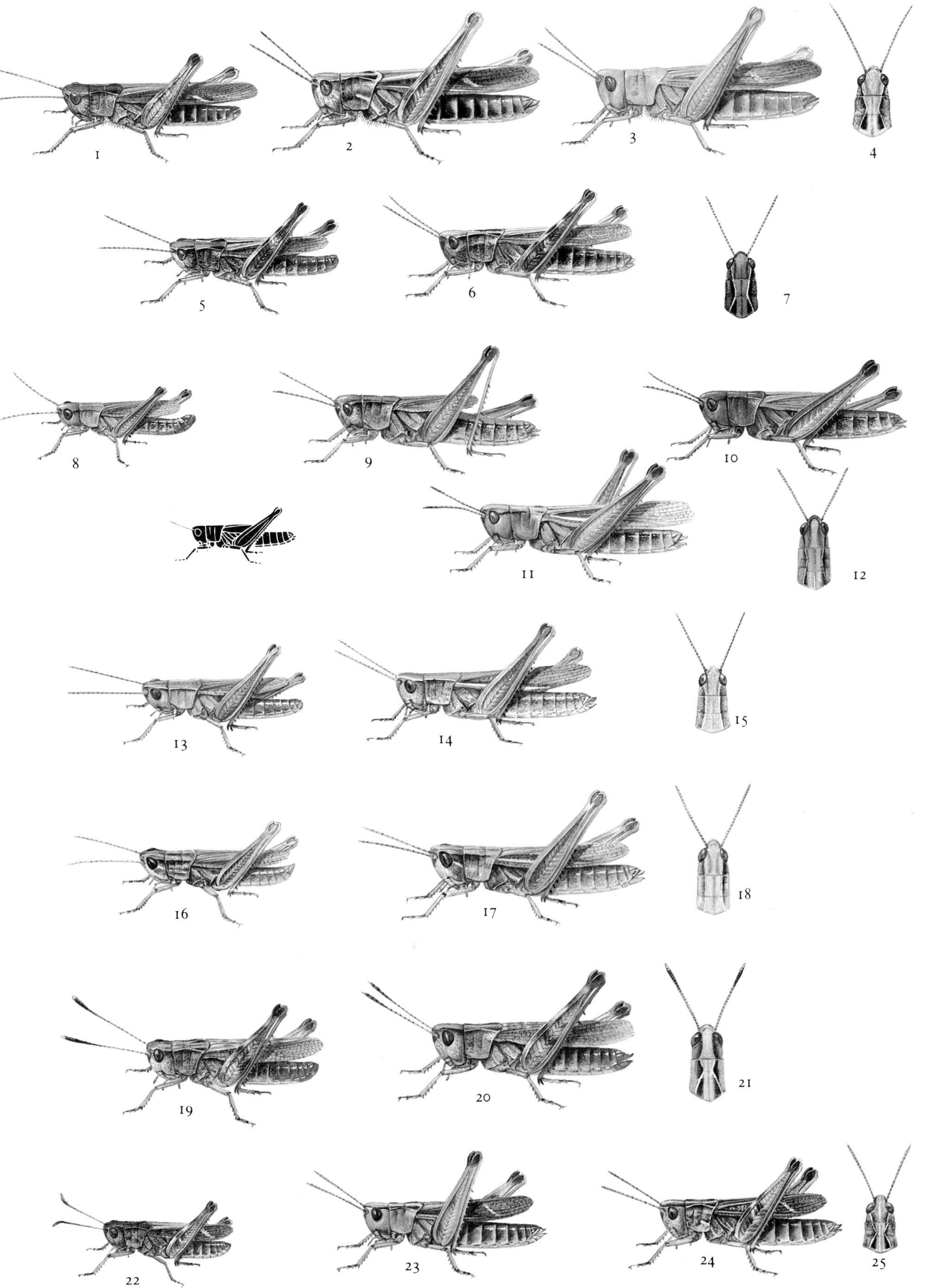

Plate 7: Acrididae

Figs 1–25, x2

Plate 8: Blattodea: Blattidae, Blaberidae

Figs 1–3, 5–11, × 1.5; 4, × 1

1 *Blatta orientalis* Linnaeus ♂
Common or Oriental Cockroach
Page 124

2 *Blatta orientalis* Linnaeus ♀
Common or Oriental Cockroach
Page 124

3 *Blatta orientalis* Linnaeus nymph
Common or Oriental Cockroach
Page 124

4 *Blatta orientalis* Linnaeus ♀
carrying ootheca (nat. size)
Common or Oriental Cockroach
Page 124

5 *Periplaneta americana* (Linnaeus) ♂
American or Ship Cockroach
Page 125

6 *Periplaneta americana* (Linnaeus) ♀
American or Ship Cockroach
Page 125

7 *Periplaneta americana* (Linnaeus) nymph
American or Ship Cockroach
Page 125

8 *Periplaneta australasiae* (Fabricius) ♂
Australian Cockroach
Page 126

9 *Periplaneta australasiae* (Fabricius) ♀
Australian Cockroach
Page 126

10 *Periplaneta australasiae* (Fabricius) nymph
Australian Cockroach
Page 126

11 *Pycnoscelus surinamensis* (Linnaeus) ♀
Surinam Cockroach
Page 123

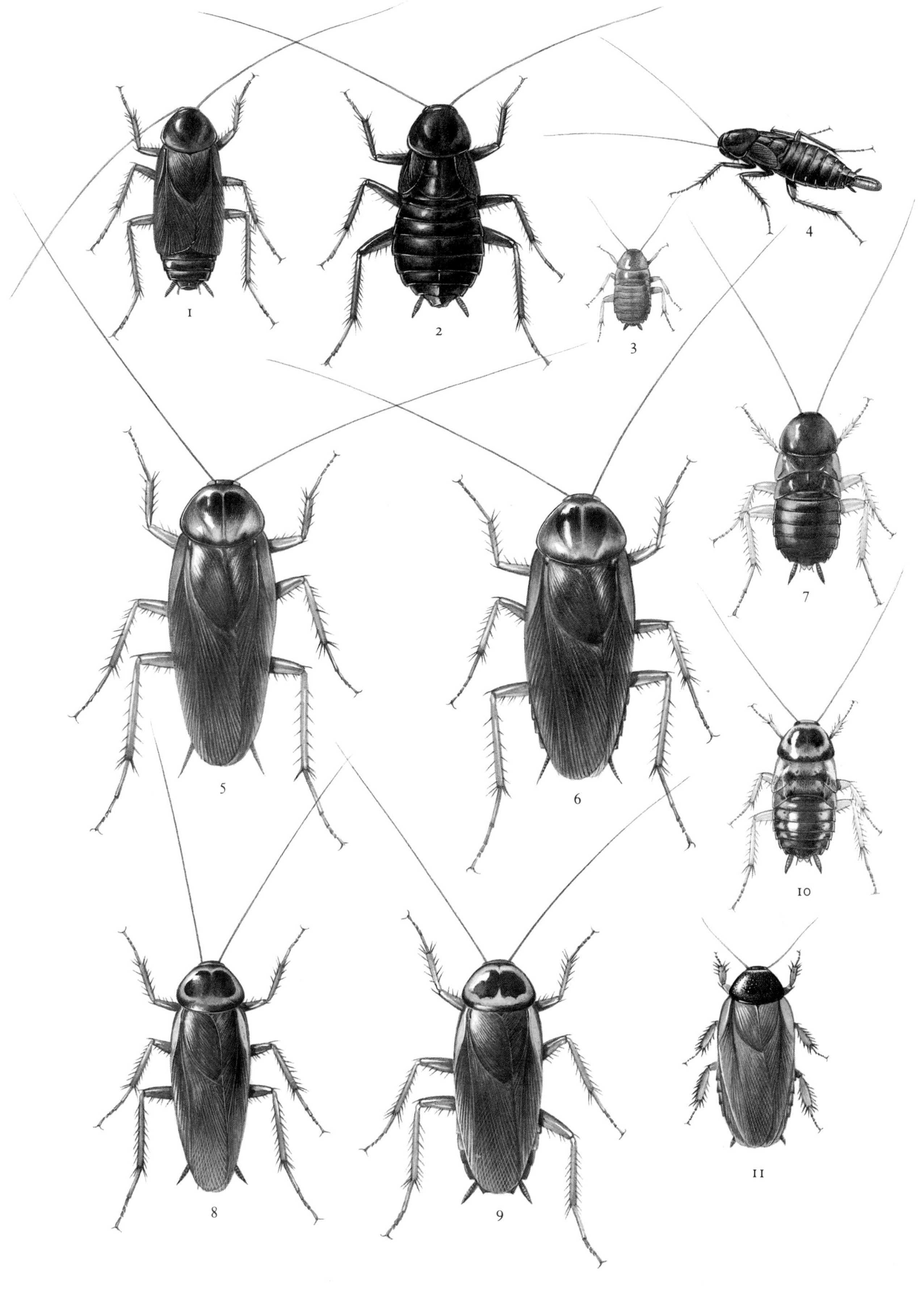

Plate 8: Blattidae, Blaberidae

Figs 1–3, 5–11, x1·5; 4, x1

Plate 9: Blattodea: Blattellidae; Dermaptera: Anisolabididae, Labiidae, Forficulidae, Labiduridae

Figs 1–3, 5–29, × 2; 4, × 2.5

1 *Blattella germanica* (Linnaeus) ♂
German Cockroach
Page 127

2 *Blattella germanica* (Linnaeus) ♀
German Cockroach
Page 127

3 *Blattella germanica* (Linnaeus) nymph
German Cockroach
Page 127

4 *Blattella germanica* (Linnaeus) ♀
carrying ootheca
German Cockroach
Page 127

5 *Supella longipalpa* (Fabricius) ♂
Brown-banded Cockroach
Page 128

6 *Supella longipalpa* (Fabricius) ♀
Brown-banded Cockroach
Page 128

7 *Supella longipalpa* (Fabricius) nymph
Brown-banded Cockroach
Page 128

8 *Ectobius lapponicus* (Linnaeus) ♂
Dusky Cockroach
Page 129

9 *Ectobius lapponicus* (Linnaeus) ♀
Dusky Cockroach
Page 129

10 *Ectobius pallidus* (Olivier) ♂
Tawny Cockroach
Page 130

11 *Ectobius pallidus* (Olivier) ♀
Tawny Cockroach
Page 130

12 *Ectobius panzeri* Stephens ♂
Lesser Cockroach
Page 131

13 *Ectobius panzeri* Stephens ♀
Lesser Cockroach
Page 131

14 *Euborellia annulipes* (Lucas) ♂
Ring-legged Earwig
Page 134

15 *Euborellia annulipes* (Lucas) ♀
detail: forceps
Ring-legged Earwig
Page 134

16 *Labia minor* (Linnaeus) ♂
Lesser Earwig
Page 135

17 *Labia minor* (Linnaeus) ♀
detail: forceps
Lesser Earwig
Page 135

18 *Marava arachidis* (Yersin) ♂
Bone-house Earwig
Page 135

19 *Marava arachidis* (Yersin) ♀
detail: forceps
Bone-house Earwig
Page 135

20 *Apterygida media* (Hagenbach) ♂
Short-winged or Hop-garden Earwig
Page 136

21 *Apterygida media* (Hagenbach) ♀
detail: forceps
Short-winged or Hop-garden Earwig
Page 136

22 *Forficula auricularia* Linnaeus nymph
Common Earwig
Page 137

23 *Forficula auricularia* Linnaeus ♂
detail: forceps of macrolabic form
Common Earwig
Page 137

*24 *Forficula auricularia* Linnaeus ♂
Common Earwig
Page 137

25 *Forficula auricularia* Linnaeus ♀
detail: forceps
Common Earwig
Page 137

26 *Forficula lesnei* Finot ♂
Lesne's Earwig
Page 138

27 *Forficula lesnei* Finot ♀
Lesne's Earwig
Page 138

28 *Labidura riparia* (Pallas) ♂
Giant or Tawny Earwig
Page 139

29 *Labidura riparia* (Pallas) ♀
detail: forceps
Giant or Tawny Earwig
Page 139

*see also silhouette (natural size)

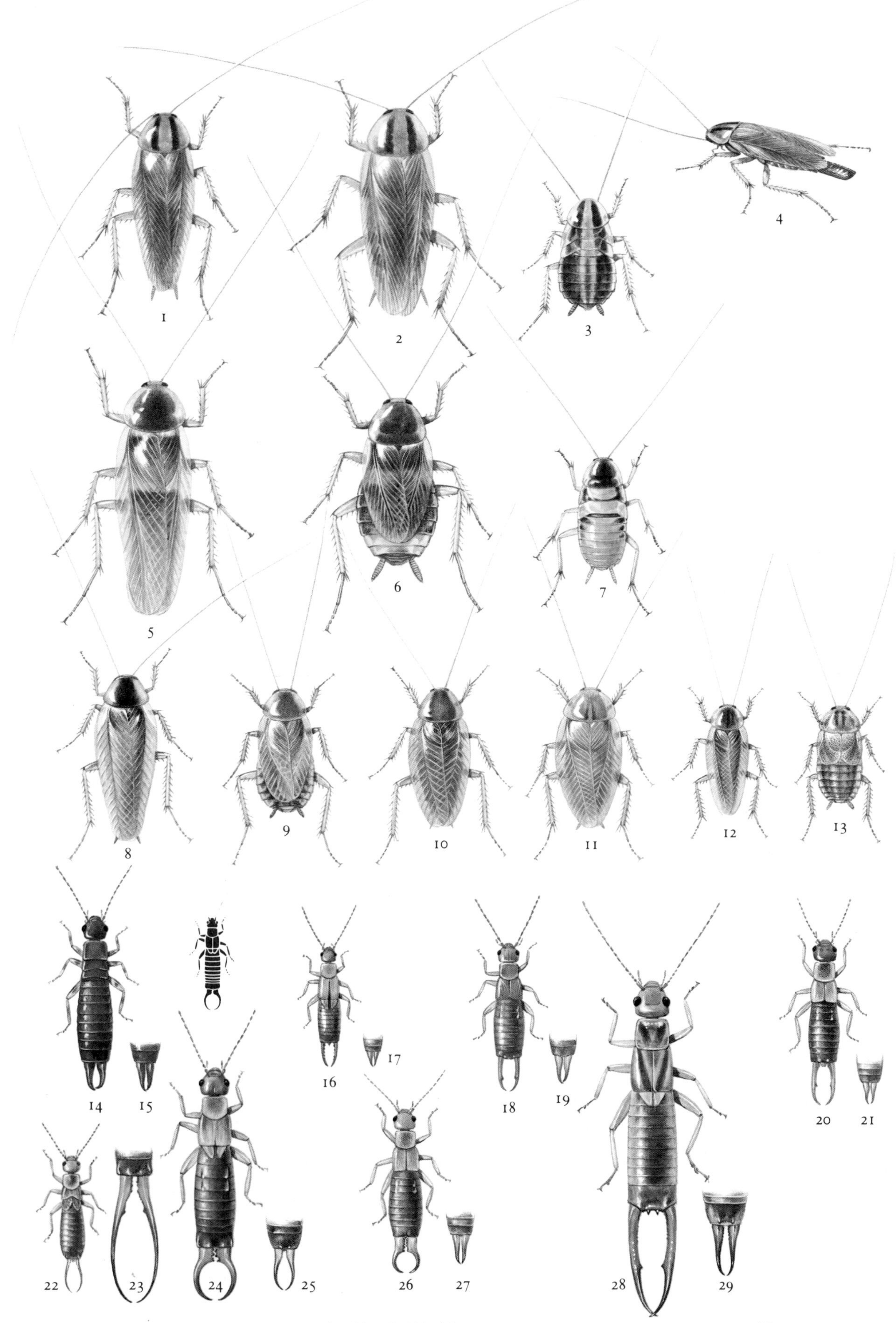

Plate 9: Blatellidae, Anisolabiidae, Labiidae, Forficulidae, Labiduridae

Figs 1–3, 5–29, x2·5; 4, x1·5

Plate 10: Phasmida: Phasmatidae

Figs 1–5, × 1.5

1 *Acanthoxyla geisovii* (Kaup) ♀
Prickly Stick-insect
Page 140

2 *Acanthoxyla inermis* Salmon ♀
Unarmed Stick-insect
Page 142

3 *Clitarchus hookeri* (White) ♀
Smooth Stick-insect
Page 143

4 *Carausius morosus* (Sinéty) ♀
Laboratory or Indian Stick-insect
Page 143

5 *Carausius morosus* (Sinéty) ♂
Laboratory or Indian Stick-insect
Page 143

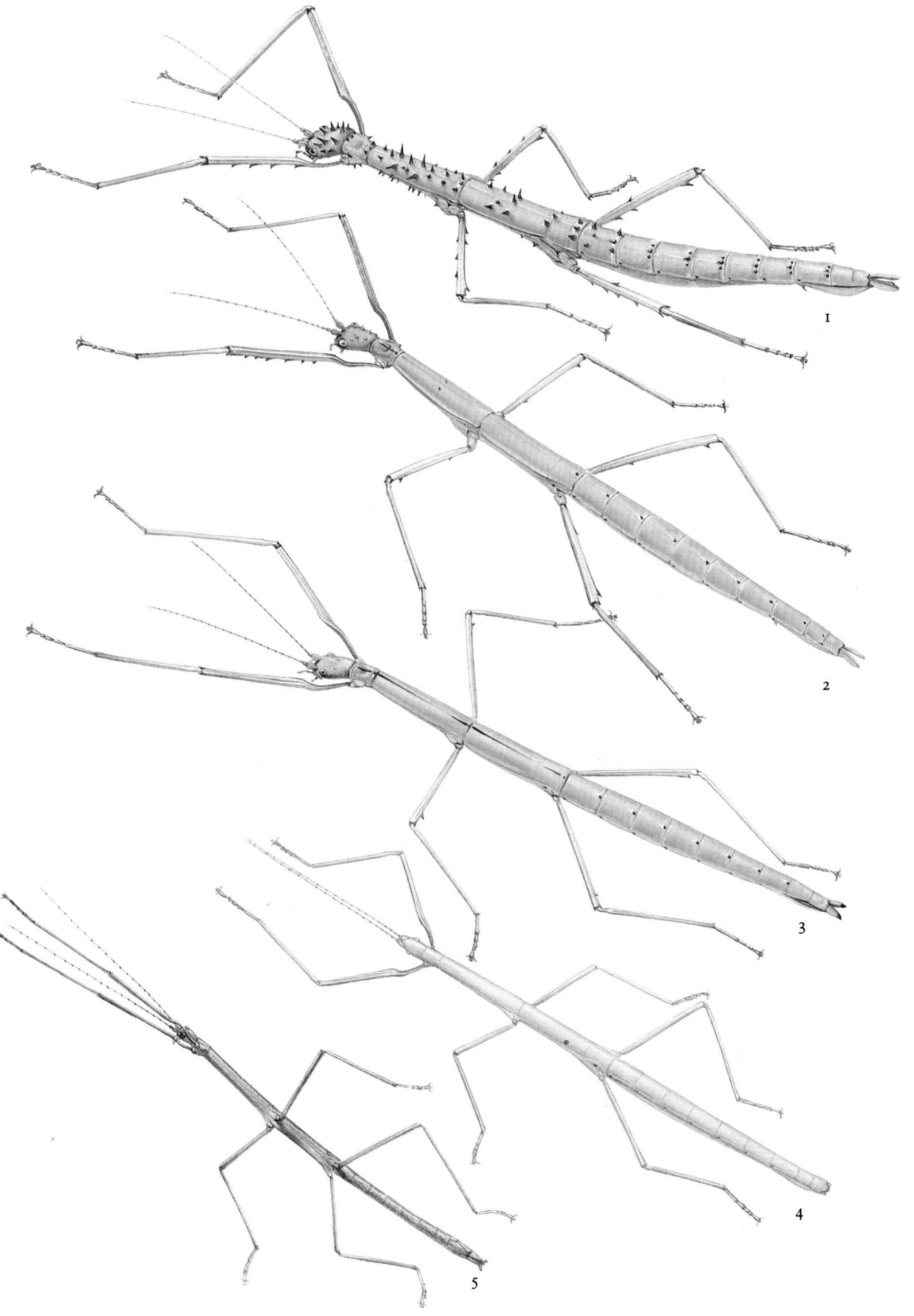

Plate 10: Phasmatidae Figs 1–5, x 1·5

Index to Animal Names

Principal entries are given in bold type, followed by reference to colour plates as **115** (Pl. 7:13–15). The index also contains references to colour plates A and B, to text figures and to keys to orders and families. Vice-county maps are to be found with each principal species entry; map references in this index refer to the dot-distribution maps: pp. 166–189.

See separate index to plants

Index of Plants

Only the scientific names of genera and species cited in the text are given in this index.